TRUMPET CALL
TO
VICTORY

JOE FARLEY

Mechanicsburg, PA USA

Published by Sunbury Press, Inc.
Mechanicsburg, Pennsylvania

www.sunburypress.com

ISBN: 978-1-62006-763-5 (Trade paperback)
ISBN: 978-1-62006-764-2 (Mobipocket)

Library of Congress Control Number: 2017959829

FIRST SUNBURY PRESS EDITION: November 2017

Product of the United States of America
0 1 1 2 3 5 8 13 21 34 55

Set in Bookman Old Style
Designed by Crystal Devine
Cover by Lawrence Knorr
Edited by Olivia Swenson

Continue the Enlightenment!

contents

AUTHOR'S NOTE

A few years ago a friend of mine gave me a book titled *Undertaker's Son* written by Richard "Digger" Phelps with the aid of Jack Colwell. It was an appropriate gift given that I was a member of the last graduating class from Hazleton Saint Gabriel's High School where Coach Phelps began his head coaching career. Naturally, I looked through the book for references to Saint Gabriel's. I discovered what I was looking for on page 59, where Phelps remembered being hired as the head basketball coach at "a small Catholic school that played some of the bigger schools."

Phelps added that after seeing the movie *Hoosiers* years later, he was reminded of his days at Saint Gabriel's. He was particularly struck by the scene where the local townspeople were telling the new coach, played by Gene Hackman, that the boys just didn't play basketball the way he had in mind. According to Phelps, when people heard about his plans to employ a press for the whole game, he was warned about upsetting the applecart. "None of the teams around here do that," he was told. "You don't press until the fourth quarter and you're down by twelve." Digger's memories struck a chord in me because I had recommended the same movie to my mother who, after seeing the film, told me that it reminded her of Saint Gabriel's.

Thus, I have mulled over doing this story for quite some time. Like many Saint Gabriel's graduates, my ties to the school span generations. My uncle and godfather Paul Flood took the court for the school in the mid-thirties. My father, John Farley, was a star on the 1947 team that until the '60s was the most successful squad in the school's history. I grew up reading about his exploits in a scrapbook my mother had compiled. Two of my cousins, Francis "Snapper" O'Donnell and Michael O'Donnell, played for Saint Gabriel's in the late '50s and early '60s respectively.

Much of what is described in this book I witnessed. The majority of people mentioned were known to me personally, and

I remain in touch with some of them, though it's been almost a half century since we roamed the halls of Saint Gabriel's as students. In some cases, writing this book put me in touch with former players who were my heroes when I was a young boy. In others I sat down with former teammates and opponents to talk about those youthful days long past.

In putting this together, I relied on my memories as well as those of the many people who were willing to share their thoughts on the triumphs and defeats they experienced or remembered from their high school days. In addition, I leaned heavily on the local newspaper coverage of the Saint Gabriel's basketball teams. In doing so, my respect relative to the talents of three Hazleton sportswriters—Phil Sarno, Ray Saul, and Don Barnes—has grown and deepened considerably. The fact that I was so much more impressed with their objectivity as I read their stories today than I was when they were first written speaks volumes about the passions that gripped my young mind decades ago.

One of the challenges in telling the story of the final years of Saint Gabriel's basketball is that I was a part of it. As a matter of fact, I was the starting point guard on the last team to take the court wearing the school's purple-and-white uniforms. I have chosen to write this account as an interested observer of the events, which in many cases I was. In those instances where I am directly involved, I have endeavored to be as objective as possible and have leaned heavily on those who shared their experiences with me.

With regard to the four coaches who led Saint Gabriel's—or the G-Men as they were often called—in what could be described as the school's "golden age," I offer the following as an explanation. I never played for or talked to Francis "Chip" Kender. I was still in grade school when he was the head coach. I remember being excited whenever he would show up to watch the school's biddy basketball games (yes, the parish sponsored its own league) or the seventh, eighth and ninth graders play in what was called the Public Parochial League because it felt like you were being scouted. My references to Coach Kender come from the recollections of some of his players and the local newspaper. As I did attend many of the games involving his teams, some observations are pulled from my memory.

When Richard "Digger" Phelps took command I was an eighth grader starting for the freshman team. As a result, I had some moments with Mr. Phelps, as we called him back then (the word around the school was that he didn't like the nickname Digger). Coach Phelps has attracted quite a bit of attention over the years after leaving Hazleton, so finding information about him was not a problem. However, his year at Saint Gabriel's has never been dealt with in any depth until now. I am indebted to those who played for him and were willing to share their thoughts on the coach when he was just beginning his career. Though he was only at Saint Gabriel's for a short time, it is my opinion that he continued to influence basketball in the Greater Hazleton area after he moved on to bigger and greater things, and I touch on that in this book.

Phelps was succeeded by a fellow Rider College graduate, Jack Cryan. Over the past few years a few former Saint Gabriel's players suggested I write a book solely on Jack Cryan. Frankly, I never gave the matter serious consideration because Coach Cryan and I found ourselves at odds almost from the beginning of his tenure. To give the reader a clear view of my relationship with the coach, I must relate that I left the team early in November of 1967. Coach Cryan and I never spoke again, not even at our last meeting two years after he had left Saint Gabriel's. If I had to sum up our relationship, I'd paraphrase an old Bob Dylan song and say, "He was right from his side, and I was right from mine." That said, Cryan was loved by the majority of his players and was arguably the most successful coach in the school's history. The only fair way for me to tell the story of the Jack Cryan years is to leave our personal relationship out of it. As a result, I have leaned heavily on the memories of those who played for him. It strikes me as something of an irony that I'm telling the story of his two-year coaching reign when he was the dominant force in basketball in the Hazleton region.

The final coach in Saint Gabriel's history was Jerry Anderson. As a player both years he coached, I had a bird's eye view of those final two seasons. Coach Anderson arrived on the scene at a time when the fans of the G-Men had become very used to winning. He didn't have the good fortune of his predecessors to coach the player who rewrote all the record books, not only at Saint Gabriel's but throughout the region. He was, however, blessed with players who were determined to carry on what had become a tradition of winning at the tiny Catholic school. My thanks go out to the former coach who agreed to share his memories with me as I worked on this book. Coach Anderson treasures his time at Saint Gabriel's to this day. He recalled the importance of basketball at the school saying that the hierarchy there was "God, the priests, the basketball coach, and then the nuns." When asked if there was anything he'd like to see in the book, he said he didn't want much about him in it; he felt the real story should be about the players. He accomplished much and was far more successful than he was given credit for at the time.

It would have been impossible for me to complete this project without the assistance of many people who were willing to share their memories and thoughts with me. My sister MaryEllen Gibson provided the scrapbook my mother had compiled on the '47 G Men, and my mother was willing to share the trophy that team received after becoming the first Saint Gabriel's team to win the Anthracite League. My brother Jimmy took the time to read my draft efforts and provide suggestions on improving the story. He also accompanied me on a number of my visits to interview former players. Francis and Mike O'Donnell, two of my cousins, shared memories of their years playing for that small Catholic school from the south side of Hazleton. Former players Ray McBrearty, Mike Heffernan, John Goryl, and Jerry Fallabel provided keen insights and great stories about their coaches and the teams they played on.

The four Saint Gabriel's players whom, to date, have been inducted into the Greater Hazleton Sports Hall of Fame (it is long past time for the aforementioned Fallabel to join them) willingly shared their thoughts on those bygone years. Those four—Paul Hoffman, Pete O'Donnell, Dennis Olexa, and Larry Walko—told numerous tales that served to awaken this writer's memory. Cathy Gallagher deserves my thanks for sharing her memories about her parent's decision to take Paul Hoffman into their home and allowing him to attend Saint Gabriel's. In addition, players who took the court opposing the G-Men—Tony Kinney, Ed Parsons, Bill Pavlick, Bobby Schlosser and Tom Andregic— provided the perspective of teams who faced Saint Gabriel's in the late sixties. Finally, Bruce Ellis was willing to share his thoughts on the many Saint Gabriel's players he came to know on the city's playgrounds. Needless to say it would have been impossible to complete this project without their assistance.

I would be remiss not to thank my co-author of the Keystone Tombstone and Gotham Graves series of books for patiently allowing me to concentrate on this work at times at the expense of a joint project. My publisher Larry Knorr should be acknowledged for his love of sports and willingness to take a chance on a book about a small catholic school's basketball history. I will always be indebted to the work done by my editor Olivia Swenson for her suggestions and deft touch in dealing with a less than computer savvy author.

In the pages that follow I have attempted to tell the story of Saint Gabriel's basketball in the final years of the school. It is difficult to recapture the excitement those teams generated throughout the Greater Hazleton area, but I've done my best. It's a story that includes agonizing and heartbreaking losses as well as unexpected and unbelievably momentous wins. It is the story of many young boys who dreamed of donning the purple-and-white uniforms and taking the court as G-Men.

In recalling those bygone times, in 2013 the *Hazleton Standard Speaker* published an article that began:

"Something magical mesmerized Hazleton's South Side about a half century ago. Make that a decent chunk of the city. Saint Gabriel's High School Basketball, that is."

The piece then quotes G-Men star Dennis Olexa: "I remember going to the pep rallies as a second or third-grader and seeing all that purple and all the excitement and not being able to wait until I could be a part of that great tradition . . . It was unbelievable."

1

THE PEP RALLY

SPEEDBOYS, SAINTS, AND G-MEN

On the night of March 14, 1970, in the Trinity Catholic High School gym near Harrisburg, Pennsylvania, five boys wearing purple-and-white uniforms bearing the name St. Gabriel's readied for the jump ball that would start a state championship basketball game. It would be the last time the small parochial school located on the south side of the city of Hazleton would compete in a high school basketball game. Looking back, one might say that a wave of history carried them to that spot.

The city of Hazleton is located in the anthracite coal region of northeastern Pennsylvania. It was surrounded by patch towns built decades ago when coal was king. Both Hazleton and the towns surrounding it experienced a steady population growth from the 1870s until the end of World War II. The 1940 census registered Hazleton as having more than 38,000 residents. After the war the demand for coal began to decline as cleaner and more efficient energy sources became available. In the 1950s, Hazleton's population decreased by almost 10 percent. The nearby towns shared that experience. According to the 1960 census, Hazleton's population had dropped to 32,000 people. Most were descendants of those who had settled in the area decades before, and for the current residents, Hazleton was where they made their living, worshipped their God, and decided to educate and raise their families.

Though football had its moments, most area high schools were too small to field football teams, and in some cases schools had discontinued that sport due to the expense. High school basketball was the sport actively followed by the area residents and had been for years. Most had graduated from local schools and continued to support their alma mater, often very passionately, into their adult lives. Their children who grew up attending those same schools followed the example of their parents. School spirit was encouraged to the utmost extent. The city hosted an annual "dream game" and the proceeds it generated were donated to charity. The game, always played before a packed house, pitted seniors from the local high schools in a post-season matchup. For years the teams were called the "Cityslickers" and the "Patchtowners" before being changed to the "Anthracites" and the "Mountaineers" in the 1940s.

By 1960, only the two large public high schools, Hazleton and West Hazleton, offered competitive sporting opportunities that went beyond basketball and baseball. These were also the only schools in the Greater Hazleton area to compete on the Class A level (AAAA today) during post-season play. During the 1960s, Hazleton High housed approximately 1,700 students in grades 10 through 12, while West Hazleton educated another 842.

Hazleton had no central Catholic high school. The mid-twentieth century was still marked by the existence of numerous parish schools. Mother of Grace, Most Precious Blood, and Holy Trinity were among the parish churches that offered a grade school and junior high education to their flock. Two area churches—Saint Ann's of Freeland and Hazleton Saint Gabriel's—supported high schools. Saint Gabriel's taught approximately 200 high school students (the majority of them female) in grades 9 through 12.

Saint Gabriel's and Hazleton High didn't take to the court as opponents until 1959. Prior to that year, the residents of the city argued back and forth as to which school had the better squad. As far back as 1935, the *Hazleton Plain Speaker* called the debate "that perennial argument." That year the paper attempted to settle the matter by noting that Tamaqua had beaten Tamaqua Catholic 36-33 and that Hazleton had beaten Tamaqua by six while Saint Gabriel's (who the paper referred to as the Speedboys) had lost to Tamaqua Catholic by one point. It was noted that the Hazleton win took place at home while Saint Gabriel's suffered its defeat on the road. For the fans of both teams, this information did little to quiet their passions.

Saint Gabriel's parish—the largest in Hazleton—occupied two city blocks on the south side of the city. On one corner was the rectory, which housed the priests that had been assigned there to minister to the church parishioners. The building, Colonial Revival in style, stood three stories high and offered comfortable living quarters for the men of the cloth who made Hazleton their home. The church stood next to the rectory and dominated the block. It was the third church constructed during the parish's history and was officially dedicated in 1927. Next to the church was the convent, home to the Sisters of Mercy. The last building on the block, which stood on the corner of Birch and South Wyoming Streets, was the school itself. Its cornerstone carried the date 1911. By the 1950s, an addition had been added to the school. This new section, located in the rear of the building, held the classrooms for the high school students. Grades 1 through 8 continued to receive their education in the original building. The gym was located on the bottom floor and included a stage used to showcase school plays and other presentations.

The school was supported by the parishioners who sent generations of children through its doors. By the 1960s, many of the students were the children of fathers and mothers who were Saint Gabriel's graduates themselves. Many had aunts and uncles and even grandparents who had received their education at the school. The Sisters of Mercy made up most of the faculty, though certain classes were taught by lay teachers, all of whom were members of the parish. Some of the nuns teaching the students in the school's last decade had taught the parents of the current students. As was the case in most Catholic schools at the time, order was strictly enforced, and the work the nuns did to ensure that order was wholeheartedly supported by the parishioners.

Though the Catholic high school had once fielded a football team, by the 1960s the Saint Gabriel's uniforms were worn solely by basketball and baseball players. That they both wore uniforms was the only thing the two teams had in common. The entire student body would turn out for basketball games while very few, if any, attended the contests featuring the baseball teams. While the parents of baseball players would attend some of those games, the basketball stands were filled with parents, proud alumni, and local residents interested in following the local teams. To get an idea of just how popular basketball was at Saint Gabriel's, consider this fact: in 1956 there were 80 boys in the four high school classes, and 67 of them went out for basketball.

Former players remember how basketball was viewed throughout the little Catholic school and the community. Mike Heffernan, a 1968 graduate, recalled, "Everybody in the student body looked forward to and attended the games." Pete O'Donnell, who was an outstanding basketball and baseball player, said, "It [basketball] was the most important thing at the school for the students and for the people in the parish."

In the mid-1950s the Saint Gabriel's moderator of athletics was Father Edward Haggarty. The good father was determined to see the school's basketball team succeed. In the fall of 1958, the school's seniors surprised Haggarty with a birthday party. After blowing out the candles the priest announced, "My wish is that we take the Anthracite League pennant!"

Haggarty was known for his love of cigars and basketball as well as his distinct habit of wearing a cape to go along with his priestly garb. Seeing Haggarty on the streets brought to mind Spencer Tracy in the film *Dr. Jekyll and Mr. Hyde*. It was Father Haggarty who made the decision to provide support for the basketball program in order to put it on a higher plane than it had reached in the past. Part of this plan involved moving the team's home games out of the small bandbox gym located in the school. He had decided that the G-Men—or the Saints, as they were commonly referred to in the local paper—would play their home games in the spacious confines of Saint Joseph's gymnasium, a facility that could handle 2,800 spectators. It proved to be a good move as the stands were often packed with fans. Jerry Anderson, a future Saint Gabriel's coach, remembered that the first time he saw the team play as a spectator he had to sit on the steps of the stands as all the seats were filled. Saying that the players grew to like their new home would be putting it mildly as Mike Heffernan, who during the 1968 season watched numerous of his own shots tickle the twine at Saint Joe's, said, "We loved the place."

Saint Gabriel's was an original member of the Anthracite Basketball League, formed in the 1937 and made up of area schools with smaller enrollments than Hazleton High. A Saint Gabriel's priest, Father Edward Lynch, was the new league's first president. The other charter members included West Hazleton, Freeland, MMI, and Foster Township. The 1937 Saint Gabriel's team was led by Billy Boyle and Johnny Pfaff. Thirty years later Boyle would be recognized as the most avid fan of the Saints. His frenzied support of the G-Men during the sixties was preserved in a series of photos taken during a game and published in the local paper. Pfaff would be the key organizer and leader of the parish's biddy basketball program created in 1964.

Hazleton High was already an established member of the East Penn League when the Anthracite League was formed. The East Penn League included large high schools in the Allentown-Bethlehem area as well as the two public high schools in Tamaqua and Pottsville. By the time the Anthracite League was founded, the East Penn League had already produced multiple state champions, including Hazleton, which had won the Class A title twice in the 1920s under Coach Hughie McGeehan.

The Anthracite League's first game took place on December 10, 1937, when Freeland visited Foster Township and returned home a winner by the score of 32-13. The G-Men faced MMI in their initial league contest on January 7, 1938. MMI prevailed by the score of 33-25. Freeland clinched the first Anthracite League title on February 18, 1937, when they beat Saint Gabriel's on the loser's home court 37-25.

By the start of the 1947 season the league had expanded to seven teams with the addition of McAdoo and Hazle Township. Saint Gabriel's had yet to wear the league crown and fans of the G-Men were more than excited about the team's chances as the season got underway. Their excitement was well placed. The year before, the G-Men had captured the Anthracite League's second-half championship before losing to MMI in the league's championship playoff game. Led by the six-foot-four All-Regional center Jerry Moye (who would go on to captain the basketball team at Fordham) and John "Swish" Farley, Saint Gabriel's compiled a fine 15-6 record. Both star players were returning as seniors along with Coach Ned Dougherty, recently discharged from the service and ready to retake the helm as the team pursued its first league championship.

The '47 G-Men lived up to expectations, not only winning the school's first Anthracite Title, but also becoming the first league champion to go undefeated in league play. Along the way they defeated the defending champion and then-undefeated

MMI 39-35 on the loser's court. Farley and Moye led the winners, scoring sixteen and ten respectively. By the time the regular season ended, the team had set a school record by winning
eighteen consecutive games. On one night they demolished
Freeland by the score of 75-24, and Moye set a school and regional record by scoring forty-seven points. That performance
broke the record Moye had set the previous year when he scored
thirty-eight against Saint Nicholas of Wilkes-Barre.

The Saints also did some traveling in 1947 when they hit the
road to Chester—along with two busloads of fans—to take on
the highly regarded Chester Saint James team. The fans found
the journey to be a satisfying one when Saint Gabriel's came out
on top by a score of 38-35. The balance of the G-Men that year
was demonstrated by the fact that Moye, Farley, and Jackie
Flood were in the top ten in league scoring. When the Hazleton
paper selected its All-Anthracite Team, Moye and Farley were
named to the first unit, Flood made the second team, and
the teams other two starters—Buddy Gallagher and Johnny
"Mouse" Marinko—were placed on the third and fourth teams.
In addition, reserve Dick Moore earned an honorable mention.

Saint Gabriel's performance resulted in an invitation to
compete in the prestigious Knights of Columbus Invitational
Tournament held in Williamsport. Outstanding Catholic high
school teams from around the Commonwealth gathered to compete. Invitations were based on the team's performance without
regard for the size of the schools. By the luck of the draw, the
G-Men were lined up against Pittsburgh Central Catholic in the
tourney's first round. Most observers viewed this matchup as
the championship game. It turned out they were right.

The G-Men led throughout the contest and were up by six
heading into the final quarter. With under a minute to go, Saint
Gabriel's was up by one when a player by the name of Bill
Darragh hit a long set shot that gave the Pittsburgh school the
lead 31-30. That proved to be the final score. With the loss, the
G-Men finished the season with a record of 21-4. Mary Corrigan
(who would later marry John Farley and give birth to this author) was one of the many Saint Gabriel's fans who attended
that game. She maintains to this day that the G-Men were the
superior ball club. Central Catholic went on to win the tournament easily, defeating a team from Wilkes-Barre 42-27 in the
championship game.

After the 1947 season, the G-Men failed to seriously contend for the league title for a decade. Between 1948 and 1958, two schools, McAdoo and West Hazelton, won ten of the eleven league championships. The Saints did have some outstanding individual performers during these years including Chico Ferdinand and Joe McFadden. McFadden graduated in 1958 as the leading career scorer in the school's history with 1,095 points.

As talented as they were, these players couldn't carry their teams to victory. For example, Ferdinand averaged 26.3 points per game in the second half of the 1956 Anthracite League season, but Saint Gabriel's posted a record of 1-6. In McFadden's senior year the G-Men finished in a three-way tie for first in the Anthracite League's second half. Any chance of playing for the title evaporated when McAdoo romped to an easy 80-58 win over the Saints in the playoff game and Saint Gabriel's finished with a record of 14-10.

Prior to the start of the 1959 season, the *Hazleton Plain Speaker* predicted a rebuilding but winning year for the G-Men. The paper noted that Saint Gabriel's had found it rough going in the Anthracite League in recent years but noted that head coach Danny Gregoria had piloted the team to a strong finish in 1958. Though the team was returning only two varsity lettermen, help was expected from a strong JV team and from a standout on the freshman team by the name of Joe Sernak. The paper also noted that the school had formed a pep club that assured the team plenty of fan support in the coming season. Playing eight foes in exhibition games, the G-Men posted a 5-3 record in preparation for league play.

Things fell into place for the Saints as they rode a balanced attack to the first-half title, going undefeated along the way. In doing so, they became the first Saint Gabriel's team to defeat McAdoo at McAdoo since 1947. The aforementioned pep club followed the team to away games on buses furnished by the school. On January 17th, 1959, the club journeyed to Freeland to watch the G-Men take on White Haven in a contest held at the MMI gym. With forty seconds left to play, White Haven led 64-63. A White Haven player, Don Meier, was taking the ball to the hoop when he collided with G-Man Paul Kostic, sending both players to the floor. Referee Lou Smith signaled charging on Meier, his fifth personal, which put him out of the game.

Meier expressed his disagreement with the call by taking a swing, which missed, at Smith.

Smith promptly called a technical foul on Meier, who sent his next punch in the direction of another Saint Gabriel's player, Snapper O'Donnell. According to O'Donnell, that swing missed as well, but the one he delivered in return connected. The stands emptied as more than sixty fans rushed the floor, including six fans from the balcony who used Tarzan ropes to join the fray. O'Donnell remembers being pulled out of the battle by Tommy Malloy, a well-known fan of the Saints who had been seated in the balcony.

It took more than ten minutes to restore order before the G-Men made their way to the foul line to convert the shots that gave them their first lead in the game. When the dust finally cleared, the Saints won by the final score of 67-66. The next day the local paper carried the headline "Fans Stage Fisticuffs during Saint Gabriel's-White Haven Clash."

Things didn't go nearly as well for the G-Men in the league's second half as the team dropped three contests, and West Hazleton emerged on top, setting up a title game between the Saints and the Wildcats. As mentioned, West Hazleton was by far the largest school in the league in terms of enrollment, and the decade to come would be marked by many spirited contests between the two schools. The '59 title game took place before 2,300 fans at what was described as Berwick High School's lavish new sports palace. West Hazleton jumped on the G-Men early and in the second quarter led 25-7. Led by O'Donnell, who was the only senior starter, the G-Men fought back to get within six points in the third quarter. That was as close as it got. West Hazleton pulled away to a 55-40 victory, capturing the league title. O'Donnell, who led the G-Men by scoring fifteen, would go on to be the first and—as far as this author can tell—the only Saint Gabriel's player to be named most valuable player in the region's annual "dream game."

After finishing with a 17-7 record in 1959 and with four starters returning, the G-Men and their fans, much like in 1947, were looking forward to the 1960 season. Saint Gabriel's opened that season on December 1st, 1959, when they made the short hop to Weatherly. The Weatherly High gym was packed with more than 600 fans, and the majority of those were Saints followers who had either traveled on one of four buses supplied by the parish or as part of a long caravan of automobiles that made the trip. The line of vehicles leaving the home town and heading to an away game must have resembled a similar scene in the film *Hoosiers*. On this night the G-Men didn't disappoint, rolling to a 71-54 victory. As expected, the win highlighted the scoring balance the team would showcase throughout the year with all five starters scoring in double figures and Jay O'Donaghue leading the way with sixteen. The starting five duplicated that feat a few days later when they demolished Saint Ann's of Freeland at Saint Joseph's gym by a score of 82-34.

This season would mark the first time that Saint Gabriel's and Hazleton High would face each other on the basketball court. Previously, the only time the rivals faced each other were in scrimmages or occasionally during the summer months on the cities' playgrounds. By the end of the 1960s, these playground games drew crowds of Hazletonians who couldn't seem to get enough of the rivalry.

The initial contest between the two local schools was scheduled for December 16th, 1959, at Hazleton High. On the day before the game, the *Hazleton Plain Speaker* carried a notice that, aside from a few standing-room-only tickets, the game was sold out. That same day, one of the paper's sports columnists, Phil Sarno, reported that the G-Men were undefeated, having won their first four contests, and that Hazleton looked very impressive after winning its season opener against Tamaqua. Sarno described the rivalry as being at "fever pitch" (yes, he made this observation prior to the two teams ever having met) and predicted that the game would be a "humdinger." The night Sarno's column ran, Hazleton recorded its second victory, easily beating previously undefeated Berwick 75-49.

The weather in Hazleton was remarkably moderate for mid-December with clear skies and daytime temperatures in the high forties. Looking over the local paper on December 16th, Hazletonians may have noticed that Fidel Castro predicting the United States would invade Cuba in 1960. However, many probably quickly turned to the sports page to find out how Hazleton had done the night before against Berwick.

Going into the game, most local observers rated Hazleton a slight favorite. They had the height advantage, more depth, and we're playing in the friendly confines of their home gym. That said, the G-Men were expected to provide a tough test for the Mountaineers. This initial contest set the tone for the many games that would follow.

From the opening tap, play was rough and the referees had their hands full controlling the spirited players. Hazleton jumped to an 11-5 lead in the early going, but the Saints fought back and led 14-13 at the end of the quarter. Early in the second period, Referee Joe Serafin called the two teams together and issued a warning about the rough play. At the half, Hazleton led 32-29 and the fans anticipated a close one all the way to the final buzzer.

It didn't happen. Hazleton scored eleven of the first thirteen points scored in the third quarter, and when the buzzer sounded ending that period, the G-Men trailed 49-36. Hazleton owned the boards, finishing with a 59 31 rebounding edge, and two of the Saints' stalwarts, Paul Kostic and Joe Sernak, fouled out. Only one player, Tom Sharkey, reached double figures in scoring for the G-Men, who were thoroughly whipped 83-45. After the game, Saint Gabriel's subdued supporters could only hope that their team could turn it around when the two squads would meet for a second time in Saint Joseph's much larger gym.

The second meeting took place on December 29th before over 2,000 fans. By that time Saint Gabriel's had a record of 6-1 and Hazleton was undefeated, having won its first six games. Hazleton jumped to an 18-12 lead after one quarter and increased that six-point margin to fourteen by halftime. The G-Men played the taller Mountaineers even in the second half and came up on the short side of a 74-57 score.

Playing Hazleton was not the only way the Saint Gabriel's players saw their rivals on the court. On January 29th, 1960, Buff Turse, a local businessman described in the local paper as an "ardent sports fan," chartered a bus to take the Saint Gabriel's team to the Penn Palestra, where they took in Hazleton playing Bethlehem for the first-half championship of the East Penn League.

As it turned out, losing to Hazleton that year became quite common. The Mounts had an outstanding team that won the highly regarded East Penn League and finished the season with a 24-3 record. Hazleton made it to the District 11 title game in the state playoffs where they lost to Catasauqua 62-59. That game was decided by a controversial technical foul called late in the contest by a referee that Hazleton officials had specifically requested not be assigned to work the game.

The 1960 G-Men also had an outstanding season, finishing with twenty-two wins and four losses. Along the way they became the second Saint Gabriel's team to win the Anthracite League Title and, like the '47 team, went undefeated in league play. The G-Men revenged the loss to West Hazleton in the previous year's championship game by topping the Wildcats twice. The first game with West Hazleton was particularly noteworthy in that both teams were undefeated in league contests heading into the game. In addition, West Hazleton had the home court advantage. With 2½ minutes left the Wildcats were in command 60-54. From that point on, the G-Men outscored their rivals 14-2, winning by a final margin of 68-62. Cy Fulton, who would return to coach at the Hazleton central Catholic high school that replaced Saint Gabriel's, scored nine points in the contest, including a key field goal in the fourth quarter comeback. Sportswriter Phil Sarno summed up the contest the next day, writing, "So, once again, the little whippersnappers from Donegal Hill out-battled and out-hustled a terrific borough aggregation."

In the Catholic state playoffs, in which Catholic teams with fourteen wins could play, the newly crowned Anthracite League champs opened with a win, beating Scranton Saint Ann's by a score of 64-58. This set up a best-of-three game playoff against Plymouth Saint Vincent's for the Diocese Championship. The two teams split the first two games, setting up the third and decisive contest where Saint Vincent's prevailed by a score of 77-65. Paul Kostic scored nineteen in this game, which made him the second player in Saint Gabriel's history to score over 1,000 points in his career. He finished with a total of 1,016 points.

Heading into the 1961 season, nobody had any idea that the school was entering its last decade of existence. Nor could anyone predict the heights the G-Men would reach in those seasons, especially from 1965 to the school's final days in 1970.

2

WARM UPS

THE EARLY SIXTIES

Fresh off an Anthracite League title and the most successful season in more than a decade, the G-Men and their fans expected future success as they entered the sixties. It was quite a time to be a student at a Catholic school. By April 1960, a dashing, young Irish Catholic was making a strong run for the Democratic Party's nomination for the highest office in the land. If successful, John F. Kennedy would become the second Roman Catholic in history to be nominated by a major party as its standard bearer for president. In addition to the Cold War, the space race, and the presidential election, Hazleton residents had plenty of local basketball news coming their way in the months preceding the start of the 1961 season.

On April 11, 1960, the Hazleton paper informed readers that Democratic leaders, including the head of the Senate Democrats Lyndon Johnson, were pressing Congress to take action on a plan to provide health care aid for the elderly. One could also follow the presidential campaigns of John Kennedy and Hubert Humphrey, who were searching for votes in the West Virginia coal fields. The local grocery store was advertising a sale on Easter hams, which could be had for forty-nine cents a pound. In addition, for every purchase totaling $10 or more, the shopper would be rewarded with a hundred free S&H Green Stamps. In local news, it was reported that two mine officials had been found not guilty of manslaughter in the Knox mine disaster, where a flood claimed the lives of nine miners. On the sports page, there were stories covering the opening of the 1960 Major League Baseball season scheduled to begin the next day.

Of more than a little local interest was an account of a banquet held the evening before to honor Saint Gabriel's Anthracite Basketball League champions. It was reported that a large crowd attended the affair held in the school's auditorium. Father Haggarty used the opportunity to announce that he was turning over his post as athletic director to Father Paul Purcell. Haggarty said the move was necessitated by the mounting pressures he faced as acting pastor of the city's largest church.

Purcell, a native of Scranton, was thirty-two years old. He had been raised in a family of five children, three of whom became priests. Purcell became an assistant pastor at Saint Gabriel's upon his ordination in 1954, and he was very popular among both the student body and the parishioners as a whole. For his part, Purcell said he hoped to continue to build on the foundation Haggarty had laid in boosting the school's athletic program. Little did he know that a major decision regarding the basketball program would be thrust upon him before the start of the next school year.

Hazleton High School had a terrific year in 1960. They handily beat their two local rivals, Saint Gabriel's and West Hazleton. They were led by Coach Frank Serany, who had manned the helm for the Mountaineers for twelve seasons. Serany was a Hazleton graduate and was regarded by many at the time as the greatest basketball player in the history of that school. Coming off a year when he led the team to an East Penn League championship, few doubted he would return to coach in the 1961 season.

Thus it was quite a surprise when the Hazleton school board received a short letter from Serany on August 9th. The letter stated, "It is with deep regret that I submit my resignation as Hazleton Senior High School Basketball Coach. Respectfully yours, Frank J. Serany."

The short letter dominated sports news the next day. The *Hazleton Plain Speaker* noted that while Serany had not stated the reasons for his resignation, he had been "at odds with some school board members on more than one occasion." There were many stories around town about school board members exerting their influence when it came to Hazleton High School athletic teams. Numerous rumors circulated that some of the directors urged coaches to start certain players or face consequences. One didn't have to go far to find people in the area who would talk about superior athletes who were denied the opportunity to showcase their skills due to the political power the directors held over the coaches.

There is no denying that the Hazleton school board was a very different animal in those days. Stories were rampant, and some would say it was common knowledge that securing a teaching position in the Hazleton school district, in some if not many cases, required a payment to a school director. In the mid-1970s, Ed Parsons, a former Hazleton student, recalled approaching a director he knew about securing a permanent teaching position. Parsons pointed out he was a graduate of the school, had participated in the basketball program, and had been active as a substitute teacher for two years when he made his case requesting consideration for a full-time position. The school director responded that he'd be happy to consider Ed and that currently that consideration cost $2,000.

Whatever Serany's reasons, within days the local newspaper was reporting that Saint Gabriel's coach Danny Gregoria was being mentioned as his successor. The board moved quickly, and at a school board meeting held on August 23rd, Gregoria was named as Hazleton's new coach by a vote of 12-1. The lone dissenting vote was cast by the president of the board, Girard Stish. Mr. Stish evidently had a long memory, for among his objections to hiring the new coach was the fact that in the late 1920s, Gregoria had transferred from Hazleton to Saint Gabriel's to finish his last two years of high school. While at Saint Gabriel's, Gregoria was a star on the basketball team and was selected to the All-State Catholic team. Stish objected to Gregoria being referred to as a basketball star, saying that Gregoria was a star in the way any major league player would be if they went to the minor leagues. Saint Gabriel's was being compared to the minor leagues and needed a new coach with a little over two months to go before the start of the season.

For Saint Gabriel's, finding a coach was complicated. Gregoria had taken the Saint Gabriel's job in December of 1956 after Tommy Orr was forced to resign the position because of Pennsylvania Interscholastic Athletic Association (PIAA) regulations. Orr resided in West Hazleton and was a teacher in Dennison Township, which was certainly within the Greater Hazleton area. Father Haggarty had hired Orr after failing to locate any interested candidates within the Hazleton school district. Five games into the 1956-57 basketball season, Haggarty received a phone call from Coach Carl Meier of White Haven, who told him that he planned to file a complaint with the PIAA relative to the rule that coaches must coach in the same district in which they teach. Haggarty exhausted every avenue, but the PIAA stood firm with Mark Funk, the organization's head, when he informed the priest that he should "drop basketball if the situation could not be remedied." With Saint Gabriel's facing this crisis, Gregoria, who taught at Hazleton High, agreed to take over at his alma mater. With Gregoria gone, Father Purcell had to quickly find a new coach who would meet the PIAA standards.

At this time two organizations were involved the administration of high school athletics in the Commonwealth. The PIAA was in charge of public school programs while the Pennsylvania Catholic Interscholastic Athletic Association (PCIAA) governed Catholic high schools. At the time Catholic schools were not permitted by the PIAA to participate in state playoffs and as a result the PCIAA had established a separate playoff system. The PIAA still exercised considerable control over the Catholic schools by restricting public schools from playing against Catholic institutions that failed to meet PIAA standards.

By mid-September, the Saints had yet to name a coach. The Hazleton paper speculated that the school was awaiting approval from the PIAA before naming Gregoria's successor. A number of names were being floated as being in consideration or interested in the position including Frank Serany, Ernie Valente, and Jim Brehony. On September 29th, Phil Sarno was reporting both Serany and Valente had turned down the position, and the person now being considered was a "borderline" case in terms of the territorial requirements of the PIAA. The paper also reported that there was a candidate ready to take the position who clearly met the PIAA standards.

For his part, Father Purcell was conveying an extremely enthusiastic attitude as the season approached. With seven players topping the six-foot mark, the good father noted that this would be "the tallest team we ever had at our school and we simply can't wait until the season opens to see how the boys perform." Purcell added that the student body was so excited about the coming season that the coaching announcement would be made at a student assembly program.

True to his word, Father Purcell assembled the school's high school classes in Saint Gabriel's auditorium on October 4th, 1960. There he announced that Francis "Chip" Kender had been hired to guide the G-Men. The students reacted with a tremendous ovation. Purcell introduced Kender as a man with a wealth of basketball experience. Kender had excelled as a player at Hazleton High and later as part of a US Army team. At East Stroudsburg State Teacher's College, he starred for the team prior to his graduation in 1959. It was noted that Kender had acquired coaching experience on the junior high level and most recently assisted the Hazleton program that had won the East Penn League Title the year before. Thus it came to be that Hazleton High was being coached by a Saint Gabriel's graduate while a member of the Hazleton alumni had taken the helm at the Wyoming Street school.

The new coach took the stage and thanked the student body for their "fine reception" and remarked how happy he was to have been named the new coach. He promised to do his best to have his teams live up to the tradition that had been set for them as "the fighting Irish." Kender, who was twenty-seven years old, met all the PIAA requirements. He would serve as head coach for five years. It would be the longest run of any head coach at Saint Gabriel's in the school's final decade.

Many of the players who made up Kender's teams still have positive feelings about the coach. Mike O'Donnell, who played on three of Kender's squads, says, "He brought us into the modern world of basketball." Pete O'Donnell remembers him as a "real gentleman" and a man who was "a teacher who coached basketball." Paul Hoffman described Kender as "a good coach." Both Ray McBrearty and Dennis Olexa recall that Kender was nothing if not an impressive-looking young man. The photo in the newspaper published with the story of the announcement supports this. Kender wears a calm but determined look that is accentuated by his sharp features and closely cropped dark hair, not one strand out of place. It's certainly in keeping with Dennis Olexa's memory of Kender as the "best dressed man in town."

A little over a month later, John F. Kennedy became the first Roman Catholic president in the nation's history. Kennedy's win pleased the vast majority of Saint Gabriel's parishioners as well as their children, who made up the student body. With that victory behind them, thoughts turned to the upcoming basketball season and the new coach. In previewing Kender's first team, the *Plain Speaker* noted that Danny Gregoria had taken a perennial Anthracite League doormat and created a champion. Adding that Gregoria hadn't left the cupboard bare, the piece pointed out the G-Men returned two starters in Joe Sernak and Tom Sharkey. Kender himself envisioned a team that could develop into a contender to repeat as Anthracite League champs.

That said, no one was predicting a repeat of the 1960 season where the G-Men and, according to the local paper, their "fantastically loyal fans" had enjoyed what many considered the greatest year in the school's basketball history. West Hazleton was the odds-on favorite to win the league title, and in the first half of league play the Saints would face three tough opponents—McAdoo, MMI and the Wildcats—on the road. In addition, due to injuries, two players expected to step in and be major contributors this season, Tom Barrett and Tim Curry, would be unavailable for action until sometime in January.

A veteran Wilkes-Barre Saint Mary's team spoiled Kender's debut when they beat the G-Men 69-58 at Wilkes-Barre. Sernak and Sharkey accounted for thirty-four of the fifty-eight points put on the board by the Saints, and no other player approached double figures as the new coach substituted freely in search of a combination that clicked. Kender snagged his first win on December 2nd, 1960, when Saint Gabriel's traveled to Freeland and beat Saint Ann's by ten. Another defeat at the hands of Saint Mary's followed, so the G-Men would face Hazleton High coming off a loss and sporting a losing 1-2 record.

Hazleton had won their first two games, and many expected an easy victory for the Mountaineers. Before 1,600 fans described by the local paper as "almost hysterical," the two teams battled to a 17-17 tie after one quarter. The G-Men were utilizing a fast break offense that became a trademark during the Kender years, and they scored twenty points in the second period. Still the Mounts showed plenty of offensive power of their own, and they netted twenty-seven in the period to take a 44-37 lead as the teams headed to their locker rooms to prepare for the second half. In the third quarter the Saints found themselves down by eleven before rallying to narrow the margin to five at 60-55 when the buzzer ended the quarter.

Hazleton was up by three, 66-63, with 3:22 to play when Coach Gregoria called a time-out. He directed his players not to shoot unless they had worked the ball inside for a high percent-age shot. On three successive possessions the Mounts ignored these instructions, taking outside shots and missing all three attempts. After the third miss Tom Sharkey took the ball the length of the floor and scored, cutting the Hazleton lead to one.

With under a minute to play, Saint Gabriel's got the ball back after another Hazleton miss and called time-out. Kender directed the G-Men to play for the last shot. With thirty-seven seconds left to play, a pass from Sharkey intended for Sernak was intercepted. Hazleton attempted to run out the clock but an aggressive Sharkey forced a jump ball with seventeen seconds left to play. Hazleton controlled the tap and called time-out. The Mounts successfully inbounded the ball and the Saints' Eddie Olcxa fouled Billy Nance, who made the one of two foul shots to put Hazleton ahead 67-65. When the second shot missed Sernak secured the rebound and passed it to Sharkey, who was fouled taking the ball up court with five seconds left to play. Sharkey, showcasing his coolness under pressure, converted both ends of the one-and-one to knot the score at sixty-seven and send the contest into overtime.

Both teams played cautiously in the overtime, and with a minute to play, Hazleton was nursing a 73-72 lead. The Mounts had possession of the ball and successfully killed the clock to the ten-second mark when the G-Men were forced to foul. Nance made both free throws, and then Sharkey was called for walking as he advanced the ball up court with four seconds left. The G-Men fouled again, and once again Hazleton converted both shots to make the final 77-72. The Mountaineers had escaped with a victory, but Saint Gabriel's faithful left Saint Joe's feeling like they had gone toe to toe with the larger school and dem-onstrated they belonged. One couldn't help but wonder if some of the Saint Gabriel's players, like Eddie Olexa, didn't leave the gym feeling like they had let one get away.

Kender's G-Men were now off to a 1-3 start. On December 17th, 1960, the Hazleton paper reported that the Saints had gotten back on the winning track by defeating Saint Ann's for the second time by a score of 73-53. Once again the G-Men were led by Sernak and Sharkey, who scored twenty-two and twenty respectively. After five games, the two stars were both averaging twenty points a game.

By this time the Anthracite League had grown to include nine teams, with Weatherly being the newest member. The addition of the Wreckers was viewed as a boost to the league as Weatherly High had a long and successful basketball history. Indeed, in the years to come Weatherly and Saint Gabriel's would battle in a number of exciting contests and memorable playoff games.

The Saints took on an undefeated McAdoo team in their first league game under the tutelage of Coach Kender. The G-Men were no match for the Maroons, falling to McAdoo 68-47 in the winner's gym. Thus the matter of a second straight undefeated Anthracite League season was settled early for Saint Gabriel's. At 2-4, Kender's head coaching career was off to a rough start.

Just a few evenings later in the waning days of 1960, West Hazleton served notice that it was going to have a significant say in the race for the league title. The Wildcats defeated Hazleton for the first time on the basketball court by a score of 67-59. Phil Sarno stressed the significance of the victory in his column when he opined that West Hazleton could hold its own with the majority of teams in the East Penn League. In Sarno's view, the Anthracite League was coming of age.

Hazleton got back in the winning column against the G-Men, winning by ten on their home court. Though the loss dropped the Saints record to 2-5, the game marked the return of Tim Curry and Tom Barrett as active players for Saint Gabriel's. Local observers agreed that as the two rounded into peak playing condition, the Saints would be a much tougher outfit.

While the duo's return aided the G-Men, the team finished the league's first half with a record of 4-4 and found themselves mid-pack in the standings. West Hazleton took first half honors, going undefeated and beating a highly touted McAdoo team by ten on the loser's court. By the time the G-Men were scheduled to face the still undefeated Wildcats in the second-half race, the Saints had dropped three of four on their second trip around the circuit. The record didn't reflect the team's talent as pointwise, few teams dominated the Saints. The losses were coming in extremely close games. That said, this edition of G-Men was finding it difficult to put together a winning combination, and Kender's preseason prediction of contending for league honors sounded hollow.

Still, when West Hazleton and Saint Gabriel's met at Saint Joseph's in their second half matchup, the G-Men gave the Wildcats all they could handle before coming out on the short end by a score of 48-45. Coach Kender used a ball control offense, and it almost resulted in what the *Plain Speaker* said would have been the biggest upset of the season. Despite the valiant effort led by Sernak, who scored twelve points while hauling down twenty-one rebounds, the game resulted in another Saint Gabriel's defeat.

Without a doubt the season had been a disappointing one for the new coach, the team, and Saint Gabriel's fans, but those same fans refused to give up on their team. Three days after the heartbreaking West Hazleton loss, three busloads of G-Men followers made their way to Freeland to watch their Saints notch a 104-72 victory over White Haven. The local paper noted that the game, played at the MMI gym, had attracted the biggest crowd of the season for a contest held at that venue.

The win over White Haven proved to be the last victory for Saint Gabriel's as the '61 season came to a close. Following a loss to Hazle Township, the G-Men closed the season at home against MMI. The Saints played tough for three quarters before being outscored 25-13 in the final stanza. As the final buzzer sounded, the scoreboard read Visitors-71, Home-54. The Saints had finished the season with an 8-14 mark overall and 6-10 in league play. Throughout the frustrating season, the team retained the support of its loyal fans. Now there was nothing to do but wait until next year.

Despite losing both Joe Sernak and Tom Sharkey to graduation, Hazleton's newest newspaper, the *Standard Speaker*, was optimistic about Saint Gabriel's chances heading into the 1961-62 season. The paper noted that Chip Kender had a year of head coaching under his belt and would be working with all his players, unlike the previous year when a fractured wrist and an appendectomy had sidelined two of his key performers early in the season. Kender himself sounded optimistic, saying that this year's team would be better balanced and faster than last year's squad. The coach spoke highly of seniors Dennis Roman, Tim Curry, and Ed Olexa, the latter being touted as one of the best ball handlers in the region. Also mentioned by reporter Ray Saul was the arrival of sophomore Frank Smith, whose family had moved to Hazleton from Philadelphia and who appeared to have secured a position as a starter. According to Saul, the G-Men "have an excellent chance on improving on last year's 8-14 mark and may do a lot better than that."

The Saints made their debut on December 8th, which happens to be the Feast of the Immaculate Conception. Most Catholics would say that would be a good omen for a team named after Saint Gabriel. However, any advantage was negated by the fact that the opening day opponent was Marian Catholic.

Approximately 800 fans found their seats at Saint Joe's to watch the contest. As always, the Saint Gabriel's student body was out in force and already in place by the time the ball was thrown into the air starting the junior varsity contest. The junior G-Men prevailed 49-41.

Almost immediately after the visitors took the floor to begin their warm-ups, the Saints took the court, breaking through the paper fastened on a large hoop held by the cheerleaders as the sounds of "When the Saints Come Marching In" filled the gymnasium. Led by Dennis Roman and Eddie Olexa, Saint Gabriel's delivered a victory for Coach Kender by holding on to beat the Colts by a score of 78-71. The next day Don Barnes, writing in the *Standard Speaker*, made the observation that the G-Men could be a dark horse for Anthracite League honors. Barnes also mentioned that Hazleton High loomed next for the Saints, and having never beaten the Mounts, "they'd give their eye teeth to do it."

The two teams met on December 12th in the Hazleton High School. The school stood high atop the city on the north side of town and was known as "the Castle on the Hill." Early in the third quarter, Olexa canned a layup and the G-Men trailed by just two, 41-39. The Mounts refused to surrender the lead and expanded it to 51-44 when the quarter ended. Hazleton was still leading by seven early in the fourth quarter when both Tom Barrett and Tim Curry fouled out. From that point on the home team took control and won by the deceptive margin of 75-55. Most observers, including sportswriter Sarno, agreed that the G-Men had exhibited "the traditional fighting spirit of Saint Gabriel's High School." All were aware that there would be a rematch on December 22nd.

By the time the 22nd rolled around, Hazleton remained undefeated, sporting a 4-0 record. The G-Men were 3-1, having won two straight after hitting that bump in the road called Hazleton

High. The local paper predicted the biggest crowd of the season would be on hand to witness the contest, which would also be broadcast on local radio station WAZL.

Sports editor Ray Saul was one of the approximately two thousand fans who made their way to Saint Joe's to take in the battle, and a battle it turned out to be. In the first quarter the score was tied at eight before Hazleton staged a mild rush to take a 16-12 lead as the period ended. In the second eight minutes, the score was tied at sixteen, eighteen, twenty and twenty-six before Hazleton scored to go up by two. The G-Men answered with five straight points and headed to the locker room at half holding a 31-28 lead.

The Saints came out strong in the third quarter and midway through the period pushed their lead to 47-37. At this point Hazleton went on a run outscoring Saint Gabriel's 12-1 to take a 49-48 edge entering the final eight minutes. Tom Barrett, who had played an outstanding floor game, scored first as the final quarter got underway, nailing a difficult hook shot that resulted in a three-point play when he was fouled. Eddie Olexa then scored successive field goals and the G-Men were in command 55-49. The Mounts fought back and with thirty seconds show-ing on the clock trailed by two at 63-61.

Trying for a steal, Hazleton fouled Barrett, who hit one of two free throws. After another missed Hazleton attempt was se-cured by the Saints, Olexa was intentionally fouled with three seconds on the clock. He also hit one of two foul shots, making the final score Saint Gabriel's 65, Hazleton 61.

The little school from the south side of the city had, in the words of Mr. Saul, "stunned previously unbeaten HHS . . . be-fore a frantic crowd." Eddie Olexa had scored twenty-five points in leading the G-Men to victory. Father Purcell rushed into the victors' locker room after the game and proclaimed, "No school tomorrow." It was a Friday night, but nobody cared. Saint Gabriel's fans celebrated the victory into the early morning hours. Fortunately, the players didn't join them. Dennis Olexa remembers his father calling his brother Eddie to breakfast ear-ly the next morning: "Eddie, get down here! Just because you're the hero of the Hazleton game doesn't mean you can sleep in."

Less than a week later, West Hazleton stated its case as the top team in the region when the Wildcats easily took Hazleton to task 65-45 on the Mounts' home court. With the win, West

Hazleton looked to be the team to beat for the Anthracite League title.

With the addition of Saint Ann's, the league had now expanded to include ten teams. By the first week of January, Saint Gabriel's had notched one victory in league play before taking on perennial power McAdoo at Saint Joe's. Many thought the G-Men would suffer a letdown after the big win over Hazleton and the over-a-week-long layoff. Instead, the G-Men looked like a definite contender as they beat the visitors 71-66. The win bolstered the enthusiasm of the Saints' loyal fan base who were still fired up by the victory over Hazleton. Indeed, it seemed like Saint Gabriel's starters could hang with anybody. What the team lacked was depth—if one of the starters got hurt or in foul trouble, there weren't any players on the bench who could fill in at their level. The big showdown with West Hazleton was but a week away. It would be played at Saint Joe's, and folks were already predicting a crowd of more than two thousand.

On January 8th, the day before the game, Father Purcell announced that there would be an advanced ticket sale for the game on the 9th between 1 and 4 p.m. at the school's athletic office. Purcell said the advance sale resulted from the numerous requests that had been made for tickets and in the hope of easing the anticipated crush for tickets at the gate. Based on superior depth, West Hazleton was rated a slight favorite.

The prediction of the game drawing the largest crowd of the season proved correct, and the game lived up to its billing. It was a hard fought contest that saw the Wildcats gradually edge ahead every quarter through to the end of the third period when the Cats led by a 46-35 margin. Once again, it was Eddie Olexa who led the G-Men on a fourth quarter comeback that saw the Saints pull to within four at 60-56 with about a minute left to play. That turned out to be the final margin; West Hazleton hung on to win 62-58. Bench strength did prove critical as the G-Men only got two points from their reserves while the Wildcats netted seventeen. Don Barnes, covering the game for the *Standard Speaker*, summed it up by writing, "Saint Gabriel's gave it a great try and barely missed. West Hazleton showed it had the stuff to meet a stiff challenge. Whoever beats either of these clubs will be beating a good one."

The lack of quality help coming off the bench came back to haunt the Saints less than two weeks later when they traveled to Hazle Township to take on the Shippers. Tom Barrett was unavailable due to illness and Tim Curry fouled out of the game and saw very limited action. Hazle Township, sporting a 3-7 record entering the contest, upset the G-Men 58-48, effectively eliminating Saint Gabriel's from the chase for first-half honors.

Although they were out of the running as far as the first-half title went, the G-Men still had a big game left against the Weatherly Wreckers who owned a 7-0 record when the two teams met at Weatherly in late January. For three quarters, Saint Gabriel's was in control and held double digit leads on several occasions. In the final period Weatherly roared back to tie the score at fifty-five with four minutes left to play. The G-Men scored twice to regain the advantage but Weatherly answered with five straight points to take a 60-59 lead. The Saints had nothing left and dropped their third Anthracite League game by a final of 67-63. The G-Men would finish the first half with a record of 6-3. West Hazleton would best Weatherly in a battle of unbeatens to take the first-half title. Heading into the second half Saint Gabriel's was dealt another blow when the PIAA ruled that Tom Barrett had exhausted his eligibility. This was the first of four significant PIAA rulings that would touch the Saints basketball program in its final years.

By late February the G-Men record in the second half stood at 4-3, and with thirteen total season victories there was doubt that the team would reach the fourteen victory mark needed to qualify for the Catholic playoffs. Such was the situation on February 23, 1962, when the heavily favored Weatherly Wreckers traveled to Hazleton to meet the Saints at Saint Joe's. Things looked very dim indeed when Weatherly raced to a 32-13 halftime lead. With their backs against the wall, the G-Men outscored the Wreckers 20-8 in the third quarter to narrow the margin to seven entering the final quarter.

With just over two minutes left Weatherly scored to go up by five, 48-43, and it appeared that the great comeback effort by Coach Kender's fired up crew was going to fall short. It didn't. That goal by Weatherly was their last, and the G-Men answered with goals by Olexa and Denny Roman to pull within one. With just over a minute left to play Olexa scored again, giving the Saints their first lead in the game. With just fourteen seconds on the clock, Frank Smith stole the ball from a Wrecker and Saint Gabriel's scored another bucket to make the final score 51-48.

The win set up a contest with Williamsport Saint Joseph's in the Catholic playoffs.

The playoffs started before the final slate of games in the Anthracite League had been played. Saint Joseph's was an impressive 21-1 going into the game. That heady record wasn't enough to deter the G-Men faithful, who arrived in Kingston aboard five chartered buses and numerous personal vehicles. Unfortunately, the Saints caught St. Joseph's on a night where they could not miss. As a team they hit more than 50 percent of their shots and their leading scorer Dave Hillyer, who scored twenty-two all on field goals, hit at a 75 percent pace. It proved to be too much for the Saints, who were beaten decisively 69-49. Once again Eddie Olexa led the G-Men with thirteen points.

Saint Gabriel's wound down the '62 season losing to McAdoo 76-66. The same night that a few miles down the road in Hershey, Wilt Chamberlain scored a hundred points, setting a National Basketball Association record. As a team, the Saints couldn't match Wilt's total. Denny Roman scored twenty-four and Eddie Olexa put fifteen on the board in the losing cause. The G-Men finished with a record of 14-9, but the season wasn't a total loss. They had beaten Hazleton for the first time and held their own with West Hazleton (which won the league title, going undefeated for the second consecutive year). Along the way Eddie Olexa had emerged as a star in big wins against Hazleton and Weatherly. A senior, Olexa had played his final game wearing the purple and white. No one knew it at the time, but it would have been appropriate for him to announce at the season's end, in true Al Jolson style, "I'd just like to say on behalf of the Olexa family, you ain't seen nothin' yet."

3

PRE-GAME INTRODUCTIONS

THE YOUTH MOVEMENT
1962–1964

Before the start of the 1962-63 basketball season, a major change in the Anthracite League membership took place. Lou Sauers, the president of the McAdoo Area School Board, announced in June that perennial basketball power McAdoo, which had won multiple league titles in the last decade, would be joining the Hazleton School District. The move would result in the closing of McAdoo High School, whose students would now attend Hazleton High School. In terms of athletics, the jointure was seen to greatly enhance Hazleton prospects in the coming years. Athletically, it also benefited Marian Catholic, a high school located just outside Tamaqua in Hometown, Pennsylvania.

Meanwhile, Chip Kender was attempting to deal with a number of issues as the basketball season approached. His team had virtually no varsity experience. Roman, Olexa, Curry, and Barrett, the nucleus of the 1962 team, had graduated. Frank Smith, who had started as a sophomore, was lost when his family relocated. Then Jim Haefner, a six-foot-three senior who had gained some varsity experience the year before, was forced to give up basketball due to a chronic knee injury. At a larger school, these problems may not have been insurmountable, but with less than a hundred boys in the four high school classes at Saint Gabriel's, it added up to an obstacle taller than JFK's pledge to land a man on the moon before the end of the decade.

Kender made the decision to start five underclassmen. He would play junior Joe Clark at center and surround him with four sophomores—Jerry Sernak, Mike O'Donnell, Mike

Yourishin, and Charlie Gennaro. When one examined Saint Gabriel's varsity and junior varsity roster, it had quite a youthful look. Of the twenty players listed, only six were from the junior and senior classes. There were thirteen sophomores and one freshman by the name of Pete O'Donnell. Coach Kender, in summing up his team's chances, acknowledged that wins were going to be hard to come by this season, but in his view it would all pay off in the following two years. The *Standard Speaker* agreed, urging the followers of the G-Men to have patience in the coming season. The student body needed no urging as they embraced this young team as if they were defending champions.

Saint Gabriel's was scheduled to open the season on December 4, 1962. National news that day included reports that conservative Republicans were meeting in Chicago to begin a drive to ensure that Nelson Rockefeller, New York's governor, would not be the party's presidential nominee in 1964. In Hazleton, the stores on Broad Street were alive with shoppers preparing for the Christmas holidays. Local hunters were busy as well, and the number of deer kills was reported as heavy on the second day of the hunting season. Bobby Darin and Sandra Dee were starring in the romantic comedy *If a Man Answers*, which was showing at the Grand Theater.

Meanwhile, the members of the Saint Gabriel's student body were making plans to meet for tonight's opening game. This support was reflected in sports editor Ray Saul's daily column, where he commented that "although Saint Gabriel's will field an inexperienced team, the G-Men have probably the most loyal fans in the region and a good-sized crowd will turn out at Saint Joseph's gym to see the G-Men battle Marian Catholic in the opener."

Those loyal followers did indeed fill the seats that evening and watched Marian get things going by winning the junior varsity game 42-35. The varsity game had to remind many in the crowd of games played by that 1947 Anthracite League championship team in terms of the final score, 39-36. The difference was that the G-Men found themselves holding the short straw at the conclusion of the contest. There was little doubt that this young group was going to struggle, as evidenced by the fact that for eight full minutes Saint Gabriel's failed to score. That said, with one minute remaining, they only trailed by one. After the game, a group of fifth graders began what would become a tradition, running from Saint Joseph's to the lobby of the *Standard Speaker* to report the score and to find out the results of other local high school games being played that night.

Three days later after the G-Men had dropped their second game to Plymouth Saint Vincent's 51-35, the local press was already looking ahead to a potentially better future. Wishing it was otherwise, Don Barnes wrote, "It's going to be a long winter for Saint Gabriel's basketball fans. With the kind of support the student body gives the team, even when it's a hopeless cause, they deserve a winner. Well, there'll be other years." Unfortunately, Hazleton High was next on the slate for the G-Men.

Hazleton had lost its opener, but everyone was sure the Mounts would break into the win column versus Saint Gabriel's. Even the local paper, noting that the G-Men had notched their first win in the series a year earlier, flatly stated, "There will be no repeat." Evidently that news did not reach the many students who attended the Saints' pep rally. For those present, it seemed like a victory for the G-Men was all but assured.

In spite of the certainty of the outcome, over 1,700 fans found their way to Saint Joe's to watch the local rivals. From the opening tip-off it was clear the youthful Saint Gabriel's squad was not going to go away easy. In the first quarter the score was tied five times and ended with a G-Men holding one-point lead, 14-13. In the second period the Saints got hot and opened up a 28-19 advantage before Hazleton went on a run of their own to narrow the margin to 34-31 at half. After totaling thirty-five points in each of their first two games, the G-Men had almost scored that many in a single half against the senior-laden Hazleton club.

Most observers felt that the Mountaineers would put it together at half and come out and take control. The Saints had other ideas, and they refused to fold, maintaining their lead at 52-49 heading into the final period. At the five-minute mark, Ron Hess hit a jumper that gave Hazleton their first lead since scoring the opening point of the game. Sernak, O'Donnell, and Yourishin had fouled out for the G-Men. A minute later Saint Gabriel's reserve Jim Gallagher picked up his fifth foul and headed for the bench. Hazleton took advantage and finally pulled away to win 73-61. Joe Clark had played a tremendous game for the losers, scoring sixteen points and consistently making his defensive presence felt in the middle. The following day, Ray Saul wrote that Saint Gabriel's "came within five minutes of pulling off the biggest upset in regional basketball history." He also echoed the sentiment expressed by his colleague the previous week when he made it a point to commend the Saint Gabriel's students for their tremendous spirit. The loss proved to be one of the high points of the season, but that spirit never wavered.

The Saints dropped to 0-4 when they traveled to Plymouth and suffered another defeat at the hands of Saint Vincent's, 62-44. Up next on the schedule was West Hazleton, the odds-on favorite to successfully defend their Anthracite League title. The Wildcats hadn't lost a league game since February 5, 1960, but this was a far different Saint Gabriel's team than the one that had defeated West Hazleton that night. As a matter of fact, West Hazleton was returning all five starters from last year's championship team. In addition, the game would be played at West Hazleton, and the Wildcats had scored as many points in two games as the G-Men had in four.

The game went according to script as the home team jumped to a 15-3 first-quarter lead and never looked back, winning by a final margin of 67-30. Not a single Saint Gabriel's player managed to hit double figures. By the time Hazletonians were ringing in 1963, the G-Men had lost two more, including an 80-28 defeat at the hands of Hazleton. Ray Saul, growing more pessimistic as the season progressed, opined that "Saint Gabriel's may go through this season without winning a game."

There was no doubt that the G-Man were struggling. After hanging tough with Saint Ann's for three quarters, they managed to score only three points in the final period and dropped a 46-32 decision. Despite the mounting losses, the Saints fans never wavered in their support. They continued to fill the stands at Saint Joe's and make the trips to the away games, never leaving until the final buzzer and cheering as loud for the last basket as they did for the first.

The next game for the Saints was scheduled for January 8th when they would face a Hazle Township team sporting a 4-1 record. The game would be played at Saint Joe's. The *Standard Speaker* on the day of the meeting described Hazle Township as a "heavy pick" to emerge victorious. Further down the sports page was a small story noting that Saint Gabriel's freshman team, coached by Vince Gallagher, had defeated West Hazleton 60-39 the night before. Pete O'Donnell, a name that would become quite familiar to G-Men fans, had scored twenty in the win.

Perhaps inspired by their younger counterparts, Saint Gabriel's upset Hazle Township 56-52 before what was described as an "appreciative crowd." Once again the Saint Gabriel's fifth graders arrived at the *Standard Speaker* breathless after making the run from Saint Joe's. The employee on duty looked up at them as they entered the lobby and asked, "So how much did you guys lose by tonight?" The excited boys duly reported that the G-Men had broken through and won their first of the season. Looking at the boys over his glasses, the man responded, "Good, you fellas deserve it."

The youthful G-Men broke into the win column, at least shedding the monkey of a winless season off their backs. What was clear about this team was that it was struggling to find both an offensive leader and identity. Generally, even weak teams have at least one scorer who can carry the load at least for a while. A list of the region's top twenty scorers at what was roughly the midpoint of the season included not a single Saint Gabriel's player. MMI, the Saints' next opponent, had three players in the top twenty.

Given their offensive woes and the opponent, one would have guessed that the G-Men wouldn't make a game of it. If you had told someone before the game that MMI would also wind up controlling the boards—snagging forty-five rebounds compared to the seventeen pulled down by the Saints—most observers would have expected a convincing win for the more experienced MMI squad. To everyone's surprise, at the half MMI held a slim lead of 32-31. The Preppers, as they are still known, opened things up in the second half by outscoring the Saints 56-33. The final score was 88-64. For the G-Men, the sixty-four points was a season high. Joe Clark had another good game, hitting for nineteen, and sophomore Jerry Sernak made his presence felt by adding sixteen. Their loyal fans were sure the team was improving and more wins would be had before the season was over. At least the fifth graders making the run to the *Standard Speaker* hoped so.

All the hope in the world couldn't help the G-Men when they met Weatherly a few days later. What was described as a good-sized crowd saw the Wreckers wreak havoc on the court at Saint Joe's building with a 28-9 advantage after eight minutes of play. The game was never in doubt, and it seemed like the Saints had taken a step backward in the 83-45 drubbing. Little noticed was a young left-handed sophomore sharpshooter by the name of Jim Barrett who led Saint Gabriel's in scoring with seventeen points. A reserve at the season's start, Barrett had worked—or perhaps shot—his way into the starting lineup.

The Saints then went on the road to face Foster Township. For three quarters Coach Kender's troops clung to small leads. With just a few seconds to play, the score was tied at 54. A Foster Township sophomore Tom Koral scored the winning goal as the buzzer sounded. The Saint Gabriel's team, dominated by sophomores, had been beaten by one of their peers. Once again Jim Barrett had paced the G-Men attack, scoring fourteen. The loss dropped the Saints record to 1-11.

Meanwhile, all but unnoticed, Coach Vince Gallagher's freshman squad continued to put together a solid season. In their most recent outing, they defeated Mother of Grace 58-42, led by Pete O'Donnell's seventeen points.

The G-Men took a week off before ending the Anthracite League first half by coming up on the short end of an 83-67 score versus Freeland. The script for the Saints was becoming familiar: keep it tight for two or three quarters and then fade in the fourth. Coach Kender was struggling to get his youthful charges to finish games.

It was at this point in the season that Saint Gabriel's played a game that would never be repeated in the short history left to the school. The G-Men returned to the ever friendly confines of the small gym located in Saint Gabriel's school to face a team made up of the school's recent graduates. The game marked the final time a Saint Gabriel's varsity team played a game in their school's gym. The alumni squad included Joe McFadden, who remained the leading scorer in the school's history with 1,095 points. McFadden would find himself busy signing autographs for the Saint Gabriel grade school students who rushed to grab the seats in the front rows to witness the contest. The alumni also featured former stars Denny Roman and Eddie Olexa as well as Cy Fulton, who had played on the school's 1960 championship team. McFadden led the alumni scoring fourteen, but the young G-Men led by Jim Barrett, who dropped in twenty-two, prevailed easily 60-44. Little known to the crowd crammed into the small Saint Gabriel's gym, it would soon no longer be necessary to invite former stars back to celebrate championships and individual achievements. The Saints' loyal followers would soon watch current players rewrite the school's individual and team basketball records in ways no one would have dared predict on February 2, 1963.

Saint Gabriel's began the Anthracite League second half on the road against the team that had beaten them to end the first half. They surprised those fans who traveled to Freeland by jumping out to a 21-13 lead after one quarter. By the end of the third period the margin was 53-43, and they slightly widened that in the final stanza, earning their second win (unless you count the alumni game) 73-60. Jim Barrett had another fine game as did Jerry Sernak, both scoring seventeen points. The consensus was the G-Men had shown marked improvement since the beginning of the season. Just how much would be measured in their next game when they would face West Hazleton, which still hadn't lost a league contest since 1960. Frankly, no one gave the Saints a ghost of a chance.

Over 1,000 fans turned out to see the once-beaten (in exhibition play) Wildcats take on the G-Men. Saint Gabriel's led once, early in the game, 5-4. After one quarter West Hazleton was on top 17-9, and the visitors continued to build on that margin, winning 84-43. Don Barnes, covering the game, once again pointed to the future: "Better days are ahead for the Saints. A rangy junior high team hoping to win its league and a better than fair JV unit give hope for the years to come."

After the West Hazleton loss Saint Gabriel's dropped three more league contests to Saint Ann's, Hazle Township, and MMI. To their credit the G-Men were competitive in all three contests and actually had the opportunity to come out on top in two of them. The close-but-no-cigar story found Saint Gabriel's sitting on a 2-16 record as they prepared for the last home game of the season against Foster Township.

Almost all of the Saint Gabriel's student body had already found their seats when the Saints' JV unit came out of the locker for pre-game warm-ups. Pete O'Donnell, a freshman, was on the court with the junior G-Men. A few members of the student body pointed at him, and a wave of murmurs spread from one end of the student section to the other. It was unusual for G-Men fans to see a freshman playing with the junior varsity squad. In two short years they would be watching another talented freshman take the floor as a member of their varsity team for the first time in the school's history. When O'Donnell scored later in the game, the students roared their approval. He would score many more points on the Saint Joseph's gym floor in the years to come.

The varsity did its job, winning 70-58 to secure their third win of the season. Three sophomores—Jim Barrett, Charlie Gennaro, and Jerry Sernak—scored in double figures for the G-Men. Two days later the team dropped the final game of the season at Weatherly and finished with a record of 3-17.

Local experts had expected a rough year for Saint Gabriel's, but this was the worst season anyone associated with the school could remember. Through it all the student body remained loyal and spirited. The G-Men, all agreed, would be better in the coming years—although nobody could have predicted how much better.

With the dismal 1963 season in the rearview mirror, the G-Men and their fans were anxious for a fresh start. Saint Gabriel's would still put a young team on the court, but the lack of experience was no longer a factor. When school started in September of 1963, one felt a renewed sense of optimism in the halls of the small school on Wyoming Street. Coach Kender, who now had a lifetime record of 25-40, was certainly ready to see if his decision to go with all inexperienced underclassmen would begin paying off.

On Thursday, November 21, 1963, the *Standard Speaker* carried its preseason prognosis on the newest edition of G-Men ready to add to the history of Saint Gabriel's basketball. Written by Ray Saul, the piece noted that few coaches could say they had a veteran squad with a roster that only included two seniors, but that was the Chip Kender's position. Noting that Saint Gabriel's could start five lettermen and still have two in reserve, Saul predicted that G-Men fans would have plenty to cheer about in the coming season. Joe Clark, now a senior and who led the team in scoring the year before, was back, as were Jerry Sernak and Jimmy Barrett, who had made solid contributions as sophomores. In addition, Pete O'Donnell had won a starting job and was said to show the promise of being the next star for the Saints. Also mentioned as figuring prominently in the team's plans were juniors Charlie Gennaro, Joe Entiero, Billy Boyle, and Mike O'Donnell. Kender himself felt that the team was "a year away" and that a lack of height could be a problem. Indeed, standing at an even six feet, Boyle was the tallest player on the team.

The following morning, the front page of the paper carried a number of interesting tidbits. It was reported that Robert Stroud, the Birdman of Alcatraz, had passed away. Republican leaders were quoted as being highly critical of President Kennedy's "mismanagement" of his legislative program. Meanwhile, it was reported that Kennedy had been greeted warmly by thousands as he arrived in Texas to begin a three-day visit.

An extra addition published that same afternoon carried the headline "President Kennedy Slain." At Saint Gabriel's the news of the popular president's assassination dropped on the students like a sledgehammer. It was up to the nuns to deliver word of the president's death to their students. Each did it in their own way. In the sixth grade, the sister began by telling the class, "Well, I guess you didn't pray for your president today." After receiving the news, the students were dismissed for the day.

Saint Gabriel's opened the season against a veteran Marian Catholic teamed coached by local legend Wink Gallagher. The game was played at the Coaldale High gym that Marian used as their home floor. Reminiscent of the previous season, the Saints led by two at half but faded in the fourth quarter, losing by a final of 71-59. What was different was the balanced attack exhibited by the G-Men. Three players hit double figures, including Pete O'Donnell, who scored twelve in his varsity debut. Mike O'Donnell remembers Pete was forced to play inside because "we didn't have much height" and playing against taller opponents required the sophomore to develop multiple moves to get to the basket. Though the loss was disappointing, it was clear that Saint Gabriel's was indeed a much improved team compared to the squad that had taken the court a year earlier.

Local interest in the high school basketball season continued to run very high. The local paper received numerous phone calls on the night's games from interested residents who couldn't wait until the following morning to get the results. It reached the point where, on December 3rd, the *Standard Speaker* requested its readers to please not call the office for scholastic basketball scores until at least 10:30 p.m. The paper noted that they really didn't have all the results on hand until that time. Naturally, this didn't apply to Saint Gabriel home game scores since the fleet-footed elementary students reported the results within minutes of the final buzzer.

Opening at home, the G-Men hoped to break into the win column against the always tough Plymouth Saint Vincent's. The Saints started slow and for three quarters continued to dig themselves a hole. After three periods they trailed 61-46. In the fourth quarter they staged a comeback led by Jimmy Barrett and Pete O'Donnell, but they fell just short, losing by a final score of 78-74. Barrett scored twenty-nine in the contest and O'Donnell added twenty-six. The lanky young sophomore was certainly living up to his advanced billing.

It goes without saying that few of the G-Men or their followers were happy opening 0-2. But with Hazleton up next there was no time to dwell on the slow start. There would be two differences playing against the Mounts this year. First, they were now coached by Fran Libonati, who had taken over midway in the previous season after Danny Gregoria resigned for health reasons. Libonati was a Hazleton graduate who had starred on the court for the Mountaineers. He was young, handsome, and very personable. Since taking over for Gregoria, his teams had displayed hustle and determination. In their first game this season they had easily won 88-72 on the road versus Mahanoy Area. The second difference was that Hazleton had joined Saint Gabriel's in using Saint Joseph's gym for their home games. The Mounts had tried this move for a short time in the '50s but were forced to abandon the idea due to poor attendance, which made leasing the space too expensive for the return on the investment.

Attendance wasn't a problem for this Hazleton home game as more than 1,800 fans found seats in the spacious gym. Saint Gabriel's pastor Monsignor John Maher made a rare appearance, joining Father Purcell in the stands. The Saint Gabriel's cheerleaders wore "snappy" new uniforms, and the same would have been true for the G-Men had their new duds arrived on time. Father Purcell expressed his disappointment over the late arrival of the uniforms to Ray Saul, and also let it be known that Saint Gabriel's would be starting a biddy basketball program. That program would begin following the New Year's celebrations and would be headed by John Coyne and Johnny Pfaff, now known as Mr. Pfaff, who had played for the Speedboys in the Anthracite League's inaugural season. The Saint Gabriel varsity players would coach the fourth, fifth, and sixth graders, who would practice on Saturdays and play games on Sundays. The biddy program would pay dividends on the court in the final years of the school.

Hazleton had a distinct height advantage in the game and they used it, controlling the boards by a 50-22 margin. The G-Men made up for their lack of height by utilizing a pressing defense that resulted in numerous Hazleton turnovers. The game was hard fought from the get-go and at half Hazleton had a slim lead of 27-22. The teams played a virtually even third quarter and the score stood at 41-37 heading into the final eight minutes. Jimmy Barrett scored the first two goals as the period started to knot the score at 41. Then Jerry Sernak stole the ball from a Hazleton player and took it to the hoop to put the G-Men ahead for the first time since the opening quarter. The Saint Gabriel's fans went wild.

That lead was short-lived and with a little less than three minutes to play, the Mounts led 55-50. Coach Kender called a time-out and attempted to rally his troops. Joe Clark was fouled with 1:49 on the clock, and he hit both fouls to cut the margin to three. Hazleton was then assessed a technical foul. Kender sent Barrett to the free throw line but he missed the shot. The Saints inbounded the ball but missed the field goal try. Hazleton's Neil Darrough then scored his only bucket of the ballgame to put Hazleton up by five with under a minute to play. The game ended with Hazleton on top 61-54. Once again the little Catholic school from the south side had given the Mountaineers all they could handle only to fall just short. The G-Men and their fans were hopeful that they could turn the tables in the next encounter between the teams scheduled for New Year's Day.

The Saints were off to a very slow start and concerns were being heard in the pubs on Donegal Hill. The G-Men needed a win badly and were hoping it would come on Friday the 13th against Shenandoah Catholic at Saint Joe's. By halftime the issue was still in doubt as Saint Gabriel's held a 34-29 lead. In the third quarter Jimmy Barrett got hot, scoring ten points. By the end of the period the G-Men led by eighteen on their way to a 77-54 win. Barrett scored twenty-three in the game, and

Joe Entiero, in a starting role for the first time, added four-teen. There was some bad news—back problems sidelined Jerry Sernak, the Saints' important inside man. Back issues would plague him for the remainder of his career.

Elsewhere in the area, basketball fever was taking hold of its many fans. Don Barnes had traveled to Summit Hill to cover the MMI game, which was won by MMI in overtime. After the game the MMI bus was surrounded by Summit Hill fans who pelted it with rocks and bottles. Barnes, who had to leave his car in Summit Hill overnight after his keys went missing from his jacket pocket, expressed hope that Summit Hill would work on cultivating some manners in their "goon squad."

With Sernak still unavailable, the G-Men traveled to Plymouth for a rematch with Saint Vincent's. The Saints were never in the game and with just four minutes to play they found themselves down 80-56. At this point the visitors staged a re-markable comeback, narrowing the margin to 83-79 with under a minute to go. Forced to foul, the Saints got no closer, losing 88-83.

A few days later the Saints traveled to face Shenandoah Catholic, a team they had handled easily a week earlier. Early in the second quarter Joe Clark was forced to leave the game with an ankle injury. Without Sernak or Clark, G-Men rebounds were rare. Joe Entiero, who had scored eleven, fouled out in the third quarter. With more than five minutes to go, starters Pete O'Donnell and Billy Boyle joined Entiero on the bench. With four starters gone the G-Men couldn't hold on, coming out on the losing end of a 77-74 score despite the twenty-nine points scored by Jimmy Barrett.

Things only got worse for Kender's struggling squad. Facing Marian Catholic on December 23rd the Saints would be without both Sernak and O'Donnell, who was out with an arm injury. Two Saint Gabriel's reserves, Jim Gallagher and Jim McBride, were also out due to injuries. Joe Clark played hampered by a sprained ankle. In spite of these adversities and the fact that Joe Entiero and Billy Boyle fouled out in the final quarter, the score was tied at forty-eight with under a minute to go. Joe Clark made one of two foul shots to put the Saints ahead. After a Marian miss, Charlie Gennaro was fouled with fourteen ticks left. Gennaro missed the front end of a one-and-one. Marian got the ball to Jerry Holubek, who tossed in the winning bucket with just seven seconds on the clock. The hard-luck G-Men were sitting with a record of 1-6 as 1963 came to an end.

Concern over the losing record was heightened by the fact that Anthracite League rival West Hazleton was off to a torrid start. The Wildcats were undefeated and were led by a sharp-shooting, smooth-ball-handling guard named Yosh Grobelny. Grobelny was regarded as the best basketball player in the region, and he showed it, running the offense and scoring twenty-four points in an 80-60 win against Hazleton.

Sports editor Phil Sarno used the recent West Hazleton domination of the region to remind his readers that years ago he had urged Hazleton to play Saint Gabriel's and West Hazleton only to be bombarded by calls and letters from Hazleton fans claiming that those teams wouldn't stand a chance against the "superior" forces of Hazleton High. Now Sarno claimed that those fans needed to reverse their appraisal since both West Hazleton and Saint Gabriel's had "completely outclassed latter-day editions of the Mountaineers when it comes to the finer points of the game of basketball." In fairness to Hazleton fans, Saint Gabriel's had hung with the Mounts but had hardly outclassed them on the court. This latter point would be reinforced on New Year's Day when Hazleton would pull away in the final quarter to beat Saint Gabriel's by a score of 73-53. That loss left the G-Men a very disappointing 1-7 heading into league play.

Having struggled through what was generally considered to be a tough exhibition slate, the G-Men would begin the Anthracite League first half at home against Freeland Saint Ann's. West Hazleton, which was undefeated in league play going back to 1960, was the odds-on favorite to repeat as champions. Indeed, the Wildcats, led by new coach Ron Gatski, appeared to have a stronger team in the '63-64 season than the squads that had won the previous two titles. Most observers felt that only MMI could challenge West Hazleton.

Saint Gabriel's led all the way against Saint Ann's but seldom by more than four points. With four minutes to play the score was tied at seventy-three. Jimmy Barrett scored eight points in those final minutes to lead the Saints to an 84-77 win. While Barrett scored twenty-eight in the contest, the G-Men were beginning to showcase a more balanced attack as three other players finished in double figures, including O'Donnell with thirteen. Injuries remained a concern as Sernak was still unavailable and Clark remained hobbled and unable to perform at one hundred percent. The team had little time to celebrate the win with MMI being the next team scheduled to visit Saint Joseph's gym.

While the G-Men were beating Saint Ann's in a heated struggle, both MMI and West Hazleton were coasting to easy wins in their initial league games. West Hazleton used the first contest to send a warning to the rest of the league when they scored forty-seven points in the first quarter of their lopsided victory over Freeland. Word on the street was that the Wildcats and their fans were already thinking in terms of post-season play as winning the league was, in their minds, pretty much in the bag.

In previewing the Saint Gabriel's-MMI matchup, the *Standard Speaker* hedged its bets: while MMI could win by twenty, it could also be much closer. It wasn't. MMI, coached by the very able Al Goedecke, took charge from the outset and won, going away 95-59. The Preppers were led by a Jack Hollis, a terrifically talented senior point guard. Hollis scored twenty-five points in the game while also accumulating a dozen assists. In the meantime, he held Barrett, who entered the game averaging 21.3 points per game, to seven. The only Saint Gabriel's player who scored in double figures was O'Donnell, who finished the game with twenty. Despite O'Donnell's fine performance, the G-Men had been totally out classed.

Coming off that loss one could have easily expected the Saints to pack it in. Instead they traveled to Hazle Township and won a hard fought contest when a healthy Joe Clark intercepted an inbounds pass with five seconds to play to preserve a 63-62 victory. Just a few days later they returned to the friendlier confines of Saint Joe's to take on Weatherly, whose lone league loss was to West Hazleton. The Wreckers were solid favorites, but the G-Men once again kept their fans on the edge of their seats, pulling out a 56-55 win before what was described as a "delirious home crowd." Saint Gabriel's was now 3-1 in league play and could force a first half playoff if they could sweep their next three games. Doing so would be a challenge considering that the last of those contests would be against West Hazleton on the Wildcats' home court.

However, before Saint Gabriel's could take on West Hazleton, the Wildcats would have to travel to Freeland to take on MMI in their bandbox gym. That game was scheduled for Tuesday,

January 21, 1964, and so great was the demand for tickets that arrangements were made to move the game to a much larger venue. On the Sunday afternoon before the game, Father Purcell telephoned the offices of the *Standard Speaker* to announce that the game had been shifted to Saint Joe's and would be part of a doubleheader with Saint Gabriel's taking on Foster Township in the opener.

The move proved to be a wise one as over 2,100 fans showed up for the games. The G-Men got things going by beating Foster Township 70-62 despite the limited availability of Jimmy Barrett, who was battling an illness. Pete O'Donnell picked up the slack, scoring twenty-one, while Joe Entiero added fifteen. The Saints were indeed performing at a higher level as the year progressed.

MMI gave West Hazleton all they could handle in the second game before falling 76-68. Jack Hollis outscored his rival Yosh Grobelny twenty-nine to twenty-four but Grobelny got more support from his teammates. Local fans were coming to realize that the Anthracite League's brand of basketball was now rivaling that being played in the East Penn League. Phil Sarno opined that West Hazleton would run away with that league title this year. The sportswriter also noted that the standard of play in the first game of the twin bill was also excellent.

On January 25th the G-Men traveled to Freeland and looked impressive, beating the Whippets 87-75. Jerry Sernak was back but seeing limited action. The team continued to show scoring balance as four underclassmen scored in double figures. The win put the Saints into second place in the league's first half race, and with Weatherly's upset of MMI they were now the only team left with a mathematical chance of tying West Hazleton and forcing a first half playoff. With the two teams scheduled to meet in just a few days, Ray Saul wrote that few would give the G-Men a "Chinaman's chance." Saul added that you could tell that to anybody but the Saints' followers, adding that "Saint Gabriel's will be a bona fide title threat next season."

On the day of the game the *Standard Speaker* preview noted that West Hazleton had now won fifty-nine straight league contests and that the last team to beat them was Saint Gabriel's. The basic feeling was that the Wildcats should have the game in hand after two quarters and that it would take a super effort from talented G-Men underclassmen to even keep the game close.

Coach Kender decided that he had to stop Yosh Grobelny if his team was going to have any chance at all, so he played a box-in-one defense. Defensively the strategy worked—Grobelny was held to a season-low four points and the powerful West Hazleton offense was held to their season low of 75. However, the Saints found out that West Hazleton could also play defense as they held the G-Men to their lowest output of the year, 48. Pete O'Donnell was the only Saint Gabriel's player to hit double figures, scoring seventeen. After starting league play 1-7, the G-Men had improved their record to 6-9. The team had a week off to prepare for the second half and to hopefully end the season with a winning record.

The Saints would open the second half on the road against MMI. The Preppers had lost three straight to end the first half but were still considered to be the only team with a legitimate shot at beating West Hazleton. In the previous meeting MMI had completely dominated Kender's squad and that had been at Saint Joe's. This game would be played in MMI's own small gym. MMI was considered a solid favorite to right their ship and start the second half with a victory.

The G-Men started five underclassmen against MMI, and from the opening tap they made it clear that the blowout in their first meeting would not be repeated. O'Donnell scored twelve points in the first quarter, flashing moves to the basket that left the MMI defenders flat-footed in his wake. After eight minutes the score was knotted at eighteen. Toward the end of the second quarter MMI staged a small rally to go into the locker room with a 36-30 halftime lead. In the third quarter the smaller Saints took control of the boards and narrowed the margin to 63-61 entering the final eight minutes. Midway through the final quarter the Preppers went on another mild run and then hung on to win 88-82. Don Barnes, covering the game for the *Standard Speaker*, seemed to come away from the game more impressed with the losing team. Barnes wrote that the G-Men were "going to be a terror next season." Then he went further: "They'll put up an argument with anyone this half, and next year should rule the Anthracite League roost."

It seemed that this Saint Gabriel's team was indeed finding their stride as three days later they totally dominated Freeland, winning by an impressive 94-60 margin. Area observers, noting the speed and offensive firepower that the Saints were showcasing, began to wonder whether they might be the toughest nut for West Hazleton to crack in the league's second half. The G-Men would get the Wildcats at Saint Joe's, and MMI, after an upset by Weatherly, had to travel to West Hazleton to take on the first-half champs in less than a week.

On Tuesday, February 11, 1964, Saint Gabriel's students paid a quarter each to board two buses waiting to transport them to Freeland for the game against Foster Township, who were 2-0 in the second half. Despite the fact that West Hazleton was squaring off against MMI, the local paper was painting the Saints' contest as the most interesting game of the night. That observation could not have been more off the mark.

Father Purcell, who never missed a game, was seated with the students who had made the trip and watched the G-Men build up a comfortable 61-44 lead over the Falcons after three periods. Midway through the final quarter, the good father was called away to take a phone call. When he returned to his seat, he was smiling and shaking his head. He then told the students around him what he had learned on the phone call. While the Saints played on, the news Purcell carried quickly spread throughout the student section. MMI had defeated West Hazleton, ending the Wildcats' sixty-two-game winning streak in the Anthracite League. While that was big news in and of itself, even more startling was the final score in the game. The Preppers had prevailed 7-5. Needless to say, on the bus ride home the main topic of conversation wasn't Saint Gabriel's 67-58 victory.

To say the least, the MMI win threw the race for the Anthracite League's second-half crown wide open. But locals, at the time, were thinking more about the 7-5 game than anything else. Calls to the *Standard Speaker* described the game as everything from "amazing" to "disgusting." The final score was picked up by national wire services and MMI's coach Goedecke heard from newspapers all over the country asking him to share his strategy and preparation for the contest. All Goedecke shared was that his team had spent time preparing for the contest and implemented his game plan. Fifty years later, Yosh Grobelny was still shaking his head about the Preppers win and their game plan. Grobelny reflected, "They had a talented team. They were as good as we were. They didn't have to take a back seat to anyone. There really was no difference between our teams."

The Saints had little time to dwell on the shake-up in the league. What promised to be a fired up West Hazleton squad was next on the schedule. On the day of the game one could feel the excitement throughout the halls in the small Catholic school. Students wondered aloud if the G-Men would employ the tactic that had proved successful for MMI and hold the ball. This matchup had become one of the biggest games of the year, and a huge crowd was expected at Saint Joseph's gym.

It was clear from the opening tap that the G-Men had no intention of slowing the game down; they were going toe to toe with the Wildcats. After one quarter, West Hazleton had a 17-9 lead, but the Saints wouldn't go away. At half West Hazleton was clinging to a 30-24 lead. In the third quarter the G-Men fought back and took a 40-38 lead when Jimmy Barrett buried one from way outside. Two goals by West Hazleton followed but Barrett made good on a technical foul called on the Wildcats coach to make the score 42-41 after three periods. It all fell apart in the fourth quarter when Saint Gabriel's didn't score a field goal. The Wildcats, meanwhile, couldn't be stopped and out-scored the home team by twenty-two points in the final stanza, making the final score a deceptive 71-48. After being taken out late in the game, Yosh Grobelny led the West Hazleton starters in saying goodbye by waving white towels at the Saint Gabriel's student section.

The loss to West Hazleton had effectively eliminated Saint Gabriel's from the race for second half honors. With an overall record of 9-11 the possibility of finishing up the season on a winning note with an equal number of wins and losses. The G-Men took a step in that direction when they beat Saint Ann's on the losers' home court 81-70. Once again the Saints were led by Barrett, who scored thirty-one. Both O'Donnell and Entiero also hit double figures. Weatherly, which sported a 5-0 second half record, was next up. The G-Men had upset the Wreckers by one point in their first meeting, but this game would be played at Weatherly.

When the G-Men entered the Weatherly gym they were greeted by a huge banner that read "Wreckers Revenge." The

Weatherly players certainly seemed to be carrying a grudge once the game began as they rushed to a first quarter lead of 22-13. The two teams played an even second quarter despite the fact that the Wreckers totally controlled the boards on both ends of the court. At halftime, the score stood at Weatherly 39, Saint Gabriel's 29. The second half went much the same way as the second quarter, and when the final buzzer sounded the Wreckers had exacted their revenge, winning 67-56. The win set up a West Hazleton matchup with Weatherly, which would be the second game of another twin bill to be held at Saint Joseph's. Saint Gabriel's would wrap up the '64 season against Hazle Township in the first game of the doubleheader.

As the season drew to an end, the Saints and their fans were already looking ahead to next year. They had stuck with Coach Kender and the team through the lean times and many expected that next year's harvest to include a league champion-ship. In addition to the foundation of experience that had been laid in the past two years, fans would have an additional reason to expect success by the time the next school year began.

The G-Men played their final game on the night that Cassius Clay, later to be known as Muhammad Ali, stunned the world by upsetting Sonny Liston to win the heavyweight championship of the world. West Hazleton took care of Weatherly on their way to winning a fourth straight league title. The Saints took care of their business, easily defeating Hazle Township 75-47. The game marked the final appearance of Joe Clark, who scored two in the contest. Clark had lost his starting job during the sea-son as Coach Kender decided to go with five underclassmen in hopes of building a championship team in the coming season. With the win, Saint Gabriel's finished with a record of 10-12. It marked the last time in the school's history that the basketball team would finish with a losing record. It was also the last time that Saint Gabriel's would finish a season without playing for either a state or at least part of a league championship.

4

THE NATIONAL ANTHEM AND THE ALMA MATER

Men in Black

On Sunday, April 5, 1964, the Saint Gabriel's biddy basketball league held its first championship game. The Orioles, led by Joe Farley and George Evancho scoring twenty-five and twenty respectively, defeated the Cardinals 54-44. All the players in the league were directed to return their uniforms to Father Deviney's office located in the school building by the following Saturday. The father himself had quite a day in the game between the biddy coaches and managers that took place after the championship tilt. He scored seventeen points and his team won 73-62.

Father Raymond Deviney had been introduced to the parish a month before when he stepped into the rather large shadow left behind by Father Purcell who had been named the director of Saint Michael's School for Boys in Hoban Heights. At a farewell ceremony held in his honor, Father Purcell had remarked, "The people of Saint Gabriel's parish will always hold a sacred place in my heart." Little did he know he would return to Saint Gabriel's years later as pastor of Hazleton's largest Catholic church.

When Purcell left to take up his new duties, he was extremely popular both inside and outside the parish. As athletic director he had earned the respect of his peers from the other schools he had interacted with. His popularity with Saint Gabriel's students was evident in the two farewells organized to honor him. It would be asking a lot for anyone to replace him. If Father Deviney was at all daunted by the challenge, he never showed it.

Father Deviney had a commanding voice and an equally commanding and dynamic personality. He never needed any equipment to amplify his voice when he made visits to the school to address the students. When the young priest entered a room, everyone knew it. If anyone had ever totally embraced a take-charge personality, it was Father Deviney. He stepped into the job as the new athletic moderator with a competitive spirit he wasn't shy of showing to the public.

Shortly after his arrival he accepted the sportsmanship award, which was presented annually to the school that had exhibited the finest sportsmanship during the past season. It would become clear that Deviney was more interested in winning championships on the court than accepting awards on behalf of losing teams. Pete O'Donnell remembered Deviney as being very energetic as he participated in pickup basketball games with the students. He also recalled that it was clear that Father Deviney wanted a successful athletic program, which at Saint Gabriel's meant just one thing: a winning basketball team. The new priest threw himself into his duties as athletic moderator with a passion that many in the parish hadn't seen before.

Father Purcell had replaced Father Joseph Conboy at Saint Michael's. Father Conboy was assigned to Saint Gabriel's parish as an assistant pastor. Basically, he and Father Purcell had switched positions. He was a bit older than Father Deviney, already in his thirties, but the two new priests shared a common interest—the well-being and development of the students who attended Saint Gabriel's. Conboy was more reserved than Father Deviney, but he shared an interest in the school's athletic program. Though Deviney held the title of athletic director, the two priests decided to split up the duties. Deviney was primarily responsible for the senior high program while Conboy focused his energies on biddy basketball and the junior high team. Conboy was more diplomatic in handling his responsibilities but just as serious about contributing to the success of the school's athletic fortunes.

Moving quickly to establish his rule, Father Deviney was often found in the school's athletic office, which he claimed as his own. He got to know the returning basketball players while participating in pickup games. There is little doubt that he liked what he saw. Jim Barrett, who had led the team in scoring with an average eighteen points a game, would be returning for his senior year. Add the return of Pete O'Donnell, who had scored sixteen per game and could only be expected to improve in his junior year, and the G-Men had a solid foundation for success. Other seniors who were expected to contribute included small but speedy playmaker Charlie Gennaro, steady Joe Entiero, and the now six-foot-two-inch Billy Boyle. Mike O'Donnell provided depth at the guard spot, and if Jerry Sernak could overcome his back problems, he promised to be a force underneath. Father Deviney had to be looking forward to the basketball season that spring as he watched Barrett, O'Donnell, and Entiero lead Saint Gabriel's on the baseball diamond.

Though he was now at Saint Gabriel's, Saint Michael's remained on Father Conboy's mind. Saint Michael's had been started in 1916 by Bishop Michael J. Hoban. One of the bishop's main goals was realized when the school opened as an institution where orphaned boys could learn a trade that would serve them through life. Thus it had originally been called the Saint Michael's Industrial School for Boys. As time went on, it was transformed into an extensive working dairy farm home to 4,000 chickens and 170 cattle. At the end of the 1964 school year, Saint Michael's closed its small high school. The closing had quite an impact on the basketball program at Saint Gabriel's that would soon make its force felt statewide.

Father Conboy knew of one boy who had just completed the eighth grade and would now be looking for a new school where he could continue his education. The boy's father ran the farm at Saint Michael's. Based on geography, one would have expected the young man to be sent to a school in the Scranton area. Father Conboy had other ideas.

Since he was taking charge of Saint Gabriel's junior high basketball program, one of the first parishioners that Father Conboy sought out was Vince Gallagher, who coached the school's freshman team, and his wife Margaret, whom everyone knew as Peggy. Conboy didn't have to travel far to find the Gallaghers as they lived little more than a block from the school. Gallagher graduated from Saint Gabriel's in the late 1930s and had stayed involved with both the school and the parish throughout his adult life. He had served as an assistant coach in 1947 when the G-Men captured their first Anthracite League title. As the freshman coach, he encouraged and developed much of the talent that would take the court for the

G-Men in the school's final years. By the time he hung up his whistle following the 1968 season, he would have coached more state championship basketball players than any other mentor in the school's history. It's somewhat ironic that he never got to coach the boy who came to live with his family and became the greatest high school basketball player the region ever produced before or since.

Father Conboy told the Gallagher's about the talented young basketball player and soon-to-be high school freshman who was searching for a school. As Vince's daughter Cathy remembers, her father didn't have to be asked—he volunteered to take the young man under his roof. The plan Conboy and the Gallaghers devised involved the Gallaghers becoming the young man's guardians, which would allow him to attend school at Saint Gabriel's. Cathy Gallagher remembers being thrilled when she heard about the news. She was an only child and this arrangement would give her the chance to be an older sister.

With half a plan in place, Father Conboy took a trip back to Hoban Heights where he found the young man milking a cow on the school's farm. Conboy approached the boy and asked, "How would you like to go to school in Hazleton"? The boy replied, "Father, you're talking to the wrong guy. First, I don't know where Hazleton is, and second, unless you go down to the house and convince my mother, I'm not going anywhere." The priest nodded and headed toward the house, and when the boy finished his farm work and returned home, Paul Hoffman learned that he would attend high school in Hazleton.

A week later, Conboy took Hoffman to meet the family he would live with for the next four years. They hit it off immediately. Cathy Gallagher then took Paul around the neighborhood and introduced him to a number of the locals who would soon be his classmates. Among those he met was Jane Ammon, a young girl who in a few years would be leading the G-Men faithful as a cheerleader, offering vocal support for the teams Hoffman would be an integral part of for the next four years.

Throughout that summer, basketball in Hazleton remained alive on the city's playgrounds. Pine Street, South Side, and the James Street courts were home to the current and future players who would take the court for Saint Gabriel's and Hazleton High. In West Hazleton, the court at the Encke School Playground was always busy. Billy Pavlick, who would be a premier point guard at West Hazleton in the late sixties, recalled, "We didn't have basketball camps in those days. You got better by heading to the playground." He added, "Of course, you couldn't go to a rival playground on your own and expect to get a game."

As the summer wore down and the new school year approached there was a feeling of optimism at Saint Gabriel's that hadn't been present for years. After all, the team would return a slew of seasoned veterans who had shown much promise as the previous season progressed. The youth movement was over and it was time to collect the dividends on that investment. Coach Kender was confident that he would put a title contender on the floor. In addition, both Father Deviney and Father Conboy knew that the team had been further strengthened by the arrival of the freshmen from Hoban Heights.

5

FINAL INSTRUCTIONS

THERe'S a NeW KID In TOWn

It was the Saturday before Labor Day, September 7, 1964. In Hazleton, many families were making preparations to spend the day picnicking at one of the local amusement parks. Children, watching grandmothers, mothers, and aunts preparing the food that would be served later on long picnic tables beneath the roof of a pavilion, knew that the weekend marked the official end of their summer vacation. Meanwhile, grandfathers, fathers, and uncles perused the local newspaper over cups of coffee.

The front page of the *Standard Speaker* carried the headline that an all-white jury in Georgia had acquitted two white men charged with killing a Negro. Further down the page there was a story about Melvin Belli, the famous attorney who had recently defended Jack Ruby during his murder trial for the killing of Lee Harvey Oswald. Belli had filed a case with the California courts asking that Republican presidential candidate Barry Goldwater's name be removed from the state ballot. Belli argued that Goldwater was not a native-born American since he came into this world in Arizona prior to that state being admitted to the union. The entertainment section advertised a dusk-to-dawn show at the Hazleton Drive-In with *Day of the Triffids* leading off the entertainment and free coffee and donuts served at dawn. The sports pages told of the Philadelphia Phillies 5-3 win over the San Francisco Giants that gave the "Fightin' Phils" a six-and-a-half game lead over the Cincinnati Reds in the National League pennant race. The Saint Louis Cardinals were in third another game back.

Of greater interest to most readers was the local sports column announcing that high school football season had arrived. The column also commented on the many schools in the area that didn't field football teams but were waiting anxiously for November 1st when basketball practice would officially begin.

The businesses on Broad Street were preparing to open. Shopping malls were a thing of the future. The Markle Bank Building towered above the other buildings on the street, which included a number of the city's banks, restaurants, and popular stores like Landau Brothers and the Leader. As the day went on Broad Street would come to life as Hazletonians went about their business.

School had been in session for a week and Paul Hoffman, newly arrived from Saint Michael's, was in the process of checking out his new surroundings. Meanwhile, word of the new student circulated the small school. There was a rumor that this new freshman would be playing on the varsity basketball team. Many found it hard to believe. Not only had a freshman never started for the G-Men varsity, but this year the team was returning all five players who had started many of the games the year before. Many wondered if he would even be allowed to go out for the varsity team, much less make it and offer any meaningful contribution.

If Hoffman knew of the stir going on around him, he didn't show it. He wasn't shy, but he certainly wasn't outgoing. He was unassuming and friendly. Though his height would be reported as up to six foot five, he stood at six foot one inch as a freshman, and his growing days were behind him. As a freshman he was thin and lanky. His glasses gave him more the look of a serious student than of a young athlete. Father Conboy may have brought him to Saint Gabriel's, but it was clear early on that Father Deviney had taken a special interest in the welfare of Saint Gabriel's newest player.

Unknown to but a few, the new student was a natural athlete. He was blessed with tremendous speed and quickness. He was agile and had developed a leaping ability that enabled him to dunk a basketball at a time and in a region where possessing that ability was the exception. He was also deceptively strong. As an eighth grader he had displayed sufficient ability to play on Saint Michael's varsity team. Bruce Ellis, who was already following high school basketball around the state, remembers, "Athletes with Hoffman's set of physical skills didn't come around often, especially in our area, in those days."

As September made its way toward November, the news regarding Hoffman was confirmed. He might be living with the freshman coach, but he wasn't going to play for him. The gossip in the school halls was that the new kid wasn't even going to have to go out for the varsity—it was a done deal. What few could believe upon first hearing was that he was going to be a starter. Given that news, the student body turned downright giddy, the general feeling being "We are going to be absolutely loaded." There was talk of doing the unthinkable and beating Hazleton and West Hazleton in the same season. Some even believed a better season than the G-Men enjoyed in '47 and '60 could be in the offing.

Almost unnoticed in the excitement over Hoffman's arrival was Father Deviney's decision to hire John Seamon to coach the JV squad. Seamon's hiring was another indication of how serious Deviney's intent was in pursuing excellence on the basketball court.

Meanwhile, the World Series came and went. The Saint Louis Cardinals, who came from behind to win the National League pennant on the final day of the regular season, beat the New York Yankees in seven games. In late October Saint Louis manager Johnny Keane resigned and Yankee skipper Yogi Berra was fired. The firing of Berra inspired Phil Sarno to devote an entire sports column to the subject of loyalty, or the lack of it, in sports. Meanwhile, much to the delight of the majority of Saint Gabriel's parishioners, Notre Dame and their new football coach Ara Parseghian were undefeated as the month of October came to a close. On the local football scene, as of November 1st Hazleton had a gridiron record of 5-3 and West Hazleton's mark stood at 5-2-1 as the two schools looked forward to their annual Thanksgiving Day battle. All that was well and good, but what November 1st really marked was the day high school basketball teams in Pennsylvania could legally begin practice.

At Saint Gabriel's that first practice marked the introduction of Paul Hoffman to Saint Gabriel's basketball. Mike O'Donnell remembered the team lining up to run sprints. After running the initial set of sprints, the upperclassmen noticed that Hoffman had led the whole way. Setting up for a second set, the seniors decided to put the young freshman in his place, but at the conclusion, Hoffman had again led the whole way. So it went for four consecutive sets of wind sprints. O'Donnell said, "Going into the year we were small but fast, so we figured our speed would carry us, and then in walks this freshman and he blew our doors off. As the practice wore on, we were amazed; it didn't take long for us to realize that he was special."

It also didn't take long for the local paper to comment on the coming basketball season. In his November 3rd column Don Barnes wrote about "those muffled thuds in the background." That's the way he described the sound of basketballs descending on freshly polished gym floors throughout the region. Barnes recognized the Anthracite League was welcoming a new member in Jim Thorpe and the Olympians, who were expected to make a lively entrance. He noted that Hazleton returned a number of underclassmen, that West Hazleton was a question mark, that sounds surrounding Saint Gabriel's on Donegal Hill were optimistic, and that Weatherly would be looking to even a few old scores. In other words, more than a few of the local teams were expecting to enjoy successful seasons.

At the time Jim Thorpe was entering the league, the town itself was facing a decision on what to call itself. It had been ten years since Mauch Chunk and East Mauch Chunk had merged into one community and picked the name Jim Thorpe in honor of the great Native American athlete buried there. Now local residents had placed a referendum on the ballot to return to the name of Mauch Chunk. These locals were upset that the name change had failed to attract some of the benefits, like the National Football League Hall of Fame, expected to accompany the body of the great Olympian to the area. Tempers ran high leading up to the vote, culminating in the vandalizing of the Jim Thorpe memorial prior to the balloting. When the votes were finally counted the people decided to keep the name Jim Thorpe, though arguments relative to Thorpe's final resting place continue to the present day.

The Jim Thorpe basketball team was held in high regard, and they were expected to contend for the league championship in their first year. Thorpe would be led by Bobby Brown, a hard-nosed, hot tempered guard who could score from anyplace on the floor. Joe Morgan and Jack Kmetz were also expected to contribute mightily to the success of the Olympians. The Saint

Gabriel's team was well aware of all that Thorpe brought to the table. Mike O'Donnell remembered, "We had heard about how they were going to waltz in and dominate the league, so we had January 22nd circled on the calendar"—the day the Olympians would travel to Hazleton to meet Saint Gabriel's for the first time.

It was clear heading into the start of the season that Saint Gabriel's wasn't going to sneak up on anybody. All the rival coaches were saying that the G-Men were among the elite teams in the league. Then there was West Hazleton. The Wildcats had ruled the league for four straight years. Though they had been hard hit by graduation losses, they couldn't be counted out.

West Hazleton's coach Ron Gatski wasn't conceding anything. In his view, the Wildcats were the league champions until proven otherwise. Returning with but one starter, the talented Richie Sypek, most observers felt that this was going to be a rebuilding year for the perennial league champions. After losing only four scheduled games in the past four years, West Hazleton had also upgraded their exhibition schedule. The tougher exhibition slate was intended to prepare the team for the district playoffs, where they had made early exits even during these glory years.

But it was Weatherly that stood out as Saint Gabriel's main competition. The Wreckers had beaten West Hazleton a year earlier in a playoff for the second half league title before bowing to the Wildcats in the championship game. They returned five players who had started most of the games the year before. Like most of the teams in the Anthracite League, the one thing they lacked was a dominating big man. Weatherly would rely on a balanced attack led by seniors Bill Gicking and Bob Van Horn. Complementing those two would be a five-foot-eight-inch junior by the name of Pat Searfoss, who was the best all-around player the Wreckers would send onto the court.

Rumors continued to circulate about the G-Men. They were said to have routed teams in scrimmages and were employing a fast break offense that was unstoppable. Joe Entiero had been named team captain. Paul Hoffman and Pete O'Donnell were providing inside scoring threats while Jimmy Barrett continued to light it up from the outside. This was a team that was going to be able to run and score with anyone. The only preseason bad news concerned Jerry Sernak. The returning senior, who was expected to be a major force on the boards, was still battling a back injury. There was doubt that he would be able to play at all. Still, most observers had nothing but positive takes when it came to the 1964-65 Saint Gabriel's cagers.

In his synopsis of the team prior to the start of the season, Ray Saul predicted that the G-Men would be in the thick of things when it came to crowning an Anthracite League champion. He summed things up by predicting "an interesting season for followers of the G-Men, who are just about the most faithful in the region." If Hoffman had hoped to make a quiet entrance on the local scene, Saul's piece ended that hope. He devoted a full paragraph to the freshman, which was introduced in bold letters by the words "Potential Great." Saul said the Saints had found a "future star" in Hoffman.

The Saints wouldn't open the campaign until December 1st, but already their fans had penciled in the game a week later versus Hazleton as the one that would show just how good this year's team might be. In the week leading up to the start of the season, Ara Parseghian took his undefeated and number-one-ranked Notre Dame football squad out west to face the University of Southern California. At half, the Irish were up 17-0 against their archrivals, but the Trojans roared back in the second half aided by several controversial calls to upset Notre Dame 20-17. Saint Gabriel's fans were hopeful that the Notre Dame loss didn't turn out to be an omen. What was a certainty was the fact that the game marked the last time the vast majority of them would give a football game a thought until next September.

On the first day of December the *Standard Speaker* previewed Saint Gabriel's first opponent, Immaculate Heart of Fountain Spring. The paper predicted a successful debut for the G-Men, noting their speed, talent and experience. This first game preview was already predicting that the team would make the post-season Pennsylvania Catholic Interscholastic Athletic Association (PCIAA) playoffs with room to spare. Yet again praising the Saint Gabriel's fans as being "fantastically loyal, even in lean years," the piece said they would have plenty to enjoy this year, perhaps even an Anthracite League title.

6

THE FIRST QUARTER

A veteran team

On December 1, 1964, the day the G-Men would begin their basketball season, the local paper noted that the weather that evening would be mild with temperatures between 0 and 10 degrees. A story on the front page told of the Vatican urging the world's Roman Catholics to pray for the success of Pope Paul VI's trip to India. In all probability, many of the prayers emanating from the pews in Saint Gabriel's church concerned the upcoming game with Immaculate Heart.

As was usually the case, Saint Gabriel's student section at Saint Joseph's gymnasium was the first to fill prior to the JV contest. The high school students filled the bleachers directly behind the G-Men cheerleaders, while those in elementary school lucky enough to find their way to the game took the next available seats. The night began with the Saint Gabriel's junior varsity easily defeating the undermanned Falcons 72-33.

Shortly before 8 p.m., the G-Men took the court for the first time in the new season to a rousing ovation and the sounds of "Sweet Georgia Brown." More than a few eyes in the crowd were on the Saints' newest edition, Paul Hoffman, as the team went through its pregame routine. After warm-ups were completed the team gathered around Coach Kender and received his final instructions. From the opening tip, the G-Men played aggressively on both sides of the court. The strategy resulted in numerous Immaculate Heart turnovers, and after one quarter the G-Men had a commanding lead of 23-5.

The crowd witnessed a bit of history when Paul Hoffman took the court as one of the Saints' starters. It marked the first time a freshman had started a basketball game in the school's history. During that first quarter he had made his presence felt on the defensive side of the ball by blocking several Falcon attempts.

By halftime the G-Men had extended their lead to 50-20, and Coach Kender had already begun to substitute freely. In all, nine players would score for the home team. When it was over the Saints had notched their first win by a comfortable margin of 87-53. Mike O'Donnell had come off the bench to score nineteen for the winners, hitting on nine of thirteen shots. Pete O'Donnell, team captain Joe Entiero, and Jimmy Barrett also scored double figures. Hoffman had scored just seven points but had been a force on the boards and a commanding presence on defense. Though Kender's pressure defense had resulted in a number of personal fouls, the G-Men performance showed they possessed the bench strength to deal with foul trouble.

In his account of the contest, Don Barnes said that "Saint Gabriel's was right on time for its first appointment with destiny." He noted that the G-Men had certainly made clear that they would contend for the league title in the coming season but cautioned a premature coronation until Weatherly, West Hazleton, and Jim Thorpe had a chance to showcase their wares. The Saint Gabriel's followers were more than satisfied with the initial win, though that satisfaction was tempered by the fact that in one week the Hazleton Mountaineers would be the opponent.

The fact was that this team was probably the most talented to date in the school's history. They were fast, had numerous offensive weapons, and had gained a future star in Hoffman. The question marks were on the defensive side of the ball, which wasn't unusual in the region at the time. Defensive basketball wasn't stressed by most coaches, and there wasn't a lot of practice time spent on the fundamentals on that side of the ball. Defense was still being coached and taught the way it had been twenty years earlier.

Jim Thorpe opened with a ten-point win over Marian Catholic. West Hazleton had a much tougher time, just getting by Berwick 55-53 in their opener. The Wildcats got more than half their points from Richie Sypek, who scored thirty-two. When one examined the box score, it was clear the Cats had won it on the foul line where they hit fifteen of eighteen shots while Berwick made only eleven of twenty-six. Anthracite

League rivals found themselves licking their chops to get a shot at this West Hazleton team. They were anxious to dethrone the team that had captured four consecutive league titles.

Weatherly took on Crestwood on the latter's court to start the season. Don Barnes described the game as having "more whistles blown than on New Year's Eve." The Wreckers were known for their aggressive—some might say undisciplined—defensive play, but on this night they saw seven of their players foul out. When the game ended, Weatherly only had three eligible players able to take the court. Given the circumstances, it was no surprise that the Weatherly came out on the short end of a 64-58 score. Despite the loss it was clear that the Wreckers were going to be a force to be reckoned with in league play

Meanwhile, Hazleton High opened at Saint Joe's against the always tough Mahanoy Area Golden Bears. This turned out to be another game decided on the foul line. Even though Hazleton ended the game with a 25-19 edge in field goals, they fell to defeat by a score of 72-64 as Mahanoy Area converted thirty-four foul tries while Hazleton only sent fourteen through the hoop. Despite the loss, the Mounts sent a message that they were going to be a tough out for any foe in the coming season. Led by the six-foot-two senior Bob Solarek, Hazleton wasn't big but they were very rugged inside as evidenced by the fact that they had out-rebounded the taller Golden Bears.

Monday, December 7th, was the day before Hazleton and Saint Gabriel's would meet for the first of two games. At Saint Gabriel's the students were abuzz talking over both the game and the pep rally scheduled to be held that night in the school auditorium. Everyone was making plans on where they would meet prior to attending the rally. There was not a seat to be had when the G-Men took to the little court in the school's gym in their pre-game sweats to go through their warm-up drills as the rally began. The cheerleaders were present but they weren't necessary as the student body erupted in a chorus of sound that filled the building and continued as "Sweet Georgia Brown" and "When the Saints Come Marching In" blared from the school's loudspeakers. Then the team completed its drills and took their seats facing the crowd, and the cheerleaders took the floor. They led the frenzied crowd in a series of cheers, most notably Thunderation, which filled the space as only a roaring crowd could. To top it off, an elementary school student, the diminutive Joe Fox, made an appearance as Little Gabe, the school's mascot. His entrance drew wild cheers that were followed by a couple of humorous skits.

Father Deviney then took to the floor with his booming voice. He began by saying, "Someone here, before the rally started, came to me to tell me that there are Hazleton High School students present and that I should ask them to leave. I said no way—I want them to see what they're missing." That remark brought the students to their feet, and Deviney let the ovation roll over him until he slowly motioned the students to take their seats. After Deviney had finished rousing the crowd, senior captain Joe Entiero addressed the throng, who by now were cheering after every sentence any speaker uttered. Then Lee Gesler, who played on the JV team, requested the floor. First Gesler almost took the roof of the place by announcing he wasn't worried about the varsity game that was "in the bag." He then noted that Saint Gabriel's had never beaten Hazleton in a JV contest and announced, "That's going to change tomorrow night." Coach Kender topped things off by telling the students how important their support was going to be and that they needed to be every bit as loud tomorrow as they were being right now. There wasn't a soul in the place who thought that was going to be a problem.

In its day-of-the-game preview the *Standard Speaker* saw the G-Men as slight underdogs. Hazleton, though not a big team, would send a taller outfit onto the court than the Saints. It was also noted that Hazleton had won nine out of ten games since the teams began meeting early in the decade. The feeling was that Saint Gabriel's was going to have to shoot well from the outside to pull off a win.

A crowd approaching two thousand filed through the doors at Saint Joe's anticipating a tight contest. Father Purcell journeyed down from Saint Michael's to catch the action, and his entrance resulted in a standing ovation from the Saint Gabriel's student body. From the opening tap the G-Men ran pressure man-to-man defense and with five minutes gone the Saints were up 14-13. It was at this point that Saint Gabriel's shots couldn't find the hole, and Hazleton ran off fourteen straight points to lead 27-14 with about six minutes to go in the half. Kender called a time-out and the Saints responded when play resumed, cutting the margin to 37-34 at the half. Hazleton had controlled the boards in the first half, and the G-Men were inconsistent from the foul line.

The two teams played an even third quarter and after three periods, Hazleton was clinging to a 54-49 lead. In the fourth period Hazleton coach Fran Libonati went to his bench and inserted Danny Gallagher into the game. Gallagher, who had transferred from Saint Gabriel's to Hazleton, responded by scoring nine critical points. Meanwhile the Saints' foul shooting woes continued as the normally accurate G-Men missed the front end on numerous one-and-one opportunities. When the game ended Hazleton had emerged victorious 76-69. The Mounts had five players score in double figures including Gallagher, who hit for fifteen. Pete O'Donnell and Barrett both scored eighteen for the losers, but they combined to hit just six of fifteen foul tries. Both Entiero and Hoffman scored twelve, and Hoffman also pulled down nine rebounds for Saint Gabriel's though the Mounts controlled both boards. Jerry Sernak made a brief appearance, but it was obvious that his back continued to be a problem, and he was ineffective. Despite the loss, the G-Men had played well enough against Hazleton to serve notice that they would be a force in the Anthracite League and in post-season play. Oh, and Hazleton easily won the JV game 64-39.

After the Hazleton game there was a difference that could be felt in the stands on the Saint Gabriel's side of the gym. The next day you could feel it in the halls walking through Saint Gabriel's High School. This loss wasn't easy to swallow. In previous years when the team was a decided underdog, those close losses could be summed up as moral victories, and in games where the margins weren't that close, the outcome had been expected. The difference this time was the fans expected a win. The days of taking solace in moral victories had passed. This was the dawn of a new era for the Saint Gabriel's faithful and the team they followed. Victories would still be celebrated, certainly some more than others, but losses were going to be much harder to live with. One sensed that Father Deviney didn't appreciate losing and didn't expect to have to put up with much of it during his stay in Hazleton.

Through two games it was easy to see the style of play the G-Men favored. Coach Kender employed a man-to-man defense from the opening tip and used the fast break whenever the opportunity presented itself. Mike O'Donnell, then a senior on the team, believes that Kender utilized the fast break offense because the team had speed and depth but lacked size. It was a way to wear down taller opponents who lacked the bench strength the Saints possessed.

After the Hazleton loss the G-Men had one day to prepare before taking on a Crestwood team that had already beaten two Anthracite League teams, including highly regarded Weatherly. Crestwood had height and controlled the boards in both of those wins. The Saints were going to be further hampered as far as rebounding went because Paul Hoffman had suffered an injury against Hazleton and would miss at least two games. However, the game would be played at Saint Joe's, and the G-Men always played well in those cozy confines with which they had become so familiar.

The Saints led from the opening tip though seldom by more than six points. After three quarters it was Saint Gabriel's 49, Crestwood 44. With four minutes left in the contest the G-Men were still up by five 63-58. Crestwood scored a goal and, after multiple Saint Gabriel misses, canned two foul shots to cut the margin to one with 2:46 to go. The G-Men brought the ball up court but were called for a double dribble with just over two minutes to go. At this point Crestwood decided to hold the ball for a last shot.

With twenty-six seconds left, Entiero went for the steal and fouled Crestwood's Fred Jones. Jones missed the front end of the one-and-one but the rebound went to the six-foot-four Irv Carter, who scored, putting Crestwood ahead 64-63. Coach Kender called time-out. With seventeen seconds to play, there was plenty of time for the G-Men to get a good shot, but Crestwood applied solid defensive pressure, and Jim Barrett sent up a hurried effort from the head of the key. The shot hit the rim and bounced away as Crestwood secured possession. That was the ballgame.

Pete O'Donnell, who Ray Saul described as having more moves than the Mayflower Van Lines, led the G-Men in scoring with twenty. Barrett scored twelve, and Gennaro hit doubles with ten. Crestwood controlled the boards as evidenced by the fact that the smaller Saints only had twenty-four rebounds. What many had hoped would be a magical season was off to a rocky start.

A letter sent to the *Standard Speaker* by a Crestwood fan a few days after the game illustrates how closely the local community followed high school basketball in those days. The writer accused the paper of biased reporting in the account of the contest. He said that Saul only grudgingly complimented the winners while being quick to make excuses for the losers. Saul responded by pointing out that he had described the game as a great win for Crestwood. He had complimented the winner's ability and predicted they would win a lot more games in the coming season. Saul pointed out that what the fan called excuses were simply facts—mainly, Crestwood was the taller team, Saint Gabriel's did in fact hold the lead until the last twenty-six seconds, and the G-Men were missing a key player in Paul Hoffman. Saul ended his response by saying, "If this is biased reporting, then, in our humble opinion, the world is flat." The Saint Gabriel's basketball team wasn't interested in excuses; they were interested in wins.

The next game was a rematch against Immaculate Heart. This was the team the G-Men had dispatched by a score of 87-53 to open the season. Once again Immaculate Heart scored 53 points, but this time the Saints only managed 58. Barrett was ill and missed the game, but it was still far closer than expected. With a record of 2-2, the G-Men had two games left before league play began. Between illness and injuries, plus the fact the next two exhibition opponents had already beaten Saint Gabriel's, things were hardly looking up.

Three days before Christmas 1964, the G-Men traveled to meet Crestwood in a rematch of the game that had resulted in the letter to the editor. In what was their worst performance of the season, the Saints hit on just eight of thirty shots in the first half, were badly out rebounded, and trailed the Comets 39-21 at intermission. Fighting back, the G-Men narrowed the margin to 58-51 with a little over three minutes to play but then ran out of gas. Crestwood pulled away to win 73-55. Carrying a losing record on their backs, the team took some holiday time off as they prepared to meet Hazleton on New Year's Day.

On the same night that Saint Gabriel's was being soundly beaten by Crestwood, West Hazleton sent a message heard throughout the Anthracite League. As mentioned previously, the athletic administrators at West Hazleton had decided to upgrade their exhibition schedule by adding historically strong regional programs to the slate. Nanticoke, a school that had won multiple Class A public school district titles, fit that bill. The Wildcats defeated Nanticoke at Nanticoke 76-61. It was the first win over Nanticoke in the school's history. The win gave West Hazleton a 4-1 record heading into their game with Hazleton a week later. Though the Cats had beaten the Mounts four straight years, most observers favored Hazleton in this matchup. It was clear that regardless of the outcome of the Hazleton game, West Hazleton wasn't going to relinquish its hold on the league championship without a fight.

In the days leading up to the Hazleton–Saint Gabriel's rematch, Weatherly finished its exhibition schedule with a convincing 85-47 win over Marian Catholic. That gave the Wreckers a 4-2 record (two close losses to Crestwood) as they readied themselves to start league play. Meanwhile, Hazleton beat West Hazleton 53-45 before more than 2,200 fans. That left West Hazleton at 4-2 and Hazleton at 6-1 heading into the game with Saint Gabriel's.

Sports fans in Hazleton spent New Year's Day much like their counterparts throughout the country—watching college football bowl games. Arkansas got by Nebraska in the Cotton Bowl while LSU was beating Syracuse in the Sugar Bowl. In the granddaddy of them all, Michigan humbled Oregon State 34-7 in the Rose Bowl. Michigan's fullback Mel Anthony set a Rose Bowl record for the longest run from scrimmage when he took the pigskin eighty-four yards for a score. A couple of thousand Hazletonians missed the Orange Bowl where Texas beat the Joe Namath-led Alabama team, opting to take in the Hazleton-Saint Gabriel's game instead.

The G-Men had employed an up-tempo offense all season long. Hoping to catch Fran Libonati's Mounts off guard, Coach Kender decided to go with a semi-possession, deliberate-type offense. From the opening tip, the Saints walked the ball up court and worked the ball, looking for a good shot. On defense they went man for man with Joe Entiero drawing the job of handling Hazleton's leading scorer, Bob Solarek. The strategy seemed to be paying off as Saint Gabriel's took a 19-18 lead to the locker room at halftime. In particular, Entiero had held up his end, holding Solarek scoreless in the first two periods. The Hazleton star hadn't even been able to get off a shot.

Midway through the third period, the G-Men were leading 32-27 when Hazleton ran off eight straight points to take a 35-32 lead. With six minutes left to play Hazleton was up 39-37 when the bottom fell out. Hazleton ran off ten straight points as the G-Men failed to convert the front end of multiple one-and-one chances from the foul line. Down by twelve, they abandoned the deliberate style and Hazleton caught fire, outscoring the Saints 27-10 in the final period to wrap up a 62-42 win.

While Entiero held Solarek to just two points, Carmen Chandler scored twenty-two for the Mounts, and Louie Fiore came off the bench in the last quarter to score all eight of his points. Barrett led the G-Men with seventeen, and O'Donnell hit for ten. Sernak remained on the bench nursing his bad back, but neither the G-Men nor their fans were using that as an excuse. They had been beaten twice by a Hazleton team many felt the Saints were equipped to handle. The loss left them limping into Anthracite League play with a record of 2-4. The day after the game, Ray Saul was more optimistic than most of Saint Gabriel's fans when he wrote that "you can bet your best bib and tucker" that the G-Men would contend for a league championship.

On the day before league play began, Saul made his annual first half predictions. In the sports editor's opinion, calling the Anthracite League this time around was tougher than any year since 1960. He predicted West Hazleton and newcomer Jim Thorpe, sporting a 6-1 exhibition record, would tie for first half honors. Saint Gabriel's and Weatherly were picked just behind the top two with Freeland Saint Ann's a dark horse contender.

The G-Men opened league play against Freeland, the tallest team in the circuit. At home in Saint Joe's gym, the Saints found their offense and ran off to a 93-70 win. Coach Kender used twelve men in the game and four of them hit double figures. Pete O'Donnell and the steadily improving freshman Hoffman led the way, both scoring nineteen. Barrett hit for fifteen and Mike O'Donnell came off the bench to score fourteen. Jerry Sernak also scored nine, but what was good news for the Saints was his very presence on the floor as his play underneath helped off-set the rangy Whippets height advantage. If this Saint Gabriel's team had a weakness, it was matching up on the inside against teams with height. It was a flaw that Sernak's presence on the floor helped address.

Elsewhere around the league, West Hazleton went on the road and took down previously undefeated Saint Ann's 84-67. Once again, the ever dependable Richie Sypek led the Wildcats with thirty-four points. Jim Thorpe let everyone know they were going to have to be dealt with before the league crown would be awarded by beating Foster Township 85-62. The only big surprise in league play took place at MMI, where Weatherly struggled to beat MMI 60-59 in overtime.

Saint Gabriel's traveled to Freeland to face Foster Township in their second league game of the season. The Saints were a solid pick to win by double digits, but the Falcons didn't get that message. Though the G-Men never trailed in the contest, Foster kept hanging around. With six minutes left Saint Gabriel's had a lead of 59-52 when things began to turn. For over three minutes the Saints didn't score, and when Jerry Sernak broke that drought by hitting a foul shot the score stood at 60-56 with 2:30 left on the clock. George Sitch scored for the Falcons at the two-minute mark, and Bill Hauze hit a foul shot with a minute left to make it 60-59. The little Foster Township gym was literally rocking when Joe Entiero was fouled with thirty seconds left. Foster controlled the ball after Entiero missed from the line, but Pete O'Donnell stole an errant Falcon pass with fourteen seconds to go and called time-out. Foster returned the favor by intercepting a G-Men pass with eight seconds left. The Falcons got the ball to Sitch. who drove for the goal and put up a contested layup. The ball rested on the rim for what seemed like an eternity before dropping outside the cylinder as time ran out.

The G-Men escaped and were still undefeated in league play but were scheduled to face the defending champion West Hazleton Wildcats in just a few days. The Cats had tuned up for the contest by clubbing MMI 88-58.

For the Saint Gabriel's student body, the West Hazleton rivalry had grown concurrent with the Wildcat's league dominance. Few could forget Yosh Grobelny leading the West Hazleton starters as they waved their white towels at the G-Men fans less than a year before. Only the older Saint Gabriel's students could remember the last time the Saints had beaten West Hazleton— for most 1960 was an eternity ago. For the Wildcats the game represented an opportunity to quiet the critics that were saying this team didn't measure up to the squads that had won four consecutive league titles. There was a lot on the line for both teams.

If there was any doubt about the significance of the game, it was dispelled by the full-page headline that appeared on the first page of the sports section of the *Standard Speaker* on game day. Bold letters proclaimed that a close contest between the two city rivals was expected in what was billed as the area's marquee matchup.

As far as the game went, the beginning of Don Barnes's column the next day said it all. Barnes wrote, "The prospect of a fifth straight Anthracite League championship for West Hazleton was reprehensible as well as unthinkable before the season opened but the league members by now have been alerted to the fact that it's entirely possible." Barnes couldn't be blamed for his conclusion after witnessing the Wildcats club the G-Men into submission 84-62. Though the game was close for three periods, West Hazleton was in control the whole way. Led by the incomparable Richie Sypek, who scored twenty-nine points despite being blanketed by Paul Hoffman, the Saints proved no match for West Hazleton. The loss was disheartening for both the Saint Gabriel's team and their supporters. More than a few Saint Gabriel followers had gone into the season believing that a league title was a sure thing, and now it didn't look at all likely. There was a rumbling of complaints among some of the older fans that coaching was the source of the problem. If Father Deviney had an opinion, he was keeping it to himself.

At this point, three teams—Weatherly, Jim Thorpe, and West Hazleton—remained undefeated in league play. The G-Men were in a position of having to hope those three knocked each other off while they beat the two undefeated teams they had yet to face to force a playoff for the first half title. Weatherly would face Jim Thorpe in just a few days, so one piece of the puzzle was about to fall into place. Meanwhile, the Saints needed to start winning.

If the loss to the Wildcats did anything positive, it seemed to light a fire under the G-Men, who traveled to Freeland to face Saint Ann's hoping to right their ship. The Saints actually trailed by one at half before exploding to win, going away by a score of 106-73. The 106 points represented a new school scoring record. Hoffman, giving the fans a taste of what was to come, scored thirty in his finest performance to date. All five of the Saints starters hit double figures with Barrett netting twenty, Entiero nineteen, Pete O'Donnell sixteen, and Sernak fifteen in addition to collecting twenty rebounds.

It was Saint Gabriel's finest performance of the season, but it wasn't without its critics. Ray Saul reported that the newspaper had received a number of phone calls after the game complaining that Coach Kender had run up the score on the Crusaders. To his credit, Saul contacted Kender, who said he felt that his team was down mentally and needed the extra work. What he didn't say was that they also needed to boost their confidence, but that was probably on his mind as well.

Meanwhile, in the game of the night, Jim Thorpe had crushed Weatherly 69-48 in a contest described as "conclusive, devastating, and final." While the Olympians were riding high, the lightly regarded Freeland Whippets traveled to West Hazleton and almost caught the Cats sleeping. The West Hazleton gym, though not the bandbox some of the local teams played in, wasn't spacious, and in its history had provided a solid home court advantage. In addition, the Cats had a devoted following and opposition fans were hard pressed to attend games there in any great numbers. Then there were the strange things that occurred to visiting teams at West Hazleton. For example, the overhead lights might flicker when the teams playing the Wildcats were on offense. To put it mildly, West Hazleton enjoyed welcoming visiting teams. On this particular night versus Freeland, West Hazleton squeaked by with a 74-72 victory. The close win kept the Wildcats undefeated in league play but illustrated that in this year's Anthracite League race, nothing could be taken for granted.

The next big game among the contenders would be the Weatherly-Saint Gabriel's matchup with the loser likely eliminated from first half title contention. On the night before the Weatherly game, Saint Gabriel's fans were treated to some good news delivered by their freshman team. The young G-Man squad coached by Vince Gallagher remained undefeated in junior high league play after beating previously undefeated Saint Joseph's 87-72. Saint Joseph's was led by a six-foot-four freshman named Darrell Farkus who scored sixty-four of Saint Joseph's seventy-two points. The junior G-Men placed five players in double figures including three—Rocco Fallabel, Dennis Olexa, and Mike Heffernan—who would play an important part on other Saint Gabriel's teams in the near future.

Most local observers tabbed Weatherly as the slight favorite based largely on the fact that the game would be played on the Wreckers' home court. Even before the JV game tipped off, the small Weatherly gym was filled to capacity with not even standing room available. The crowd was treated to a whale of a prelim as Weatherly pulled out a 76-74 win in the first game. That contest set the tone for the encounter to follow.

The home team led throughout the night, though never by more than eight points. After three quarters it was Weatherly 50, Saint Gabriel's 46. The Wreckers continued to employ an aggressive man-to-man defense in the final quarter despite being deep foul trouble. Before the final buzzer sounded, three of their starters would foul out. Meanwhile, the Saints had abandoned their pressing defense after Weatherly had exploited it for several easy buckets. With time running out, Weatherly was clinging to a two-point, 63-61 lead. It was at this point that little Charlie Gennaro launched a shot that tickled the twine just before time expired, sending the game into overtime.

The two teams started the overtime period by trading field goals. What followed was the turning point in the game. The Saints worked the ball to Hoffman, whose jump shot from the right side off the court hit the mark. Weatherly's John Hart was called for fouling Jerry Sernak underneath while both players were positioning themselves to secure a potential rebound. Sernak converted both ends of the one-and-one and the G-Men were on top 69-65. Weatherly missed their next try from the field, and the Saints secured the rebound and were instructed by Coach Kender to hold the ball. The Wreckers were forced to foul to gain possession, and the G-Men converted the foul shots to come away with a 75-67 win. Kender's Saints were back in the thick of the first half title race thanks to a balanced attack led by Sernak's nineteen points and fifteen rebounds. Pete O'Donnell added sixteen, and Barrett and Hoffman scored thirteen apiece.

In other league action, Jim Thorpe had remained undefeated, easily taking down Saint Ann's while West Hazleton struggled before putting away Foster Township 81-69. On Friday, just three days away, the league would showcase its top teams in action against each other when Jim Thorpe would travel to Hazleton to take on Saint Gabriel's and Weatherly would visit West Hazleton. Most thought those games would go a long way in determining the Anthracite's first half.

Despite the win at Weatherly, Jim Thorpe was favored to beat the G-Men at Saint Joe's. The Olympians were undefeated in league play and had dominated the same Weatherly team that Saint Gabriel's required an overtime period to beat. On the day of the game, the halls in Saint Gabriel's school buzzed with news and it wasn't good. A number of the players on the basketball team were home sick with what Father Deviney later called a virus. Efforts were made to postpone the game until Sunday, but nothing could be worked out. As the news traveled student to student, the word was that Jim Thorpe officials had refused to reschedule the game. That really wasn't true. Ironically, public schools weren't permitted to play on Sundays, and with a regularly scheduled game against West Hazleton already on their slate for Tuesday, the Thorpe forces didn't want to play on Monday. So it was decided the game would be played that night. Needless to say, the Saint Gabriel's student body, already keyed up for the important contest, was further fired up by what they misconstrued as Jim Thorpe's apparent willingness to take advantage of the situation.

Jim Thorpe featured a balanced attack led by senior Jack Kmetz who had been described as "the soul of the team." Along with Kmetz, Joe Morgan and Keith Miller could be counted on for consistent play. The team also boasted a talented sophomore named Bobby Brown who had already established a name for himself as a player who sometimes let his temper get the best of him. As Pete O'Donnell recalled, "He [Brown] got into a few fights in some games."

As usual, by the start of the JV game the Saint Gabriel's student section was full. As that game was being played, the stands filled on both sides of the court. By game time a crowd approaching two thousand had gathered to see the two teams in action. Determined to let the Jim Thorpe officials know they were being unfair for their refusal to reschedule, the Saint Gabriel's students, known for their spirit, were even more vocal than usual. Tensions inside the gym ran high.

From the beginning of the game the Saints didn't look like a team battling illness. Hoffman in particular was on fire, playing some of his best basketball of the season. Sernak was a terror under the boards, and Entiero was running an offense that slowed down only when there was a whistle—and there were a lot of them. At times it seemed like the referees were sure to run out of breath as they took the tiny instrument to their lips to blow again and again. After the first half the score was tied at thirty-six, and Thorpe's ace Jack Kmetz was in foul trouble with three.

Early in the third quarter Kmetz picked up foul number four. Rather than protect their star by taking him out for the remainder of the quarter, the Thorpe coaching staff allowed him to remain in the game. With a little over three minutes to play in the quarter, Kmetz picked up his fifth foul and headed to the bench. With the loss of Kmetz, the air seemed to go out of Jim Thorpe's balloon as the G-Men hit the gas and scored on multiple fast breaks. The buzzer bringing the third quarter to an end found Saint Gabriel's on top 65-50.

The Olympians tried to comeback in the final period, but the hole was too deep. The Saints had capped one of the biggest basketball weeks in the school's history with the upset win 88-76. Hoffman, the talented freshman, scored twenty-eight to lead the G-Men. Sernak had scored eighteen and pulled down thirteen rebounds. Entiero added sixteen and Barrett, fifteen, while O'Donnell just missed doubles with eight. Saint Gabriel's shot forty-three fouls and hit on thirty of them. Jim Thorpe was led by Bobby Brown with twenty. Don Barnes described Brown as "a truly fine player who would be great if he learns to master his temper thoroughly."

While the Saint Gabriel's students were celebrating the win, the two teams headed for the stairs leading to the locker rooms across the gym floor. As reported by the *Standard Speaker*, a teenager was directing verbal assaults at the Jim Thorpe players as they left the floor. One of the players (some say it was Brown) headed into the stands after the heckler. Soon that corner of the gym was filled with a crowd of people described as a "pushing, shoving, punch throwing mob." It took several policemen to restore order, but the incident left a few of the participants with "cracked heads." The paper noted that the youthful fan whose remarks started the ruckus was neither a Saint Gabriel's nor a Jim Thorpe student. Though never officially identified, the fan's identity was soon known to the Saint Gabriel's student body. He was a Hazleton High student who for some reason hated Saint Gabriel's with such a passion he would come to games to cheer against the G-Men. On this particular night, he was apparently upset about the way the Olympians performed, and he was letting them know it.

With the Jim Thorpe win in hand, the Saint Gabriel's contingent was anxious to learn the outcome of the Weatherly-West Hazleton game. The news was disappointing as the Wildcats had remained undefeated by getting past Weatherly 70-67. All of a sudden the same fans who had rooted so passionately for a Jim Thorpe loss became big fans of the Olympians who would face West Hazleton at home on Tuesday. A Jim Thorpe win in that one would, in all probability, create a three-way tie for the first half title, necessitating a playoff.

Both Saint Gabriel's and West Hazleton had two games left. They shared one common opponent, Hazle Township, where the Saints and the Cats would be heavy favorites. The other team the G-Men would face would be MMI in the Preppers' very small home gym that had seen its share of upsets. Still, most felt that Saint Gabriel's would beat the Preppers by double figures. West Hazleton's other foe would be Jim Thorpe at Jim Thorpe, and the Olympians were the pick by virtually all the pundits.

The G-Men held up their end by beating MMI 106-96. The combined total of 202 points was more than two area teams had ever put on a scoreboard. Hoffman, fast emerging as a star, led all scorers with thirty-four while hitting on thirteen of seventeen shots from the floor. Four other Saint Gabriel's players— Sernak, Entiero, Pete O'Donnell, and Gennaro—also scored in double figures. Barrett missed the game due to illness.

In the big game that evening, West Hazleton and Jim Thorpe played what many considered to be one of the classic games in Anthracite League history before a packed house of 1,200 screaming fans at Jim Thorpe. A tight first quarter saw the Wildcats jump to a 14-11 lead. Early in the second period the Olympians tied it at seventeen and then took a 19-17 lead. That was the first of eleven lead changes in the second period, which came to a close with Jim Thorpe on top 35-32.

West Hazleton caught fire in the third quarter, quickly scoring nine straight points to take a 41-35 lead. Thorpe called a time-out. When the Olympians returned to the floor, they employed a full-court press and despite another time-out, called by West Hazleton's coach Ron Gatski, Thorpe outscored the Cats 18-2 in the last six minutes of the quarter and went into the final period with a 53-43 lead.

The fourth quarter started with a Thorpe field goal extending the lead to twelve. Over the next three minutes West Hazleton chipped away at the lead and narrowed the margin to 57-53 with a little over four and a half minutes left. With just two minutes left, Keith Miller scored to put the Olympians up 62-57.

Within ten seconds West Hazleton answered that bucket with one of their own to cut the margin to three. With just forty-five seconds left, the ever-reliable Richie Sypek scored a layup that rolled around the rim twice before dropping in.

The Thorpe lead was down to one and the Olympians, an excellent ball-handling club, decided to run out the clock. With fourteen seconds left Sypek fouled Joe Morgan, who went to the line to shoot the front end of a one-and-one. The first shot ripped the cords and Morgan stood on the line with a chance to end it. His second effort bounced off the rim into the hands of the Wildcat Ron Christina, who called a time-out with twelve seconds showing on the clock.

The score was 63-61 as West Hazleton set up their final play. After inbounding the ball to Ed Martnick the Cats set up their offense. With three seconds left the ball was in Martnick's hands again, and he fired up a shot from about twenty-five feet. The ball touched nothing but net and the two teams were tied at the end of regulation time. Martnick's shot took all the air out of the Olympians. West Hazleton outscored Thorpe ten to five in the overtime to emerge with a 73-68 victory. The win was one of the greatest in the Wildcats' storied history, and it served notice they were a team that wouldn't quit when they found themselves down by double digits. As expected, both West Hazleton and Saint Gabriel's went on to defeat Hazle Township. What wasn't expected was the Wildcats going undefeated to win the league's first half title. Saint Gabriel's was alone in second with a 7-1 record but would face both West Hazleton and Jim Thorpe on the road in the second half. Winning the second half and forcing a title game with the Cats was going to take some doing, but both the G-Men and their loyal fans felt they were up to the task.

7

OFFICIAL TIME-OUT

CHIP'S LAST HURRAH

By the start of second half play, Saint Gabriel's had added a new player to the roster. Ray McBrearty was a transfer from Pottsville Nativity who would play a lot of JV ball for the rest of the season. McBrearty was a guard who was a tenacious defensive player and a superb ball handler. Though new to the school, he carried himself with a sense of confidence and soon became a leader on the court.

The first week of second half play in the Anthracite League had some key games on the schedule that would go a long way in identifying who, if anyone, was going to challenge West Hazleton. In that first week, Jim Thorpe would travel to West Hazleton to take on the Wildcats. Three days later Weatherly would host West Hazleton, and the G-Men would travel to Jim Thorpe for a highly awaited rematch with the Olympians.

West Hazleton took care of business against Jim Thorpe 82-76, and in doing so passed a major obstacle in their bid to add another Anthracite League trophy to the many already gleaming in the school's trophy case. Once again it was Sypek who led the way, scoring thirty for the Wildcats. The Olympians, who gave the home team all they could handle, were led by Brown, who took scoring honors in the contest by scoring thirty-one.

Meanwhile, the G-Men dominated MMI in their first half opener, winning by a score of 92-61. Twelve players saw action in the contest for the Saints, who were led by Hoffman's twenty points. Hoffman emerged as a potent offensive weapon as the season progressed. Hazleton area fans were hard pressed to recall a freshman who had ever made such an impact on the local sports scene. Other Saint Gabriel's players who made it into double figures in the contest were Barrett, Entiero, and Pete O'Donnell. Coach Kender, with an eye to next year, used the game to get varsity action for a number of JV players including Ed O'Donnell and Ray McBrearty.

Those initial second half games set the stage for some key Friday night matchups in the league. Weatherly, which had taken West Hazleton to the wire in the first half, would entertain the Cats before what promised to be a packed and frenzied crowd in the small Weatherly gym. On the same night the G-Men would invade Jim Thorpe in what many expected to be one of the most interesting games of the year. Thorpe's coach Tony Romano had refused to shake hands with Coach Kender after the Saints had beaten his squad in their initial meeting—which had ended, readers may recall, with police breaking up a fight of fans and players. Adding more coal to the fire was the basic fact that Jim Thorpe absolutely had to win this game; a loss would eliminate them from the second half championship race.

Tickets to the contest were sold out in advance, and more than a few folks were worried trouble would erupt among the 1,200 fans who would surround the Olympians court. On the day of the game, Phil Sarno expressed his hope in writing that the fans not cause any disturbance that would force the PIAA to assess penalties on either school.

This time it was West Hazleton coach Ron Gatski who riled up Weatherly fans by failing to offer a congratulatory handshake to Weatherly's Skip Ebling after the Wreckers beat the Wildcats easily, 83-69. Weatherly outshot and out-rebounded West Hazleton from the opening whistle. While the win moved Weatherly ahead of West Hazleton in the second half race, they still had to face two teams—Saint Gabriel's and Jim Thorpe—that had already bested them in first half play.

Speaking of the Saints and the Olympians, while Weatherly was beating West Hazleton, they were putting on quite a show in Jim Thorpe. Though it turned out to be a white-knuckled battle, it didn't start out that way. The Thorpe players were fired up, and they jumped all over the G-Men early, scoring thirty first quarter points and taking a sixteen-point lead. Gathering themselves, Saint Gabriel's outscored the Olympians 23-11 in the second quarter and trailed by only four, 41-37, at the half.

Coach Kender, who had made free use of his bench in previous games, went with the same five players the entire first half.

In the third period the teams battled back and forth, and when the buzzer sounded Saint Gabriel's was up by one, 58-57. That lead had changed five times in the quarter, which set the stage for a final eight minutes few of the participants or fans on hand would soon forget. With 1,200 spectators on their feet throughout the quarter, there were ten lead changes. Coach Kender never went to his bench, riding his five starters the full thirty-two minutes.

A Pete O'Donnell field goal knotted the score at seventy-seven with forty seconds to play. Jim Thorpe waited until ten seconds were left before launching a shot that missed, and with both teams desperately going for the rebound, a tie-up resulted. The Saints' Sernak controlled the tap, sending the ball to Hoffman, who passed to O'Donnell, who then called a time-out.

Coach Kender gathered his team around him and diagramed the final play. Entiero inbounded the ball beneath his own basket. He found O'Donnell open in the corner. O'Donnell fired a twenty-five-foot jump shot toward the hoop, and it sailed cleanly through the net, giving the G-Men a 79-77 victory.

All five of the Saints' starters scored in double figures. The balanced attack was led by O'Donnell and Hoffman, who scored eighteen each. Barrett and Sernak hit for fifteen, and Entiero, who had become the team's floor leader, scored thirteen. It now looked like the Saints and Weatherly were in the driver's seat for the second-half title. Fans wouldn't have to wait long to see one of them take control as they were scheduled to meet four days later.

Saint Gabriel's had now won seven in a row and were meeting the expectations their legions of fans had entertained entering the year. After the slow start, the G-Men were 11-5 and a win against Weatherly would all but assure them, at the very least, a share of the second half title. A big crowd was expected to witness the pivotal battle. Weatherly was coming off their big win over West Hazleton where they did something unheard of in league play—they dominated the Wildcats. The G-Men were gelling as a team. All of their starters were legitimate offensive threats and the freshman starter Paul Hoffman had been steadily improving as the season progressed. The local paper rated the game a toss-up.

Another crowd of two thousand fans were in their seats at Saint Joe's when the JV game ended with the junior G-Men emerging on top, 78-53. Prior to tip-off of the varsity game, Saint Gabriel's fans rose to their feet and joined in a thunderous ovation when Father Purcell entered the gym to take in the action. Everyone in the student body agreed that Purcell's arrival was a good omen. Coach Kender had decided to center his defense on stopping Weatherly's top scorers, Bill Gicking and Pat Searfoss. On Weatherly's first possession the G-Men employed a triangle-and-two defense with Hoffman on Gicking and Entiero smothering Searfoss. After one quarter, the Saints were on top 20-14 and the Wreckers were clearly struggling on offense. As a team, Weatherly was forcing the ball and taking bad shots. Clearly, they hadn't prepared to face a gimmick defense.

When the second quarter began it was apparent that Weatherly had decided on a strategy to attack that defense. The Wreckers were using Gicking and Searfoss to feed the ball to those players not facing man-to-man defense. Lew Kistler responded, scoring fifteen points in the second stanza, but it wasn't enough to stop the Saints who were utilizing a fast break offense with great success. At half the G-Men had stretched their lead to 47-33, much to the delight of their followers, who were practically rocking the large gym after every goal. The G-Men cheerleaders were being greeted with wild cheers as they took the court during the time-outs Weatherly used to try to curb the Saints' momentum. The tactic failed to slow the G-Men. As was often the case when the Saints were on a roll, the crowd noise was so intense that talking to the person sitting next to you was a challenge. This was one of those nights when more than a few of the Saints supporters strained their voices while urging their team to pour it on.

Early in the third period Weatherly went on a run and narrowed the margin to eight, but after a time-out the Saints regained control and went on a scoring spurt of their own, leading to a score of 69-50 heading into the final quarter. When Pete O'Donnell scored to start the period, the G-Men were coasting with a twenty-one-point lead. In its report of the game, the *Standard Speaker* stated that at this point in the game, it looked like Saint Gabriel's was "quite capable of playing with the Celtics." Most of the fans, especially those cheering for the purple and white, thought the game was over.

Then it all turned around as Wreckers scored twelve straight points before Hoffman responded by scoring for the Saints. Still Weatherly wasn't finished. They continued to battle and a Kistler goal with three minutes left made the score 73-68. Saint Gabriel's fans breathed a sigh of relief when Barrett converted a three-point play ten seconds later. With a minute left, the G-Men still led by a score of 80-72 when Weatherly's John Hart, a Wrecker reserve, came off the bench and scored six points in twenty-six seconds. The Saints' twenty-one-point lead had shrunk to two.

Weatherly employed a full-court press, but the G-Men successfully inbounded the ball to Entiero, who was intentionally fouled. The team's captain headed to the line and calmly sank both ends of the one-and-one. He sank six more fouls in succession, and the Saints survived the scare, winning 88-78. The G-Men had held on for the win and now were the only undefeated team in the second-half race. It appeared that only West Hazleton stood between them and a second-half title. They were now the team to beat. Meanwhile, the Wildcats had stayed alive in the race, barely getting by Foster Township 58-55.

Don Barnes, reflecting on the game, wrote, "That was a real basketball treat, served up Anthracite League-style at St. Joe's last night. A big win for the Saints in a big year and a rough one for Weatherly. If Saint Gabriel's gets through the second half without a scratch, the Wreckers are out of the title picture and in our book that would be a shame. It was Weatherly that put West Hazleton on the defensive in the second half race and the Wreckers deserve a better fate than sitting on the sidelines in any title playoff. That was one of the greatest comebacks ever at St. Joe's."

These were happy times at Saint Gabriel's. The success of the basketball team was shared by the entire student body and, to a lesser extent, the entire parish. Few of the grade school students could remember the 1960 championship team. Few in the school knew anything about the 1947 team beyond the fact that a trophy from that year could be seen in a trophy case that held more items celebrating debate victories than athletic ones. A basketball fever had infected the place, and it wasn't likely to end anytime soon.

There was basketball virtually every day of the week. When the varsity wasn't in action the junior high team was, and on weekends the biddy players took over the little gym in the high school. Future G-Men like Dennis Olexa, Rocco Fallabel and Mike Heffernan were leading the way on the freshman team. John Darraugh, Pat Curry, Jerry Gallagher, and Jimmy Brown were standouts for the eighth graders. Seventh grader Joe Farley was in a great spot playing with the eighth graders while seeing action with the freshman in some of their games, and he was still eligible to play biddy basketball. Tommy Boyle and Jerry Fallabel were honing their skills playing in the school's biddy league. The future looked bright, but for now everyone's main concern was capturing that elusive Anthracite League title.

Those who felt the league's second half depended on the outcome of the Saint Gabriel's-West Hazleton contest, which was less than two weeks away, were mistaken. The G-Men had Foster Township up next, and the Falcons had just given West Hazleton all they could handle. Meanwhile, West Hazleton would have to travel to Freeland to take on MMI, a team that was always a tough out on their home court.

The Saint Gabriel's Foster Township game was close from the start. At half the Saints were clinging to a slim 35-34 lead as the Falcons served notice that no one could take them lightly. In the third quarter, the Saints utilized their most powerful weapon, the fast break, scoring ten straight points to take a 51-41 lead into the final eight minutes. In that final period, Foster began to slowly chip away at the Saints' lead. With three minutes left the lead had been sliced to 59-55, and for the next two minutes the team's traded scores. With just under a minute to go, Sernak, who up to that point had just one field goal in the game, scored to put the G-Men ahead 65-59. The Falcons quickly answered with a score of their own. O'Donnell was fouled and made both shots, but then the Saints committed a foul of their own and Tom Breznitsky converted two for Foster Township.

Rather than hold the ball and force a foul, Saint Gabriel's missed a field goal attempt and Foster scored yet again. The G-Men were able to inbound the ball as time ran out and they escaped with a 67-65 win. Once again, Coach Kender had gone all the way with his starters and four of the five hit double figures with O'Donnell leading the way with twenty-two. Meanwhile, while he had only scored four points, Sernak led the Saints on the boards, collecting sixteen rebounds. If there was a lesson to be learned from this and the second game with Weatherly, it was that this Saint Gabriel's team couldn't consider a lead safe until they heard the sound of the final buzzer.

On the same night the G-Men were squeaking by the Falcons, West Hazleton found itself in a struggle with MMI. In a high-scoring affair the two teams were deadlocked at forty-seven after two periods, and then at seventy-two going into the final quarter. With a little over three minutes to play the Preppers' Bob Woodring, who scored thirty-six in the game, fouled out. At the time the Wildcats led 85-84. With their leader gone, MMI collapsed and West Hazleton converted twelve of fourteen foul shots in the final three minutes to win going away 97-84. Once again, Sypek led the Wildcats in scoring with thirty-three.

Both the Wildcats and the G-Men would be heavy favorites in their remaining contest before their scheduled meeting, now a week away. With the second half drawing to an end, the Saints could end all speculation by winning that game, setting up a rematch for the league championship. A Wildcat win would create the possibility of a three-way tie in the second half if Weatherly could get by Jim Thorpe. The Olympians, after losing to Saint Gabriel's and West Hazleton, were taking out their frustrations on the rest of the league in a big way. They had won three straight, topping the 100-point mark in each victory—103 against Saint Ann's, 106 against Hazle Township, and 109 against Freeland. Whatever the outcome of the Saints-Wildcat game, it was clear that Weatherly would have its hands full with Jim Thorpe.

The G-Men and the Wildcats tuned up for their pivotal encounter with easy wins over Freeland and Saint Ann's. Saint Gabriel's remained the only unbeaten team in the second-half race by disposing of Freeland 107-85 while West Hazleton was beating Freeland's parochial high school 84-59. Weatherly remained tied with West Hazleton for second place after beating MMI, and Jim Thorpe, though out of the second-half race, continued to pile up points by taking out Foster Township 125-92.

With the stage set for what many were calling the biggest Anthracite League game of the year, tickets were at a premium. Days before the contest Phil Sarno accurately predicted that "they'll need a shoehorn just to get the faithful fans into West Hazleton's gym Friday as St. Gabriel's visits the West End borough to tangle with the Wildcats." On game day it was announced that no tickets would be available at the door. Saint

Gabriel's was viewed as a much improved team when compared to the squad West Hazleton had easily handled a little over a month earlier. The G-Men boasted a balanced attack that had all five starters averaging in double figures. Freshman Paul Hoffman was the team's leading scorer, averaging nineteen points a game. The Wildcats were led by the region's leading scorer Richie Sypek, who was scoring at a 25.6 clip. Even with West Hazleton playing at home, where they very seldom came up on the short end, the game was rated a toss-up.

Fans arrived early so the JV game, won by Saint Gabriel's, was played before a crowd where even the standing room was occupied by a warm body. Coach Kender's defensive strategy was evident from the opening tip. The G-Men would concentrate on stopping Sypek by having Entiero play him man-to-man while the rest of the Saints played a zone defense the classic box in one. After one quarter the G-Men had the advantage 19-15. The teams played evenly over the next eight minutes, and the score at half stood at 34-30. Kender's defense had been successful in holding Sypek to just three points. However, on the offensive side of the court the G-Men had squandered numerous chances to take control of the contest. Unforced turnovers because of errant passes coupled with walking and three-second violations had kept the game close.

In the third quarter the Wildcats began feeding the ball to their second leading scorer Ed Martnick, and he responded by scoring ten points in the period. At the same time the Saints seemed to tighten up and their vaunted fast break offense was nowhere to be found. Heading into the final quarter West Hazleton was up by six, 51-45.

In the final eight minutes, Cal Ferrari came off the bench for West Hazleton to score three quick buckets and put to bed any hope of a Saint Gabriel's comeback. When the final whistle sounded the Wildcats had come out on top 67-59. They had done so on the backs of Martnick and Sypek, who came alive late. In the second half the two West Hazleton players had displayed what could only be called spectacular shooting, nailing field goal after field goal despite being closely guarded. Based on the result, a tie for the second-half crown was virtually assured. But would it involve two or three teams? The outcome of the Weatherly-Jim Thorpe contest would answer that question.

One of the very interesting spectators who took in the Saint Gabriel's-West Hazleton game was Frank Sullivan, the head basketball coach at Williamsport Saint Joseph's. The G-Men were scheduled to meet his team in the first round of the PCIAA state playoffs. Despite the loss, Saint Gabriel's had impressed Sullivan, who said, "Nobody could do much against the kind of shooting West Hazleton displayed in the second half." When asked to compare his team with the G-Men he said he thought talent-wise the two were "on par" but his team would have a height advantage. There was no doubt that Saint Joseph's was a tough club; they had lost only three games by a total of eleven points. To Saint Gabriel's fans, the game against the Williamsport team seemed far in the future since, in all probability, the G-Men would play at least one league playoff game and perhaps as many as three.

Most observers believed Jim Thorpe would handle Weatherly even though the game would be played on Weatherly's home floor. After all, the Olympians had beaten the Wreckers with ease in their first-half matchup, and Jim Thorpe was seemingly playing their best ball of the year. The game would also decide who would represent the Anthracite League in the Class C state playoffs. There was a lot on the line when the Wreckers and Olympians met.

Weatherly had one of their finest shooting nights of their whole season, hitting on eighteen of twenty-nine attempted in the first half. Coupled with strong play under the boards, the Wreckers headed for the locker room with a 45-33 lead at halftime. Thorpe made a game of it in the second half, coming within four points in the final period before Weatherly put the game away. The final score was 79-72. Weatherly and West Hazleton had now finished the second-half race with identical 7-1 records, and Saint Gabriel's could join them with a win over Saint Ann's. The G-Men were heavy favorites to do just that— after all, they had throttled Saint Ann's in their first meeting 106-73, and this game would be played at Saint Joe's.

Coach Kender knew he was going to be starting the state Catholic playoffs in less than a week. He also knew that beating Saint Ann's would set up league playoffs, some if not all of which would be played before those playoffs began. With this in mind, he was determined to rest his starters against Saint

Ann's. The G-Men took a 19-12 lead after one quarter, and Kender then inserted five new players into the game. The Saints reserves played well and midway through the third quarter, Saint Gabriel's led by a score of 49-29. For the remainder of the quarter Saint Ann's chipped away at the lead, and the period ended with Saint Gabriel's up by a score of 53-41. Kender sent in his starters to begin the final period and they quickly expanded the margin to twenty points. At that point, Kender began to substitute freely, and the G-Men, led by reserves Bill Boyle and Ed O'Donnell, emerged on top, winning 81-56. There was now a three-way tie for the top spot in the second-half race.

Lots were drawn to determine the playoff. West Hazleton drew the bye and would sit back and watch Saint Gabriel's and Weatherly play Friday. The winner would face the Wildcats the next night. Should West Hazleton, the first-half champs, lose that Saturday contest, the championship game would be held on Monday. The Catholic playoffs would start Tuesday. Saint Gabriel's was looking at the possibility of having to play four games in six days.

The first playoff game would be played at the Castle on the Hill. The reference to a castle didn't mean that the gym was spacious. With standing room, it would be possible to get about 1000 spectators in to watch the game. No one had any doubt that the place would be packed.

The day after the game Don Barnes wrote in the *Standard Speaker* that "close to 1,000 fans braved the teeth of a raw night to watch two of the league's elite battle it out and were rewarded with another in a series of hectic Anthracite League scraps for which the circuit is noted." Both teams came out blazing. Led by Hoffman's thirteen first quarter points, the G-Men took a 22-18 lead after one quarter of play. Barrett and O'Donnell got hot in the second quarter, and at half the Saints led by a nine-point margin, 48-39.

In the middle of the third period Weatherly went into a full-court press. At first, led by Entiero, the Saints made it look like a mistake, as they broke free for two easy baskets. Then the pressure began to take a toll as sloppy passes fell into the hands of the Wreckers who often converted the chances the turnovers presented. After twenty-four minutes the G-Men still led, but by the slimmest of margins: 63-61.

Weatherly hadn't led in the game since the first quarter, but with just a minute to go a field goal by Lew Kistler gave the Wreckers an 83-82 lead. Entiero took the ball onto the Weatherly side of the court and delivered it to O'Donnell. O'Donnell faked a shot, and then, using one of his patented moves, drove to the basket scoring from in close with just forty-four ticks left to put the Saints back on top by one. Weatherly was working for a shot to regain the upper hand when O'Donnell stepped in front of a pass, intercepting it and finding Sernak open for a layup to put the G-Men up 86-83 with only nine seconds left. Weatherly scored a final bucket as time ran out. The G-Men beat the Wreckers for the third time, this time 86-85, to secure a spot against the Wildcats in a game that would decide the second-half title.

It was a total team victory with four of Saint Gabriel's five starters hitting double figures. Hoffman and O'Donnell led the way with twenty-five and twenty points respectively. Barrett connected for sixteen, and Entiero netted fourteen while running the offense and collecting thirteen rebounds. Sernak, who had missed a good portion of the game due to foul trouble, scored nine. Billy Boyle came off the bench to score two, and he would later joke that his field goal had won the game.

There was really no time to celebrate the win. The Saints had come out on top on two consecutive nights but would only have one day to prepare for West Hazleton in a game to decide the second-half crown. Just like in 1959, the two teams would meet on Berwick High's gym floor. Win that one and the same two teams would play Monday for all the marbles. Then the state playoffs would begin. Don Barnes was blunt about the hill the G-Men were facing: he called it "a killing schedule."

The morning of the game the sports headline in the *Standard Speaker* read "Wildcats Can Wrap Up 5th in Row by Beating Saints." Despite the fact that West Hazleton had won the previous two meetings, the paper rated the game dead even. The paper also reported the fact that the Wildcats had won four straight league titles since the G-Men had won one back in 1960. Saint Gabriel's, with its balanced and potent attack, was given the offensive advantage while West Hazleton was viewed as the superior defensive team. Phil Sarno predicted that the game would be decided by one shot that would barely fall over the rim or roll around and fall outside the cylinder. He didn't know how right and wrong he was at the same time.

On the night of the game, February 27, 1965, in the vicinity of 1,600 fans made their way to Berwick to witness the contest. Saint Gabriel's fans had taped a huge banner to the wall behind them imploring the G-Men to "Tame the Wildcats." Once the game started, those in attendance witnessed what Don Barnes described as "one of the most exciting, most improbable—even incredible—Anthracite League playoffs in the gaudy history of the league."

The Wildcats controlled the opening tip and scored quickly. The first-quarter pace was frantic, and the West Hazleton players couldn't miss. Facing a team on fire, the Saints did all they could not to get blown out in the game's early going. After the first eight minutes West Hazleton was up by ten 28-18, and it was clear that Saint Gabriel's needed to make some adjustments to get back in the game.

Coach Kender directed his troops to employ a three-quarter court press to start the next period. The move caught the Wildcats unprepared. Turnover followed turnover as the momentum shifted to the G-Men. When West Hazleton was able to manage a shot, their misses were gobbled up by Saint Gabriel's defenders, who immediately found an outlet man to start a fast break offense that often resulted in layups. The G-Men outscored the Wildcats 26-10 in the quarter and headed to the locker room on top, 44-38.

The third quarter resembled the second for the first four minutes when West Hazleton's Ron Gatski signaled for a time-out with his team down 57-42. By this time many Saint Gabriel's fans were thinking about making plans to attend the league championship game. The time-out seemed to settle Gatski's team, but they weren't making up ground, and with just a minute and a half left in the period the Saints were still comfortably ahead 63-50. Then Sypek scored for the Cats, and when the G-Men failed to answer, two more field goals by big Ron Christina narrowed the margin to 63-56 as the quarter ended.

In the first three minutes of the final quarter, West Hazleton scored seven straight points to tie the game. Now it was Kender's turn to call a time-out in an effort to settle down his ruffled chargers. The move seemed to work when goals by Hoffman and Sernak put the G-Men ahead by four. With just ninety seconds left, the score stood at 69-67. Saint Gabriel's led and had the ball. They moved it around the perimeter of the Wildcat defense until Jimmy Barrett took a shot from the outside that missed.

West Hazleton grabbed the rebound and called time-out. Most observers thought that the Wildcats would get the ball to their ace Sypek, but Coach Gatski had another idea. Instead, the ball was fed to Martnick, who had already scored twenty-four points, but his attempt missed. The rebound caromed off a West Hazleton player and went out of bounds. Now West Hazleton was pressing as the G-Men inbounded the ball to Barrett, who was immediately double-teamed. Barrett attempted to pass the ball crosscourt, but before it reached its destination, Sypek intercepted the ball and took it to the basket, scoring to knot things up at sixty-nine. Just a few seconds later another Barrett pass was deflected and picked up by West Hazleton's Jim Beach, who was fouled and went to the line where he sank two shots.

After another time-out Charlie Gennaro scored for the Saints, making it seventy-one apiece with just ten ticks left. West Hazleton inbounded the ball against Saint Gabriel's pressure defense. They got the ball to Cal Ferrari, who got just past half court when he heaved a shot toward the rim, releasing the ball as though he were competing in the shot put. It hit nothing but net. As the buzzer sounded, Jim Beach ran up the steps right by the stunned G-Men fans and, reaching the top, tore down the huge banner that had been placed there. West Hazleton had won their fifth straight league title, and they had beaten the G-Men three times doing it. If Saint Gabriel's fans were disappointed, that feeling was shared by Father Deviney, who cradled his head in his arms after Ferrari's shot hit the mark. Pete O'Donnell led the Saints in scoring that night and, reflecting on that game, remembered it as "one we had won and let get away." It may well have been the toughest loss ever experienced by a Saint Gabriel's team.

Since the game was played on Saturday night and the Hazleton paper wasn't published on Sunday, the headline and story didn't appear until Monday. Though it was of little solace to Saint Gabriel's fans, right next to the account of the big Wildcat win was a one sentence story and a box score. The story was titled "St. Gabriel's Win" and the one sentence read, "St. Gabriel's All-Stars defeated the Weatherly All-Stars, 64-49." The box score showed the individual scoring in the biddy basketball game that had taken place the day before. Among those who played for Saint Gabriel's were Joe Farley, Tommy Boyle, Jerry Fallabel, and Brian McBride. Those four names would appear in another box score years later on March 14, 1970, when the Saint Gabriel's basketball team would take the floor for the very last time.

The loss to West Hazleton was a crushing blow, but if there was a blessing to be found, it was the fact that there was no time to dwell on it. Some may have even thought that the loss did have a silver lining in that it gave the team a couple of days' rest before they started the PCIAA state playoffs on March 2nd against Williamsport St. Joseph's. Back in 1962, the last time the G-Men had won the fourteen games required to qualify for the post-season play, it was Saint Joseph's who had shown them the door in the first round, winning convincingly 69-46. This game was expected to be much closer. In addition to the fans who drove themselves to Montoursville to attend the game, three busloads of supporters departed from the front of Saint Gabriel's school to cheer on the Saints.

In the first half, Saint Joseph's took command behind a tremendous shooting performance. In Coach Kender's own words at the break, "We tried everything in the book—two-three, box-and-one, triangle-and-two, man for man—and we still can't stop them." When the buzzer sounded sixteen minutes in, Saint Joseph's was leading 41-31. Of even bigger concern for the Saints was the fact that Pete O'Donnell, who scored six points in the first quarter, had suffered an ankle injury and was for all intents and purposes unavailable for the remainder of the game.

The two teams played an even third quarter and entered the final eight minutes with Saint Joe's holding a 53-44 lead. After the first three minutes in the final quarter, the G-Men had narrowed the margin to 53-48, and the Williamsport team went into a freeze. The Saints countered with an aggressive defense that proved ineffective when they gave up two easy field goals and a pair of fouls making the score 59-48. At this point Barrett took over, scoring seven straight points to make the score 59-55 with just over a minute remaining.

According to the *Standard Speaker*'s Don Barnes, what followed was the key play of the game. Jim Kline had the ball for Saint Joseph's when he found himself surrounded by three

G-Men. He reacted to this pressure by committing an obvious walking violation that went uncalled before passing the ball to an unguarded teammate who scored an easy goal to put the game out of reach. The final score was Saint Joseph's 65, Saint Gabriel's 61. Saint Joseph's would go on to the state title game before losing.

Looking back at the game, Pete O'Donnell remembered it as "the most disappointing loss" in his illustrious Saint Gabriel's career. He added that part of the frustration came from the fact that he was hurt and couldn't contribute, and ending the season with two losses was hard to swallow. O'Donnell, like the majority of the team's fans, had expected more from this experienced and talented team. While it was true that the team's 17-8 record was the best mark a Saint Gabriel's team had finished with since 1960, not many were satisfied. Talent-wise, this was the finest team ever to wear the purple and white, and there wasn't a championship trophy to show for it.

After five years at the helm, Chip Kender had compiled a record of 52-60. It was true that a number of those losses occurred while he was playing underclassmen and building for the future. In addition, he just had his best season and had come within a whisker of playing for a league title, not to mention he had a win against Hazleton High on his resume. In Ray Saul's opinion, expressed in his column after the season, the G-Men had played good basketball and "Coach Chip Kender has done an excellent job."

Nobody can say for sure when it was that Father Deviney decided that Saint Gabriel's needed a new coach, but it wasn't long after the season ended that the good father made a move. On May 20, 1965, the headline on the sports page of the *Standard Speaker* proclaimed "St. Gabriel's Hires Teacher-Coach; Physical Ed Program." Immediately below, the story was introduced by another headline that read "Kender and Seamon Out in New Setup." According to the paper the move in no way reflected "on the abilities of Francis 'Chip' Kender." Deviney explained the change saying the move gave the school an in-house coach who could start the school's first physical education program. The new coach was also a qualified typing and bookkeeping teacher, so the school could begin offering a commercial course. Finally, an in-house coach could direct the entire basketball program, starting with biddy ball and including intramurals.

As far as anyone could remember, Deviney was breaking new ground, not only for Saint Gabriel's but for the Hazleton area. Up to that time the vast majority of coaches had been born and raised in the Hazleton area, but Deviney had hired a Trenton, New Jersey, resident who grew up in Beacon, New York. The new guy was young as well, just twenty-three, and he had no head coaching experience. For the past two years he had served as an assistant basketball coach at his alma mater, Rider College. According to the paper, he had been recommended for the job by Rider's head coach and by William van Breda Kolff, the head coach at Princeton University.

Saint Gabriel's basketball players and coaches had a long history of nicknames. Back in the late twenties and early thirties, there were the two O'Donnell's, Doc and Specs. In the forties, Swish Farley and Mouse Marinko took the court for the G-Men. In the fifties, Danny "Ace" Gregoria was the coach and Snapper O'Donnell was one of his best players. The new young coach from Jersey didn't need a nickname; he was bringing one with him.

8

THE SECOND QUARTER

DIGGER

It was a warm, sunny day in August a few weeks prior to the beginning of the 1965-66 school year when a young Saint Gabriel's student made his way to the White Birch golf course. The student, who would be entering the eighth grade that fall, had intended to play a round by himself, but when he made his way to the first tee he was joined by an older boy he knew from playground basketball. The older boy was Danny Gallagher, the same Gallagher who had left Saint Gabriel's for Hazleton High School and had played an important part in Hazleton's win over the G-Men a year before.

The two walked the course together and their conversation quickly turned to the upcoming basketball season. Gallagher asked, "How do you think you'll do against Hazleton this year?" The young man answered, "I think we'll win. We have Hoffman and Pete O'Donnell back, and they led us in scoring last year." Gallagher smiled and replied, "Yeah, when I was at Saint Gabe's, I always thought we'd win, but it only happened once. You know, Hazleton has guys on the bench that would start at Saint Gabriel's. Heck, there are guys that don't make the team who would play a lot for your team. Hoffman and O'Donnell are both good, but you guys also lost an awful lot of players. Plus, who can say how your new coach will do."

Richard F. Phelps was named the new head basketball coach at Saint Gabriel's on May 19, 1965. The new coach was born on July 4, 1941 in Beacon, New York. His father was an Episcopalian and his mother was a Catholic. The couple decided to raise their children as Catholics. Phelps grew up and was educated in the Beacon public school system. He attended

Beacon Junior High School which, like Saint Gabriel's, was in the same building that housed the high school students. It was here that the young Phelps earned the moniker that he would carry through life.

His father's profession as an undertaker was part of the reason he was tagged with the nickname "Digger." As Phelps tells the story (in his book *Undertaker's Son*), he was the batboy for the high school team. Prior to one away game while the team was taking batting practice, he returned to the school bus and discovered some tasty treats that were to serve as the team's after- game snack. Phelps helped himself, devouring all he found. When the game ended, the angry players were ready to square things with their well-fed batboy, but the coach intervened. Using the name of a character who appeared in the popular TV show *The Life of Riley*, the coach said, "If you don't stop eating the team's cupcakes, I'm going to put you in one of your old man's boxes. Do you understand, Digger O'Dell?" The nickname Digger stuck.

Phelps graduated from Beacon High School in 1959. As one might expect, he was active in the sports scene during those high school years, playing on both the varsity baseball and basketball teams. He then attended college in New Jersey at Rider University. He decided to major in business administration with an eye toward eventually joining his father's business. At Rider he lettered in basketball in both his junior and senior years. As a player Phelps was described as a "defensive specialist," and in just a few years he would bring a new defensive mindset to Pennsylvania's coal region.

Phelps was introduced to coaching after his graduation from Rider. He had moved back to Beacon where the head coach at the high school had begun a summer basketball league. That coach approached Phelps about taking charge of Beacon's players in the newly formed circuit. His experience in the summer league resulted in a desire to pursue coaching as a life's profession. He decided to head back to Rider to obtain a master's degree while working as a volunteer assistant coach for the basketball team. His experience coaching at Rider convinced the young Phelps that he had indeed found his vocation. What he needed now was a coaching job.

In his book, Phelps recalls hearing of a coaching opening at a small school in Pennsylvania and applying and then getting the job. If there was an opening, it wasn't advertised. There is little doubt that Chip Kender hoped to return. As Vince Gallagher remembered, it was Father Deviney who went looking for a new coach. Deviney was friends with P. J. Carlesimo, who was the head coach at Fordham University, and Jack Gallagher, the head basketball coach at Scranton Prep High School. When Deviney sought their guidance, they both mentioned Phelps. It's likely that these contacts led Deviney to Phelps, who impressed the priest with his energy, self-confidence, and knowledge of the game. Deviney was determined to make a bigger success of Saint Gabriel's basketball than the school and its fans had ever enjoyed. He felt he had found the leader and coach needed to do just that in Phelps.

Within days of the announcement of the coaching change, local sportswriters expressed their thoughts. Ray Saul praised the work that Chip Kender and John Seamon (who tendered his resignation as assistant basketball and head baseball coach when he was informed of the Phelps hiring), saying both had done a tremendous job at the Saint Gabriel's. On the day after the Saint Gabriel's baseball team ended their first winning season in the history of the school by beating West Hazleton, Phil Sarno wrote that he felt sorry for the two coaches but added that the change "augers well for Saint Gabriel's," stating that the Saints "are off to greater heights" in both baseball and basketball.

To prepare for the coming of the new coach as well as the school's first physical education program, the parish set about renovating the athletic facilities. The locker rooms were changed to offer, according to the *Standard Speaker*, "the latest in design and equipment to accommodate the needs of a daily physical education course." The work, which was completed during the summer months, included the installation of a new tile basketball floor, which could be used for "basketball, volleyball, kickball and other indoor games." Monsignor Maher expressed his hopes that the program would result in the school taking a step forward in the direction of producing sound citizens. A further benefit of the program not mentioned was the fact it would give the new coach the opportunity to identify athletic talent that could contribute to the school's success on the basketball court and baseball diamond.

The young coach made quite an impression when he arrived on the Hazleton scene. He gave Chip Kender a run when it came to being the best dressed man in town. He was handsome, tall, and slim. He was accompanied by a beautiful wife who was pregnant with the couple's first child. Ray McBrearty, one of the captains on Digger's first team, remembers that he drove a '65 Mustang. "He already had a collector's item before it was a collector's item." For a man taking on his first head coaching position, he carried an air of confidence. He also was adept at dealing with the local press, a very important skill in an area where the populace followed local athletics closely through the words that appeared in the columns and stories composed by the local sportswriters.

In Pennsylvania, high school basketball practice wasn't permitted to begin until the first of November. Saint Gabriel's students had generally never seen the basketball coach at the school until the days approaching that date. That all changed when Phelps arrived. Not only was he teaching at the school, but he implemented an after-school hour conditioning program that, coincidentally, seemed to attract the students that would make up that year's basketball team. From early September, those boys gathered in front of the school to begin their two-mile run to and around the parish cemetery before ending back at the starting point.

Phelps also kept an eye on the students as he ran the new physical education program. McBrearty recalls a gym class one day when Phelps looked over the students in front of him and, in a gruff and deep-throated voice, ordered two of them—Tom Sock and Bill Ferry—to their feet. Addressing the two, Phelps asked, "What are you two going to do with your life?" Sock responded first, saying that he helped his dad out at his gas station. Phelps said, "I'm not talking about now, I'm talking about your future." Ferry spoke up, saying, "I'm going to be a draftsman." Phelps shook his head, proclaiming, "Who the hell ever saw a six-foot-five-inch draftsman? You two are going to be basketball players." Sock had some junior high experience and Ferry had never played organized ball, but that quickly, the two juniors, who happened to be the tallest boys in the high school, became part of the varsity basketball team.

Phelps took an interest in the young players as well. Joe Farley, an eighth grader, was playing a pickup game in the gym after school one day when he heard Phelps growl, "Farley, come over here." "Yes, Mr. Phelps?" said Farley after running over to face the new coach. "Do you know how to do a pushup?" Farley nodded that he did. "Show me," said the coach. After Farley hit the floor and did one, Phelps said, "Do ten of those a day every day for a week. The next week increase that by five and keep doing that until you're up to fifty a day." Farley said he would do as ordered as the new coach walked away muttering, "Jeez, we need a weight room around here." Jerry Fallabel, who was just starting the seventh grade, can recall Phelps watching him play and calling out, "Fallabel, you call that defense? That stinks. Where do you think you'll get to play if you keep that up?"

Phelps was just twenty-three years old when he took the helm at Saint Gabriel's, and he intended on making a big, early impression on his basketball team. The new coach was addressing his team for the first time when, as McBrearty remembered, "he pulled a Bobby Knight on us," hurling a chair across the court as he hammered home the loyalty he expected from the young men in front of him. The chair-throwing story may have had a bigger effect on the student body, as the rumor of the event spread from class to class, than it did on the audience who witnessed it. What really impressed the players was Phelps's knowledge of the game. Pete O'Donnell, who has nothing but kind words to say about Chip Kender, says it's simply not fair to compare the two coaches. "In fairness to Chip, he was a teacher who coached basketball. Digger was a basketball coach."

Phil Sarno came away impressed with the new coach after sitting in on one of his practices. The sportswriter noted that the practice began with an endurance development workout Phelps called the "twenty minutes of death." After the practice Phelps laid out his philosophy of the game in an interview. He stressed the importance of endurance, noting that many teams "run out of steam" in the third and fourth quarters. Described as pleasant but firm, the coach stated that one of his goals was to have every one of his players "take the upcoming game as though it is a championship contest." He was careful about raising expectations, noting that he didn't expect to set the local basketball scene afire, but his aim was to "get the best out of the material" he had on hand. He described himself as a defensive coach, stating a team that can play disciplined defense can give any team a good battle. In terms of predictions, the farthest he would go was saying, "I think we will have a very exciting club this year."

The Saints had lost a ton of talent to graduation, but expectations remained high. The team's two leading scorers were returning, and the JV squad had been a strong one. Still, it would take some doing to win the league championship. West Hazleton was always going to be in the mix, and both Jim Thorpe and Weatherly were expected to suit up strong teams. Marian Catholic, new to the league, was also expected to make some noise. Marian was a newer high school created when three Catholic parishes decided to close their individual high schools and join forces. Phelps's decision to temper expectations appeared to be a wise one. The schedule included only four exhibition games, and they would be tough—two games against both Hazleton, one of the favorites in the East Penn League, and Crestwood, which had beaten the G-Men twice the previous year.

As the first game neared, rumors about the new coach and the team flowed throughout the school. Phelps was playing Beatle albums during practice, and he didn't like the nickname Digger. Hoffman, who had led the team in scoring as a freshman, had gotten better and was proving impossible to handle inside. Sock and Ferry were practicing, often by themselves, on one end of the floor doing big man or Mikan Drills while the team worked at the other basket. Toward the end of November came the happy news that Phelps and his wife had welcomed their first child, a daughter, into their family. By this time the first game of the season, against Hazleton no less, was about a week away.

Ray Saul's preseason preview said that the team had a number of question marks. Who would be the other three starters after O'Donnell and Hoffman? How fast could Phelps bring the two new big men, Sock and Ferry, around to help with the inside game? What new wrinkles would the fans see under the first-year coach? Could the Saints find a way to fill the holes left by graduation? Phelps himself was noncommittal: "Pete O'Donnell and Hoffman should have good years. How fast the others mature will determine how we make out." Those others included Ed O'Donnell, Ray McBrearty, Bob Entiero, Tony Joe Barletta, Jimmy Rondash, and Rocco Fallabel. The closest Phelps came to a prediction was saying, "If we're cold on offense, at least we'll know what to do on defense." Saul predicted another good season for the G-Men and saw them as a factor in what was going to be the most hotly contested Anthracite League race in years.

Looking over the league heading into Phelps's first season, local sportswriters were at a loss to pick a clear-cut favorite. Balance was the buzzword. Freeland High was said to have its best team of the decade featuring five lettermen, good height, and new coach Casimir Lasecki. The league's newest member, Marian Catholic, was also hoping to make its presence felt. Led by local legend Coach Wink Gallagher, Marian was returning three starters, and Gallagher promised he would send an aggressive squad onto the local basketball courts. Don Barnes was also on record as saying that both Foster Township and MMI couldn't be taken lightly, though he felt that West Hazleton, Weatherly, Jim Thorpe and Saint Gabriel's would be the teams to emerge from the pack.

West Hazleton had now won five Anthracite League championships in succession, and six out of the last seven. Like the previous year, nobody was conceding the 1966 title to the Wildcats, but nobody was taking them lightly. They were another team that had been hit hard by graduation losses. Gone was the team's leading scorer Richie Sypek and strong inside man Ron Christina. Still, Coach Ron Gatski's cupboard wasn't bare with Ed Martnick and the hero of last year's second half title game against the G-Men, Cal Ferrari, returning. As Don Barnes noted, "The fact remains, West Hazleton is the defending champion, and any club wanting the championship will have to take it away from the Cats."

Weatherly was seen as one of the prime contenders as the new season neared. Coach Skip Ebling returned two solid starters in the talented Pat Searfoss, rated as one of the top players in the region, and the dependable and rugged inside man Lew Kistler. New to the varsity were a number of players who finished first the year before in the race for the unofficial JV title of the Anthracite League. These included Jimmy Van Horn, Dick Ritter, and Paul Romano, not to mention a sixth man by the name of Henry Panckeri Jr., who would have been a good bet to start for any other team in the league but found himself coming off the bench for this talented Weatherly bunch.

Another team sure to be in the mix was Jim Thorpe, who also had a new head coach. The Olympians would be guided by Phil "Pip" Radar, who had coached the Thorpe junior varsity the year before. Though a lack of height would be a problem, Thorpe was returning four starters from a team that had made quite an impact in their Anthracite League debut. The league's leading scorer Bob Brown was back along with Keith Miller, Joe Morgan, and Mike Tessitore. Also expected to contribute to the team's success were Dennis Balliet, Ken Detweiler, Jim Dugan, Ed Jordan, and Clem McGinley. Coach Radar's team had depth and he made that no secret, saying he expected results on the court all the way, and that if he didn't see it the boys would find themselves sitting next to him on the bench.

Before a Phelps coached squad would take the court against any of the Anthracite contenders, they would face Hazleton High in their opener. When tryouts opened at Hazleton, forty-eight boys had reported, and they would be joined by others currently playing football. The number of players trying to make the Hazleton team was about equal to the number of boys enrolled at Saint Gabriel's in the tenth, eleventh and twelfth year classes. In Coach Fran Libonati's third season, the Mountaineers were considered one of the prime contenders for the East Penn League crown. Returning starters included Rich Fuddy, Joe Tito, Jim Williams, and Danny Gallagher. The JV team, which had gone 20-2 the year before, had a leading scorer in Joe Marnell who was now ready for bigger things. Added to the mix was what many considered one of the most talented sophomore classes in the school's history, which included the six-foot-four-inch Darrell Farkus, Bob Farnell, Rich Babon, Bob O'Donnell, and Tom Scarcella. Ray Saul predicted that with a few breaks, this Hazleton team could put together "a banner season."

As practices progressed at Saint Gabriel's, the team began buying into what their new coach was selling. Pete O'Donnell remembered, "It didn't take long to realize that this guy really knew his basketball." Paul Hoffman called him a "technician" when it came to the game. Dennis Olexa described Phelps as a "thinking man's coach." Mike Heffernan recalled "an excellent X and O man." Ray McBrearty, who was a co-captain with Pete O'Donnell on Phelps's Saint Gabriel's team, said that Digger clearly had a handle on the game and beating him would be "a feather in anybody's cap."

Though the new coach had downplayed expectations, his efforts had done little to subdue the enthusiasm of Saint Gabriel's supporters who felt a championship was overdue. The first test would come versus Hazleton on Pearl Harbor Day at Saint Joseph's before what was sure to be a huge and enthusiastic crowd. For a young coach in his first game as the head man, it promised to be a baptism of fire.

9

FULL-COURT PRESS

THE ROLLER COASTER SEASON

On the morning of December 7, 1965, Hazletonians were greeted by near-freezing temperatures that promised to drop into the low teens by evening. The headlines in the *Standard Speaker* reported that *Gemini 7* piloted by astronauts Frank Borman and James Lovell Jr. continued to orbit the earth. President Johnson had summoned his secretary of state and secretary of defense to his ranch in Texas to discuss Vietnam. Local movie theaters advertised their offerings, including the film *Darling* starring Laurence Harvey and Julie Christie. When readers made it to the sports page they found the Hazleton-Saint Gabriel's game touted as topping the local cage card.

Don Barnes accurately reported that few could remember an opening basketball game generating as much interest as the one about to be played by the G-Men and the Mountaineers. On Saint Gabriel's new head man, Barnes reported that Phelps felt that you couldn't tell much about a ball club in December. The coach expressed his view that a team's true potential couldn't be reached until later in the season. While Phelps wasn't promising any championships, Barnes noted that G-Men fans were expecting some "basketball miracles." Hazleton High, based on history as well as the talent and experience the Mounts had on hand, were installed as the favorite heading into the contest.

The stands at Saint Joseph's filled early on the night of the game, and spectators were making their way to the balcony before the first half was completed in the JV game. If that game was to serve as a barometer for the rest of the night, the G-Men were going to be in trouble. Led by Darrell Farkus and Bob

Farnell, the Mounts cruised to a 105-47 win against the junior G-Men. Dennis Olexa scored eighteen in the game for the Saints, but many of the Hazleton fans were making fun of Phelps and his emphasis on defense by the end of the easy win. During the preliminary contest, members of the G-Men varsity were seated behind the Saint Gabriel's bench sporting new blazers bearing the emblem "S G" purchased by Saint Gabriel's benefactors. By the time the first game ended, more than two thousand fans had braved the cold weather to find their seats at Saint Joe's.

The initial indication that Phelps had changed things at Saint Gabriel's came on the first Hazleton possession. Ray McBrearty, who the year before as a JV played defense by wildly waving his arms as he covered his opponent, had assumed a classic defensive stance, and the G Men were in a man-to-man press from the opening whistle. Early in the initial period, Hazleton's Fran Libonati went to his bench and inserted Joe Moran in the hopes of sparking his offense. Moran responded by scoring seven points in the period as Hazleton took a 19-13 lead. In the second period the G-Men came back and tied the score at twenty-two on a tap in by Hoffman. The Saints sophomore was playing like a senior, scoring on drives, rebounds, and jump shots. Hoffman scored nine in the quarter, but Hazleton used a balanced attack to head to the locker room with a 39-31 lead.

The G-Men had stayed within reach in the initial half relying on Hoffman and Ed O'Donnell to put points on the board. Saints fans were well aware that Pete O'Donnell had been held scoreless through the first sixteen minutes. The feeling was that O'Donnell would come alive in the second half. There wasn't a fan in the stands who thought this game had been decided.

The third quarter saw Hazleton lead by as few as five and as many as twelve points, but try as they might they couldn't drive the last nail into the coffin. Pete O'Donnell broke through, scoring six in the period, but Hazleton's guards Joe Tito and Joe Marnell got hot, scoring seven each to extend the lead to ten heading into the final eight minutes. Early in the last quarter Hazleton went up by a 63-51 margin. At this point Pete O'Donnell scored five straight points and Ed O'Donnell added a bucket to bring the G-Men within five before Joe Tito scored for Hazleton to quiet the fans on the Saint Gabriel's side of the court. The G-Men then scored twice after Hazleton misses and with a little over three minutes left, Libonati signaled for a time-out with his team up 65-62. Neither team slowed down after the time-out, but as the clock was winding down, Saint Gabriel's was forced to foul to gain possession of the basketball, and Hazleton made good on enough of their free throws to win 77-72.

The G-Men had come up short in their first game under their new mentor, but a few things were obvious. Phelps had promised his team would play hard for thirty-two minutes, and on this night they did. Down by twelve in the final period to a team like Hazleton would have made past Saint Gabriel's teams fold. This one came back to give a veteran team all they could handle. In addition, while strong performances were expected from Hoffman and Pete O'Donnell, the Saints showcased another offensive threat in Eddie O'Donnell, who scored seventeen on shots launched from the perimeter of the Hazleton defense. The other starters, Ray McBrearty and Tony Joe Barletta, had played clearly defined roles in the game. McBrearty was going to draw the toughest defensive assignments and guide the offensive attack while Barletta would concentrate on inside defense and rebounding. The big concern coming out of the initial contest was the lack of depth. Bob Entiero was a capable outside backup, but the undersized G-Men needed their new big men, Sock and Ferry, to mature in order to provide some quality inside strength off the bench.

Despite the loss, Saint Gabriel's students left Saint Joe's optimistic. The team answered a lot of questions. The significant graduation losses had not stung as much as one would have expected. Hoffman, now a sophomore, had clearly been the best basketball player on the court, and he was only going to get better. Pete O'Donnell had recovered from his slow start to lead the Saint Gabriel's comeback, scoring nine points in the final period. Eddie O'Donnell had shown that, given time, he was going to be an offensive threat from anywhere on the floor. Ray McBrearty displayed leadership qualities expected of a co-captain, bringing the ball up court and starting the G-Men offense. Tony Joe Barletta had held his own underneath against the taller and deeper Mountaineers. The thinking was this team was going to win a lot of games, and a league title wasn't out of the question.

While the students remained upbeat, the same couldn't be said for some of the alumni. In their view they had a new coach but the same results. They were weary of moral victories and wanted to see the scoreboard proclaim the wins. For them, the Phelps honeymoon was officially over and only wins over West Hazleton, a league title, and a victory over Hazleton the next time would satisfy them.

Meanwhile, West Hazleton's early performances were raising some questions. The Wildcats had opened the season by losing consecutive games, dropping contests to Berwick and Pottsville by more than twenty points. Don Barnes was openly questioning the Cats ability to hang with the likes of Weatherly, Jim Thorpe, and Saint Gabriel's. Against Pottsville not a single West Hazleton player scored in double figures as Coach Rom Gatski used ten players in his search to find a combination that clicked. Jim Thorpe and Weatherly, on the other hand, were both undefeated after two starts in the young season.

Saint Gabriel's next game was versus a Crestwood squad that had defeated the G-Men twice the previous year. Weatherly had already beaten the Comets, and the Saints were favored heading into the game, which would be played in the comfy confines of Saint Joe's. Unlike previous years when Saint Gabriel's students had gathered for a pep rally prior to the Hazleton game, Father Deviney scheduled one the day before this matchup.

Crestwood wasn't the same team they had been in the previous year, but they were expected to give Saint Gabriel's a challenge. It didn't happen. The Saints threw their hat into the Anthracite League championship arena by crushing the Comets 100-61. This was a Crestwood team that had hung close to Weatherly before fading in the final quarter to lose by thirteen. Phelps used eleven players in the game and ten of them scored. Hoffman, noted by the local paper to be a fifteen-year-old who couldn't miss greatness, led the way with twenty-seven points, and Eddie O'Donnell once again made his presence felt scoring twenty-three. To top off the evening, the junior G-Men also hit the century mark winning by a score of 100-50. After the win Phelps invited sportswriter Phil Sarno to his home along with Fathers Deviney and Conboy. The following day in his column, Sarno commented on meeting the coach's lovely wife and sensing "the skipper's second love is coaching."

With the addition of Marian Catholic, the Anthracite League membership had swelled to ten teams. Playing eighteen league games required starting league play earlier than usual. Three days after trouncing Crestwood, Coach Phelps took his team on the road to Hometown to face the league's newest member. Marian already had one league game under its belt, having traveled to West Hazleton where the Colts came out on the short end of an 81-67 score. The game was closer than the final score indicated; the Colts had given the Wildcats all they could handle until West Hazleton went on a thirteen-to-two spurt in the final quarter. This game would be played at Marian Catholic in the new school's modern gym (described by Don Barnes as "scrumptious") that would be the site of several historic games in the final years of Hazleton's lone Catholic high school.

Led by Pete O'Donnell, Saint Gabriel's jumped on Marian early and led by thirteen after one period. Once again Coach Phelps had the G-Men in a pressing defense from the opening whistle, and it rattled the Colts. The final score was 79-58, and Pete O'Donnell, playing his best game of the young season, scored thirty-one. Ed O'Donnell scored eighteen, and Hoffman added fifteen while leading the Saints in rebounding. It was obvious that Saint Gabriel's was going to rely on those three players to do the bulk of the scoring. Ray McBrearty and Tony Joe Barletta would be important role players. Phelps used eleven players in the game as he sought to add depth, particularly on the inside where the new coach hoped that Sock and Ferry would contribute before the season's end.

The Saints would travel to Crestwood in another exhibition contest before resuming Anthracite League play. Though it was December and the state playoffs were still three months away, Don Barnes was already speculating on which local teams would be playing in the post-season. In his December 21st, 1965, column titled While the Cats Away, the sportswriter predicted Saint Gabriel's was a sure bet to make the Catholic playoffs, and Jim Thorpe and Weatherly would fight it out for the league's spot in the PIAA post-season run. Meanwhile, Phil Sarno continued to express his admiration for the new coach at Saint Gabriel's, saying Phelps had his team "fired up" and playing "highly aggressive basketball."

Having already defeated Crestwood by thirty-nine the G-Men were heavy favorites to run their record to 3-1, and they did just that. The final score of 60-47 was deceiving as Saint Gabriel's carried a 45-23 lead into the final period before Phelps sat all his starters for the final eight minutes. Once again, the O'Donnells, Pete and Ed, led the G-Men in scoring with nineteen and fourteen.

Paul Hoffman scored but one field goal in the game and finished with six points. The following day at practice, Coach Phelps made it a point to express his dissatisfaction with the performance of his superb sophomore by asking him if he had been spending too much time reading his newspaper clippings. Even at a young age and in his first head coaching job, Phelps had that raspy gruff coach's voice that he used to great effect when he wanted someone's complete attention. On this day that someone was Hoffman. The team's captains, Ray McBrearty and Pete O'Donnell, made it a point to reassure Hoffman after practice that he had just suffered a subpar night and that it happened to everyone. The good cop, bad cop routine had the desired effect, and Hoffman was determined to return to form in the next game.

Though a few league games had already been played, it was time for league action to take the main floor. That happened two days before Christmas with a full slate of Anthracite League contests scheduled, including Weatherly at Freeland, Saint Ann's at Jim Thorpe, and MMI at Saint Gabriel's. Jim Thorpe walloped Saint Ann's 93-39 in their league opener. Bobby Brown led the Olympians, scoring twenty-one while three of his teammates also hit doubles. Coach Phil Radar went to his bench early and often in the contest that saw ten of his eleven players score for the winners. Thorpe had been a force in their first year in the league, and they served notice that they would be heard from again in the current season.

Weatherly had a much tougher time in their game against the Freeland Whippets. Freeland led by four twice in the final quarter and the score was tied at sixty with a little less than two minutes to play. Pat Searfoss, who scored thirty-one, then hit four consecutive fouls to put Weatherly up by four, but a three-point play by Freeland narrowed the margin to a single point when Weatherly turned the ball over with just thirty-nine seconds to play. After Freeland put the ball in play and was setting up their offense, Searfoss took control, stealing the ball and going the length of the court for a layup that provided the winning three-point margin. The Wreckers had held onto a win and would next travel to Jim Thorpe to take on the Olympians.

Meanwhile, West Hazleton took command early and belted Hazle Township 81-47. As for the G-Men, they found themselves on the short end of a 30-24 score after two periods at Saint Joe's. Phelps, who assistant coach Vince Gallagher remembered as a leader who made superb halftime adjustments, was able to light a fire under the Saints at halftime. Saint Gabriel's put on a second-half performance described by the local media as "one of the most fantastic halves ever played in these parts." The G-Men outscored MMI 51-17 in the second half to win by a score of 81-47. Four Saint Gabriel players hit double figures with Pete O'Donnell leading the way with twenty-four, just ahead of Hoffman's twenty-two. Ed O'Donnell added fifteen and Barletta scored fourteen. In his sports column, Ray Saul listed the gifts he hoped Santa would bring to local sports personalities. With an eye to the future for Dick Phelps, Saul's list included "a crack at the PCIAA state playoffs." Though nobody was thinking about it at the time, Saul's wish would more than be fulfilled.

It would only be the second league game for both squads, but the Jim Thorpe-Weatherly pairing was being billed as a key matchup. The two talented teams were both undefeated at 5-0, and in addition to being an important league game, the winner would have the early advantage in the race to determine which club would represent the Anthracite League in the state playoffs. Most observers viewed Thorpe as the slight favorite based on the home court advantage. The game surpassed expectations.

The Olympians gym was packed before the JV game ended with Jim Thorpe winning the opener 67-56. From the opening tip Thorpe held the lead in the varsity contest, but they found the Wreckers impossible to shake. With five minutes to play the home team was up by eight, 59-51. Despite Weatherly's significant height advantage, Thorpe had battled the visitors off the boards to make any edge in that area slim. At his point the momentum swung Weatherly's way, and in two minutes they outscored the Olympians 10-1 to take a 61-60 lead with just three minutes to play.

Over the next minute and a half, the lead would change hands five times. Pat Searfoss finally put Weatherly on top 65-64 when he scored a goal with 1:37 left to play. Thorpe turned the ball over but got it back when Weatherly's Paul Romano was called for an offensive foul with fifty-six seconds left to play. Following Coach Pip Radar's instructions, the Olympians played for the last shot. Joe Morgan's jumper from about twelve feet bounded high off the rim where it was corralled by Weatherly's Lew Kistler. Kistler was surrounded by three Thorpe players who tried to foul him as time ran out. The win put Weatherly in the driver's seat early in the league's first-half chase.

Don Barnes noted that the Wreckers would have little time to rest on their laurels as they would host Saint Gabriel's in one week. Barnes described the G-Men as Weatherly's newest challenger and "possibly the most dangerous of all." The fact was with a win over Saint Gabriel's, only West Hazleton would stand between Weatherly and the first-half title.

That same night the G-Men ran their record to 5-1, easily defeating Hazle Township 99-56 at Saint Joe's. Paul Hoffman scored twenty-four, almost all of them in the first half. Phelps went to his bench early and often in the game as he worked to develop depth on his team. The new coach clearly had his eye on future contests, and he was determined to give his new big men Sock and Ferry significant playing time whenever he could.

Prior to the game with Weatherly, a number of Saint Gabriel's fans, including Coach Phelps, would find their way to Saint Joseph's gym on Sunday, January 2, 1966, to watch Saint Gabriel's junior high team take on Saint Joseph's. The junior G-Men didn't disappoint, winning 68-46 led by Jerry Gallagher and John Darraugh. Coach Vince Gallagher was sending another quality outfit onto the court to represent Saint Gabriel's in the Public Parochial League. The G-Men had a talented JV and freshman team and while the in-house talent looked good, Phelps also took in games played by the Mother of Grace freshman team led by Tony Kinney.

On the day of the big game the headline on the *Standard Speaker*'s sports page declared "Saint Gabriel's at Weatherly in Anthracite League Showdown Tonight." The paper predicted that the game would feature "Weatherly's raw power against the Saints' finesse." Don Barnes saw the Saint Gabriel's defensive pressure as being the key as to which team would emerge with a victory. In his view, if Weatherly could handle the full-court press the G-Men would throw their way, the home team would come out on top.

To say the Weatherly gym was crowded on the night of January 4, 1966, would be an understatement. As reported by Ray Saul, many loyal G-Men followers were turned away at the door. Every conceivable spot was occupied. If the fire marshal was present, he was there as a fan and too interested in the upcoming contest to check on the number of people crowded into the limited space. The gymnasium rocked from the opening tip. Locals had at one time derided the Anthracite as the alley basketball league, but on this night two fine squads squared off against each other. That said, there was plenty of alley left in both teams as the game was described as "the most physically bruising game seen in these parts in a long time."

To no one's surprise, the Saints pressed from the get-go and jumped to a six-point lead after one quarter 20-14. Then early in the second quarter the Wreckers appeared demoralized when they were outscored by a twelve-to-two margin, making the score 32-16. Weatherly called a time-out to regroup. The pause had the desired effect for the home team, who suddenly came alive. Led by Pat Searfoss, Lew Kistler, and sophomore Henry Panckeri, Weatherly took total control, solving the Saints' press and scoring numerous baskets on easy layups on the way to a 36-35 halftime lead.

In the third quarter the teams traded field goals, and it was Weatherly who scored last to extend their lead to 54-51 with eight minutes to play. In the fourth period Phelps went to his bench and sent Bob Entiero into the game. The senior guard responded by hitting two foul shots and a driving field goal to give the G-Men a 57-56 lead. Weatherly responded with a quick goal to regain command.

The Wreckers weren't finished, and the lead changed hands several more times before the game ended. With just forty seconds to play, Pat Searfoss scored, giving Weatherly a 64-63 advantage. The Saints missed a shot on their next possession, and when Weatherly secured the rebound, things looked bleak for Saint Gabriel's. Weatherly tried to hold the ball but turned it over in the face of a pressing defense. With just seven seconds on the clock, Barletta sent a shot toward the rim from the right side of the court. The shot missed the mark but the rebound was corralled by the Saints defensive specialist Ray McBrearty, who dropped in the winning goal as time ran out. The Saint Gabriel's fans who had managed to get a ticket for the game erupted while the Weatherly supporters sat in stunned silence.

Pete O'Donnell remembered one play early in the contest involving the Saint Gabriel's staunchest supporters, the cheerleaders. "I was chasing a ball that was heading out of bounds off us and one of our cheerleaders, I can't remember who, batted the ball back into play as it was about to hit her. The referees didn't see it, and I took the ball and scored on an easy layup. I guess we owe the cheerleaders an assist on that one." While the play went unnoticed by the referees, many in the crowd saw it and some G-Men fans remember the game as the one won by the girls in purple and white.

After the game, Coach Phelps gave the credit to his players: "The kids did it all, they were just great. I've got great kids." Then the first-year coach singled out Ray McBrearty and Pete O'Donnell as terrific team leaders while adding that the G-Men, though not disciplined to his coaching plan yet, were improving with every game. At this point in the first half of league play, only Saint Gabriel's and West Hazleton remained undefeated. The Anthracite League was also gaining respect in some important local corners. The day after the game, Phil Sarno wrote that most of the teams in the league "show as much class as some of the clubs in the Eastern Penn League."

Just three days later the Saints entertained a strong Freeland team while Weatherly traveled to play West Hazleton, both key contests. Freeland had taken Weatherly to the wire before coming out on the short end of a 68-65 score. Based on the fact the game would be played at Saint Joe's, the G-Men were slight favorites, though some worried that the home team might be looking ahead to their next contest at Jim Thorpe. West Hazleton, in the familiar position as defending league champs, was considered to be the underdog against the talented team from Weatherly.

Freeland started fast jumping to a 9-3 lead, which led to Phelps calling a time-out. The coach settled the G-Men down during the break, and they responded by taking a 16-14 lead at the end of the first quarter. The second quarter began with Ed O'Donnell hitting a field goal from the outside, putting the Saints up by four, and the Whippets never got any closer. Led by the two O'Donnells and Hoffman, the G-Men pulled away and were leading 63-39 after three periods. Phelps substituted freely from that point on, and the game ended with Saint Gabriel's on top by a comfortable margin 82-65.

Meanwhile, Weatherly pulled off something they had never done since entering the league in 1960. They beat the Wildcats on the loser's home floor, 53-50. The Weatherly victory made Saint Gabriel's the lone undefeated team in league play. The Saints would travel to Jim Thorpe in a few days, and the rest of the league would be pulling for the Olympians to knock off Phelps's high flying club.

The Saint Gabriel's coach spent his Sunday afternoon taking in a junior high contest. Two local teams—Most Precious Blood and Mother of Grace—battled it out in front of 1,000 excited fans. Phelps watched a gifted left-handed freshman by the name of Tony Kinney score thirty-seven points as he led the Gracemen to an 86-68 win over their archrival. Phelps undoubtedly thought about what a team with both Hoffman and Kinney would look like.

The following day Phil Sarno wrote about a conversation he had with Phelps while they took in the game. Phelps said he was impressed with the level of play in the area and predicted that within a few years the level of play in the Anthracite League would equal that in the East Penn League. Sarno echoed the feeling that some "pretty high-class basketball" was being played in the league that many locals had underestimated for years.

On Tuesday, January 11, 1966, the big game between Saint Gabriel's and Jim Thorpe was at hand. The Saints were riding a wave of wins and were regarded as slight favorites against the very talented Olympians. Don Barnes was obviously impressed with Saint Gabriel's new young coach and predicted that the Saints' mentor would find a way to slow down the fast-paced, and at times explosive, Thorpe offense. He also noted that while Phelps had arrived on the scene talking the importance of defense, his squad was scoring on average eighty points a game. One thing was clear: with a win the G-Men would be in the driver's seat for the league's first-half title.

While the Saints and Olympians went head-to-head, there were a few surprises around the league that made the aforementioned matchup more important than anyone realized as they watched the contest. West Hazleton traveled to Freeland where the fired up Whippets stunned the Wildcats by a score of 92-66. The defending champs now had two league losses and still had to face Saint Gabriel's and Jim Thorpe in the first half. Meanwhile, Weatherly traveled to Marian Catholic and Wink Gallagher's Colts handed the Wreckers their second defeat by a 59-53 margin.

Before a packed house at Jim Thorpe, the fans were treated to a classic battle. Led by Hoffman, the G-Men totally controlled the boards in the first half. The problem was there weren't many defensive rebounds to be had. The Olympians were red hot, and that shooting kept them in the game. When the teams headed for the locker rooms at half Saint Gabriel's was clinging to a slim 32-31 lead.

The second half was much the same as both teams battled against aggressive defenses. After three quarters the teams were knotted at forty-four. While the Saints were playing steady basketball, it wasn't one of their best performances. Phelps had the G-Men playing deliberately on offense in an effort to slow down the explosive Olympians. While it had that effect, it also led to a number of possessions where the Saints turned the ball over without taking a shot. In the final eight minutes Thorpe remained hot, hitting every field goal they attempted. The G-Men didn't wilt and when the final buzzer sounded Thorpe fans celebrated a well-earned 65-63 win. After the game Phelps praised his opponents saying, "They played a fine game and deserved to win. We had seventeen turnovers and that made the difference."

The game stayed with Phelps. Years later when he was coaching at Notre Dame, he invited Pete O'Donnell and Ray McBrearty to South Bend to watch the Irish take on DePaul. The two former G-Men were invited to the Notre Dame locker room after the game. DePaul prevailed by two and with his team gathered around him after the contest, Phelps looked in McBrearty's direction and said, "Hey Mac, just like Jim Thorpe."

Despite suffering their first league loss the Saints remained in excellent shape in the first-half race. Having already defeated Weatherly and Freeland, only West Hazleton appeared to stand in the Saints' way of finishing in no worse than a tie for the first half title. Meanwhile, Phelps's comments relative to the Anthracite League being on par with the East Penn League had started a debate as multiple letters poured into the local paper challenging the new coach's conclusions. Though many schools in the league would close within the next twenty years, an honest appraisal of the region's basketball history would tend to support the conclusions Phelps voiced during his stay in Hazleton. Shortly after the discussion of the merits of Phelps's statement began, Ray Saul chimed in. "The Anthracite League has come a long way in the past decade." The sports editor added that while he wouldn't care to see the weaker Anthracite teams play East Penn foes, "St. Gabes, Weatherly or Thorpe might be interesting." Throughout the discussion, Phelps stood by his original points and added he thought it probable "that a new central Catholic high school will be here in the near future."

Three days after losing to Thorpe the G-Men set a new school scoring record while beating Foster Township 113-71 at what the *Standard Speaker* termed "the cricket cage known as the Foster gym." Both teams pressed the entire game, but the Saints had little trouble handling the pressure as six G-Men scored in double figures. Noteworthy among the six was Tom Sock, who came off the bench to score thirteen. All told, eleven players took the floor for Saint Gabriel's and all of them scored. Things didn't go as smoothly for Jim Thorpe as they needed overtime to beat Freeland 79-77 to keep pace with the Saints in the first-half race.

The next big league game pitted Jim Thorpe against West Hazleton on the Olympians home court, where they were favored to defeat the defending champs. Wildcat fans were well aware that a loss, their third in league play, would eliminate them from the first-half race. Thorpe dispatched West Hazleton with little difficulty, winning 72-50 in a game that was never close.

Saint Gabriel's had no trouble beating Saint Ann's 91-40 on the same night. Coach Phelps continued to use these games to give his two inexperienced big men, Sock and Ferry, playing time, and they responded, scoring thirteen and seven points respectively. Now all that stood between Phelps's G-Men and no worse than a tie for the first-half title were their long-time rivals at West Hazleton, a team everyone figured had to be licking their wounds.

Tickets for the Saints-Wildcat game scheduled for Tuesday, January 25th, went on sale at both schools the day before the game. They sold out and it was announced there would be no tickets available at the gate. Led by the two O'Donnells and Hoffman, the G-Men were averaging over eighty points a game. Though the game would be played at West Hazleton where the Wildcats were always tough, most observers installed the Saints as solid favorites. Confidence was high among the students roaming the halls in the small south side high school, and the feeling was Phelps would lead this team to victory and then revenge the earlier loss to Thorpe in a playoff, clinching the first-half title.

The small West Hazleton gym was packed to the rafters with ardent supporters of both teams before the JV game got underway. West Hazleton took that one by the slim margin of 44-41, which kept the junior Wildcats undefeated in league play. From the opening whistle of the main event, both teams played rough basketball, particularly under the boards where G-Men ace Hoffman picked up a couple of quick fouls. There were whistles being blown in the crowd as well, and two boys from West Hazleton had theirs confiscated after blowing them in order to distract the Saint Gabriel's offensive attack. Still led by Pete O'Donnell, who couldn't be stopped as he scored on an assortment of shots launched from all angles, the Saints jumped to a 19-10 first-quarter lead. The Cats got on track in the second period after Hoffman picked up his third foul. With the Saints leading rebounder on the bench, West Hazleton seized control of the boards and, to the delight of the home crowd, headed to the locker room with a 35-32 lead at the half.

Coach Phelps was unhappy with his team's first-half performance. He didn't care that they were missing their key rebounder for most of the second quarter. In his view, turnovers, not rebounds, had put the Saints in the hole. In the locker room he told his team, in no uncertain terms, they needed to clean up their play in the second half.

Early in the second half Ed O'Donnell stole the ball and scored, putting the G-Men on top 41-40. From there Phelps's club stubbornly extended the lead to four, 52-48, after three quarters of play. The fourth quarter was evenly played, and with just two minutes left Saint Gabriel's was on top 66-61. West Hazleton cut the margin to three on a driving score by Bob Seamon. The Saints responded by getting the ball to Pete O'Donnell, who had already scored twenty-seven points in the game. O'Donnell made a great move to blow past his defender and was heading to the bucket when he slipped and fell to the floor. Referee Sam Esposito signaled a walking violation, and West Hazleton had the ball with a minute and a half to go. The Saints then fouled Wildcat ace Ed Martnick, who converted both free throws and all of a sudden the G-Men led by a single point. Once again the Saints went to Pete O'Donnell, whose shot from about eight feet missed the mark. West Hazleton won the battle for the rebound. A shot by Seamon from the top of the key missed the mark, but a whistle sent him to the foul line where he calmly hit both shots, giving the Wildcats their first lead since early in the third quarter.

Phelps called a time-out to quiet the crowd, which had erupted when Seamon's second shot hit the mark. With both teams battling for the ball, there were three successive jump balls and the G-Men controlled all three taps. With just twenty-three seconds to go Cal Ferrari, West Hazleton's big man, stepped in front of Pete O'Donnell and intercepted an errant pass. Ferrari whipped the ball down court to a wide open Jim Platukis, who scored to put the Cats up by three. The Saints moved the ball up the court quickly, and Pete O'Donnell was fouled but he missed the front end of the one-and-one. West Hazleton secured the rebound and the Saints were forced to foul. Martnick made both fouls. West Hazleton pulled off the upset 71-66, making Jim Thorpe the first-half champions.

After the game a disappointed Phelps offered no excuses, saying only that "West Hazleton deserved to win it." For Saint Gabriel's fans, the loss was the most disappointing in recent memory. Older followers were grumbling about this young coach who wasn't getting it done despite having what many considered the two top players in the school's history on the same team. On the other hand, Saint Gabriel's students were looking forward to the second half of league play when the Saints would play Jim Thorpe, Weatherly, and West Hazleton at home in Saint Joseph's gym. If there was one constant in a Saint Gabriel's basketball season, it was the fact that, win or lose, the student body stood solidly behind their team.

Criticism of Phelps also found its way into the local paper. In his column the day after the game Phil Sarno wrote "the G-Men offensive strategy in the last quarter—by depending on one player—was one good avenue toward complete demoralization of a unit which worked so hard collectively to come so far in the league race." Sarno went on to point out that he and the spectators at the game observed four Saint Gabriel's players stand in one corner while the "key performer" tried to score against the entire Wildcat team. If older Saint Gabriel's fans needed fuel added to their fiery criticism of Coach Phelps, Sarno provided it.

Sports editor Ray Saul had been dead on in predicting that Jim Thorpe would win the Anthracite League's first-half title.

Saint Gabriel's fans were hoping he would be as accurate in his second-half predictions when he picked the G-Men to top the standings once the dust cleared. Saint Gabriel's was already 1-0 in the second-half race based on their win over Marian, a game that due to a scheduling quirk had been played earlier in the year. On a night when the rest of the league was idle, West Hazleton and MMI played their first second-half game at Freeland. West Hazleton may have still been celebrating their upset of Saint Gabriel's when they were upset by the Preppers 53-49 in overtime. The loss put the Wildcats in a deep hole as they attempted to defend their league title.

On Monday morning, January 31, 1966, the headline on the front page of the *Hazleton Standard Speaker* read "Region Paralyzed by Blizzard." The storm dumped more than fourteen inches of snow, and gale force winds of up to sixty miles an hour created drifts reaching as high as fifteen feet. Temperatures hovering around zero complicated snow removal efforts. Schools, stores, and factories closed. An Edwards Lakes to Sea bus traveling to Philadelphia with thirty-seven passengers was stranded in Hazleton, and the city responded by housing the travelers in city hall, where a number of the group spent the night sleeping in jail cells.

Later that day Father Deviney announced that the Saint Gabriel's-Jim Thorpe basketball game scheduled for the following evening would be played. One would have to surmise the good father had verified that the Saints' star sophomore Paul Hoffman was going to make it back to town in time for the game. However, as of Tuesday morning, reports were that Hoffman was stranded at Saint Michael's of Hoban Heights, where he had gone to visit his parents over the weekend. With no bus service available due to the storm, Don Barnes opined that he wouldn't be surprised to see Father Purcell arrive on the scene with the young superstar in tow.

Though early in the second-half race, the game was already being touted as perhaps the biggest game on the road to the title. Every other game on the league's schedule had been postponed until Wednesday, but that option wasn't available to Father Deviney since Hazleton High School was going to be playing on the Saint Joseph's court that night. Based on home court advantage the G-Men were the slight favorites.

Despite the weather and the total unavailability of parking options, more than 1,300 hundred fans were in the stands when referee Joe Barletta tossed the ball into the air for the opening tap. The game, as expected, was tight from the start. As far as Saint Gabriel's was concerned, the fact Paul Hoffman had made it back for the game had calmed more than a few fans' jitters. Hoffman was playing one of the best games of his still young career, scoring and controlling both boards as the Saints opened up a 37-30 lead at the half.

In the third quarter, Coach Phelps stopped pressing the Olympians. He would later say he made the move because he had control of the boards and didn't want to give a team with the shooting prowess displayed by the Thorpe players any easy chances. With the score tied at forty-nine and time running out in the third period Pete O'Donnell, who had been kept under wraps by the Thorpe defense, fired in a forty-foot shot as the buzzer sounded, giving the G-Men a two-point lead with eight minutes to play.

Ed O'Donnell started out the scoring in the last quarter by hitting a long set shot from the right side of the court. The Olympian's Joe Morgan matched that goal, but the aforementioned O'Donnell responded with two more quick scores. Then Hoffman, who had already drawn Phelps's ire by not shooting enough (a criticism Hoffman would hear from coaches throughout his high school career), drove to the basket and scored on a beautiful reverse layup. Just like that, the G-Men had spurted to a 59-51 lead.

Desperate to gain control of the ball, the Olympians discarded their zone defense and began playing man-to-man. With sixteen seconds to play, they had narrowed the margin to three but were forced to foul Hoffman to stop the clock. Hoffman, who scored twenty-five in the game as well as being the leading rebounder, sank both free throws and the Saints emerged winners by a score of 67-62. Paul Hoffman and Ed O'Donnell had supplied the offensive firepower for Saint Gabriel's, accounting for forty-one of the team's points. After the game, Phelps talked about how proud he was of his squad, and he singled out Ray McBrearty, who had scored but six points, for special praise, saying the senior captain had played a tough game in leading the G-Men to the win. The victory put the Saints in the driver's seat as the second half got underway.

After fourteen games under Phelps, the G-Men had a record of 11-3. Hoffman and the O'Donnells were among the scoring leaders in the region. On the defensive side, their opponents were netting sixty points each contest, and many of those had been scored late in games long decided when Phelps had gone deep into his bench. McBrearty had emerged as a true leader on and off the court and Barletta was doing his job as a role player, taking up space underneath and playing solid defense. Bob Entiero and Jimmy Rondash were providing offensive spark off the bench, and Sock and Ferry were getting valuable experience. The team was certainly the finest to wear the purple and white since the 1960 league champions.

The other evident factor was that this was a well-coached team. Bruce Ellis remembers, "Phelps pressed for thirty-two minutes. No teams around here had ever done that. He brought new ideas about the game into the area, especially on the defensive side of the ball. He was a step ahead of the other coaches, and he changed the way coaches approached the game even after he left the area." Saint Gabriel's student body wasn't concerned with any of that—they were hungry for another championship team, and it seemed like this just might be the year.

The G-Men hosted Foster Township in their next league contest, and they had no trouble winning easily 99-62. Once again the trio of Hoffman and the O'Donnells led the scorers, and the margin would have been much larger had Phelps not gone to his bench early and substituted throughout the game. The Saints then took a break from league play to meet Hazleton in a rematch of their December tussle.

Meanwhile there was trouble at Jim Thorpe and to the surprise of few, it involved the Olympian star and defending league scoring champion Bobby Brown. Brown benched himself at the beginning of Thorpe's game with Freeland. Then in the third quarter he walked from the bench to the locker room, where he dressed and left the gym, telling friends he was done for the season. Thorpe prevailed in the game 59-52, but few saw the first-half champions as legitimate overall title threats without Brown.

The Hazleton-Saint Gabriel's game was a much-anticipated event. A crowd in excess of two thousand was expected. Father Deviney announced that season tickets would not be honored for the game and that individual game tickets would be available on a first come, first served basis. The local paper rated the game a toss-up, and Phil Sarno wrote that spectators could expect to witness a "wild and woolly one" that would have Saint Joseph's gym rocking.

The Sunday prior to the clash, things were rocking in Saint Gabriel's small gym where the Saints' junior high squad took on crosstown rival Most Precious Blood. With three minutes to play the Most Precious Blood coach, Tony Scarcella, tossed his folding chair across the court with his team down by a 42-37 margin. The chair narrowly missed Saint Gabriel's player Jimmy Brown. His teammate Joe Farley turned to Ray Saul, who was one of the two referees, and pointedly made the signal for a technical foul, but that call never came. After order was restored, Scarcella's squad ran off nine unanswered points to win 46-42.

An enormous crowd made their way to St. Joe's to witness the second game of the season between the Saints and the Mountaineers. From the opening tip both teams played at a ferocious pace, and after eight minutes the score was knotted at twenty-two. The pace of the game favored the Mountaineers, who had a far deeper bench than the Saints. As the game progressed only the outstanding play of Pete O'Donnell and Hoffman kept G-Men close. Hazleton led by a single point at half and by seven after three periods. By this time, Hazleton's coach Fran Libonati had used ten players while Phelps had played only six.

First-time Hazleton starter Phil Andras was having the game of his life, playing outstanding basketball on both ends of the court. In addition, Hazleton was shooting lights out hitting on 47 percent of their field goal tries. In the fourth quarter, Libonati went to his bench and sent Lou Fiore into the game. The diminutive guard responded by scoring all eight of his points in the final period. When the dust cleared Hazleton had emerged with another hard-fought win by the final score of 82-70. Pete O'Donnell scored thirty-two points in the game, including the 1,000th of his illustrious career with about two and half minutes left in the game.

Talking to reporters afterward, Coach Libonati said that O'Donnell and Hoffman were the equal of any players in the East Penn League. Coach Phelps said his team had been beaten soundly, especially "off the boards," and he wished Hazleton the best of luck for the rest of the season. Ray Saul opined that better balance and depth had made the difference in the game.

Phil Sarno used the game to once again voice his displeasure with the tactics employed by the G-Men. Sarno wrote that
the Saints became a two-man team against the "sharpshooting"
Mounts and the strategy was doomed to failure. Coach Phelps
had lost the support of the sportswriter who had been solidly in
his corner. The criticisms also fed the disappointment of older
Saint Gabriel's fans who had fully expected to beat Hazleton.
The feeling among the student body was quite different. The
students enjoyed supporting the best team many of them
could remember. Their sights were still set on winning a league
championship.

On February 11th, the big league game featured Jim Thorpe
at West Hazleton. Meanwhile, Saint Ann's announced that the
school was leaving the Anthracite League at the conclusion of
the season. The Freeland Catholic high cited a dwindling enrollment and the inability to compete as the reasons. It was also
announced that Saint Gabriel's would open the Catholic state
playoffs against the defending eastern champions Williamsport
St. Joseph's.

At West Hazleton the Wildcats bared both their teeth and
claws, beating Jim Thorpe 71-60. If ever a team had a home
court advantage, it was West Hazleton. At halftime with his
team trailing by four, Thorpe coach Pip Radar was heard to
say, "They ought to outlaw gyms like this." Fans noted Bobby
Brown back in the Thorpe lineup, but even his return wasn't
enough for the Olympians. On the same night, Saint Gabriel's
joined Weatherly as the only undefeated teams in the second
half by beating Saint Ann's 81-59, paced by Hoffman's twenty-
nine-point performance.

The G-Men would face West Hazleton next and a win would
virtually clinch no worse than a tie for the top spot in the second
half race. The game would be played at Saint Joe's and judging
by the early ticket sales, a huge crowd would be on hand. Saint
Gabriel's was favored in the game, but observers noted a loss
would eliminate the Wildcats from the second half race and they
wouldn't go down easy.

Al McGuire was a thirty-seven-year-old head coach who had
recently taken on the job of rebuilding the Marquette University
basketball program. During a 1965 interview McGuire had
remarked that in the game of basketball, the home court advantage was huge. He said the crowd, particularly a vocal one,

worked "on the subconscious of the official" and that judgment calls go to the home team. Upsets, added McGuire, only occur when the visiting team wins. Based on his analysis and the fact that the G-Men would put superior talent on the court, it was difficult to imagine the home team not coming out on top.

West Hazleton's coach Ron Gatski went with a gimmick defense aimed at stopping the Saints' big three, Hoffman and the two O'Donnells. He played man-to-man defense on those three and put his other two players in a loose zone defense guarding the middle of the court. The defense had the desired effect. Pete O'Donnell, averaging more than twenty points per game, was held to nine. His first field goal didn't occur until late in the third quarter, and that came on a fast break after Hoffman intercepted a West Hazleton pass. Hoffman was also held below his scoring average, managing to score sixteen while being hounded by Cal Ferrari. Ed O'Donnell just topped his normal output by scoring sixteen on an assortment of outside shots.

The Saints had sixteen more attempted field goals than the Cats but made only two more than their league rivals. West Hazleton outscored the G-Men from the foul line 16-7. When the dust settled, West Hazleton had pulled off what Al McGuire had described as an upset, winning 62-57 on the road. The game probably marked the only time in his first season that Phelps had been out coached. The win, in addition to keeping the defending league champs in the race, had provided additional ammunition for the critical element of the Saint Gabriel's fan base to use against their young coach. In their view, Phelps had failed to prevail against Hazleton or West Hazleton, an unpardonable offense with the talent he had on hand.

By the middle of February, Weatherly stood alone atop the Anthracite League standings at 6-0. Saint Gabriel's and West Hazleton each had one loss. The next big game scheduled to take place on the 21st had Jim Thorpe traveling to Weatherly. Hazleton High was having one of its best seasons since the late fifties, having broken Allentown Dieruff's fifteen-game winning streak 30-28 in double overtime. Elsewhere in Pennsylvania sports news, Penn State football coach Rip Engle was staying true to his promise to retiring at age sixty after leading the Nittany Lions for sixteen years. A youthful assistant by the name of Joe Paterno was rumored to be the front runner to take over the head job.

That final week in the month of February was billed as the "Week of Decision" in the Anthracite League. Weatherly would meet Jim Thorpe, Saint Gabriel's, and West Hazleton within five days, and the results of those contests would decide the second-half championship. Weatherly scratched out a 64-61 win over Thorpe to remain undefeated while eliminating the first-half champs from the second-half race. The Wreckers had little time to celebrate their win since they had to prepare to take on the G-Men just two evenings thence at Saint Joseph's. Phil Sarno wouldn't hazard a pick as the G-Men and Wreckers prepared to meet, using his indecision to take yet another shot at Coach Phelps: "We won't go out on a limb and predict any more on this situation because we had to crawl in a corner for three vital games when a just-the-opposite style of offensive came into disastrous prominence."

Once again the G-Men filled Saint Joseph's with the home team facing an absolute must-win situation. Phelps opened the game by employing the full-court press that had served him so well throughout the season. Weatherly wasn't fazed by the pressure and broke it consistently with deft ball handling that led to easy scores, most being made by their two aces Pat Searfoss and Lew Kistler. Phelps abandoned the press, but by halftime Weatherly was sitting on a nine-point, 38-29 lead.

Little changed at the beginning of the second half when the hot-shooting Wreckers extended their lead to 52-37 with just three minutes to go in the period. After a time-out Phelps again instructed the Saints to employ the full-court press. This time Weatherly wavered and the score after three quarters stood at 54-47. In the final eight minutes the G-Men continued to apply pressure, and with two and a half minutes to go they had clawed their way back into the game, tailing by four, 63-59. At this point, Weatherly's star Pat Searfoss took over. Weatherly scored ten quick points while holding the Saints to a single point. When the final buzzer sounded, Weatherly remained undefeated, winning convincingly 73-60.

It was an understatement, but it struck home when Don Barnes described the game as a "crushing disappointment to hordes of St. Gabriel's fans." Phil Sarno continued to blame coaching decisions for the failure of the G-Men to take the league title. He wrote, "With an inherited team of outstanding talent and basically a unit that could outrun any other foe off the floor this year, the club shifted from high into low gear for four vital games and lost them all."

Later that week, Weatherly downed West Hazleton to win the second-half championship and set up a league title showdown with Jim Thorpe. The winner of that game would also represent the Anthracite League in the state playoffs. Meanwhile, Hoffman scored thirty-three points and Pete O'Donnell added eighteen in leading the G-Men to a come-from-behind 81-77 win at Freeland. The Saints overall record stood at 16-6 after going 14-4 in league play. The season wasn't over as they had qualified for the Catholic state playoffs, but post-season play hadn't been kind to Saint Gabriel's. The G-Men would start the playoffs against their old nemesis Williamsport Saint Joseph's the night before Weatherly and Jim Thorpe met to decide the league title—a title the Saints felt had slipped through their fingers.

10

ON THE LINE FOR ONE

THE FIRST CHAMPIONSHIP

The Saints opened what they hoped would be a long run to a state title against the team that had eliminated them a year earlier. Williamsport Saint Joseph's represented an outstanding foe with a winning tradition in the state playoffs. Coach Phelps scouted the Williamsport team personally, and he gave handwritten copies of his report to his five starters. The game would be played at Marian Catholic, a gym that would figure prominently in Saint Gabriel's basketball history in the next few years. Don Barnes was calling the game a toss-up.

Phelps's scouting reports (he would personally scout every team Saint Gabriel's would face in the post season) were detailed and offered a glimpse into a great basketball mind at a young age. They contained specific details on the strengths and weaknesses of each opposition player. The notes included tendencies his team could take advantage of as well as diagrams of the opponent's offensive sets. Phelps also showed faith in his team leaders, Pete O'Donnell and Ray McBrearty, as he allowed them to take an active part in running the team's practices. Years later, McBrearty would wonder whether this was a sign Phelps had already made some decisions regarding his coaching future at Saint Gabriel's.

When the game began, it became clear that it wasn't going to be one of the better nights for the G-Men. With the stands at Marian Catholic filled largely with their fans, the Saints struggled losing the battle off the boards to the smaller Saint Joseph's squad, and they repeatedly turned the ball over with careless passes and poor ball handling. At halftime Saint Joe's was up seven and Marian head coach Wink Gallagher remarked, "If Saint Gabriel's played like that all the time, we'd give them some action."

Things didn't get better in the third quarter and the margin between the teams spread to as many as thirteen points. Some Saint Gabriel's fans seated in the rows behind the team's bench began to let their coach know that they were displeased with his team's performance. When the buzzer sounded after three quarters, the team from Williamsport led 49-39.

In the final quarter the G-Men woke up. A steal-and-layup goal by Ray McBrearty made the score 50-45 with just over six minutes to play. Two long field goals by Ed O'Donnell followed by two more by Pete O'Donnell knotted the score at fifty-three. The G-Men had erased a ten-point deficit in four minutes. Saint Joseph's responded with a goal a few seconds later. No one in the crowd realized that they had witnessed the final points St. Joe's would score.

With just over two minutes left, Paul Hoffman and St. Joe's Jim Cummings went up to rebound a missed attempt by the Saints. Many in the crowd thought that Cummings, who had the inside position on the play, was the player who touched the ball. Still feeling Hoffman's pressure, he was unable to control the ball and it bounded off someone's fingers into the goal, tying the score at fifty-five. Hoffman, who led the G-Men in scoring with eighteen, was credited with the goal.

Saint Joe's then went into a stall hoping to hold the ball for a final shot. That plan failed when the Saints deflected and intercepted a pass. Pete O'Donnell was fouled and with just a minute to go he made one of two shots to put the Saints in front 56-55. Saint Joe's again tried to hold the ball for a final shot. With twelve seconds to play, Hoffman knocked a pass out of bounds and then stole the ball on the subsequent attempt by Saint Joe's to inbound the basketball. Hoffman was fouled and he made one of two to make the final score 57-55.

Saint Gabriel's had overcome a significant hurdle in beating their old nemesis from Williamsport. When the buzzer sounded, Coach Phelps turned to the crowd behind him and shared a few words with those fans who had been heckling him earlier. His assistant Vince Gallagher was successful in pulling the coach away from the bench and toward the locker room. Father Deviney, who was an ardent Phelps supporter, joined the team in the locker room to celebrate the win.

Pete O'Donnell remembered the game as, all things considered, probably the biggest win in his remarkable career. He has good reason to remember it fondly. When he scored his eighth point (he would finish with thirteen), he became the leading scorer in the history of Saint Gabriel's High School. O'Donnell now had a career total of 1,101, surpassing Joe McFadden, who had tallied 1,095 while wearing the purple and white.

The G-Men didn't have a lot of time to celebrate. In just three days they would meet Plymouth St. Vincent's, who had easily dispatched Wilkes-Barre Saint Mary's in a playoff game. Phelps had witnessed that game with other members of what the local paper called "Saint Gabriel's official family." The word on the street was that "the family" returned home marveling at the play of the Vinnies.

The night after the Saints' win, Jim Thorpe and Weatherly met at Saint Joseph's gym to settle the Anthracite League title. The Olympians emerged on top by beating Weatherly 80-77 in a game that took an overtime period to settle. In addition to the league title, the win earned Thorpe a spot in the Class C PIAA state playoffs.

Saint Gabriel's and Saint Vincent's met on the night of March 4, 1966, on the same Marian Catholic floor where the G-Men had squeaked by Saint Joe's. Saint Vincent's was coming off a big win and celebrating its second Wilkes-Barre area Catholic League title in as many years. The second round of the playoffs was an unfamiliar spot for Saint Gabriel's, and a win would send them to the Diocesan final the following Tuesday. The *Standard Speaker* noted the Saints were used to close games and their loyal and sometimes rabid fans could expect another tight contest against the Vinnies.

Coach Phelps had started the year by stating you can't tell how good a team is at the beginning of a season; you had to wait until a group had time to gel and mature. On this night his squad played what may have been their finest game. By halftime, the Vinnies were exhausted and on the ropes as the Saints press and overall play led to a 42-20 margin after sixteen minutes. The second half was much the same as Phelps substituted freely. Hoffman received a huge ovation from the fans when he fouled out in the last quarter after scoring thirty-one points and leading both teams in rebounding. Ed O'Donnell scored nineteen and Pete O'Donnell added sixteen in the 76-57 rout. Ray McBrearty led the team on the defensive end and played an awesome floor game in initiating the offense. The G-Men would travel to Scranton for their next game against Scranton St. Paul's in their playoff quest.

The game against St. Paul's took place on the South Scranton Junior High court, much to the chagrin of the G-Men, who were unsuccessful in getting the game moved to the more spacious confines of the Scranton CYC. The smaller gym was sure to be packed with Saint Gabriel's fans catching playoff fever after the disappointing Anthracite League finish. Meanwhile Jim Thorpe, who had won the league title, was representing the league well and had advanced to the District 2 final in their state playoffs.

When Saint Gabriel's took the court on March 8, 1966, they were playing for a Scranton Diocese title, a title they hadn't captured since 1942. The gym was packed to its capacity of about 1,000, and the vast majority of the spectators had made the trip from Hazleton to cheer the G-Men on. Among those who took in the game was Father Purcell, who still harbored a love for the Saint Gabriel's team and student body. The Saints were considered the favorites as the game got underway, but it became clear early on that Saint Paul's wasn't going to go away quietly. The underdogs from Scranton showed tremendous hustle and backed that up with an excellent shooting performance to head to the halftime locker room trailing by a single field goal 35-33.

Coach Phelps was satisfied with the job his team had done in the face of the fine effort by his opponents. At halftime he decided that the G-Men would employ an aggressive full-court zone press to start the third quarter. He also urged Saint Gabriel's career scoring leader, Pete O'Donnell, to get more involved on the offensive end. As the team made its way to the court to prepare for the second half, Ray McBrearty remembers Pete O'Donnell drew him aside and said, "I didn't feel right out there in the first half but I'm okay now. I'm going to turn it around this half."

Whether it was Phelps's adjustments or Pete O'Donnell's prediction, the third quarter was all Saint Gabriel's. The Saints' zone press paid immediate dividends when the aforementioned O'Donnell stole an errant pass, scored, and made a foul shot, completing a three-point play. St. Paul's called multiple time-outs to try to stem the G-Men tide, but it was to no avail. Saint Gabriel's scored twenty-eight points in the quarter while allowing thirteen, and the score stood at 63-46 after three periods.

For all intents and purposes it was over, and the final score of 85-63 reflected the dominance of the G-Men in the second half. All five Saint Gabriel's starters hit double figures with Hoffman leading the way with thirty. Pete O'Donnell came alive in the second half and scored seventeen, and Ed O'Donnell was a shade behind with fifteen. Tony Joe Barletta and defensive ace Ray McBrearty contributed ten each. Saint Gabriel's was headed to the eastern final against St. Pius X of Roseto in a game played at Marian High.

The G-Men werc hoping for a twenty-win season as they prepared for the eastern state final. Their record stood at 19-6 and even in those games where they had come up short they had been competitive. Coach Phelps prepared his team well, and for the most part he had been successful in making half-time adjustments when needed. Offensively the team was led by their big three weapons. Paul Hoffman led the way, scoring 21.2 points per game. Pete O'Donnell averaged eighteen even, adding to his school scoring record with every score. Ed O'Donnell contributed 13.1 in every contest, and the other starters, Ray McBrearty and Tony Joe Barletta, played the roles the coach had mapped out for them. Phelps had also made good use of his bench and underclassmen, including the two big men he had recruited in gym class. Saint Gabriel's students could taste a state title. The school's halls were filled with an excitement and enthusiasm that had generally disappeared by mid-March. Still, there were a number of older fans who just couldn't forgive Phelps for the losses to Hazleton and West Hazleton.

The gym at Marian Catholic was becoming a second home to the Saints. Phelps sent a confident team onto the court to face Pius X in the eastern final. Midway through the first quarter, Saint Gabriel's held an 11-6 lead when they went on a run the like of which is seldom seen and actually extended into the second quarter. Over the next eight minutes of play, the G-Men took complete control, outscoring their opponents with thirty straight points. With the score 41-6, Phelps sat his starters. They returned to the court for a short time to start the third quarter before returning to the bench. By the game's end,

Phelps had used fourteen players and his starters less than a half in the 96-43 romp that moved the G-Men into the game for the state title. Despite the limited playing time, four of the Saints' starters hit double figures, led by Ed O'Donnell who netted twenty-three. Sophomore Dennis Olexa scored eight points in a reserve role.

On the same night the G-Men dispatched Pius X, Tony Kinney scored twenty-five points in leading Mother of Grace to a 68-61 win over Freeland, leading the Gracemen to a junior high title. The talented Kinney, who was widely viewed as the most talented freshman in the Greater Hazleton area, would soon be facing the decision as to where to continue his high school career. He had two choices: Hazleton High or Saint Gabriel's.

Coach Phelps and Father Conboy made the trip to western Pennsylvania to scout the foe Saint Gabriel's would face in the state championship. There they saw Masontown Kolb Memorial take down Erie Saint Gregory 83-64. Phelps reported that the winners were a "tall, talented outfit that were very tough off the boards." Father Deviney's announcement, appearing in the local paper, stated the title game would take place on Sunday, March 20th, at the Scranton CYC with a tip-off time of 2:30 p.m. Father Deviney also encouraged all students to buy their tickets in advance to avoid paying an extra fifty cents at the door. He also noted the school would be running several chartered buses to the game.

The *Standard Speaker* installed the G-Men as slight favorites heading into the championship tilt. The paper noted that Kolb Memorial hailed from the same diocese that had produced last year's state title winners, Uniontown St. John's. Ray Saul wrote that the best wishes of the entire region would be with the Saints in their quest to win the school's first state championship. Phil Sarno continued his silence relative to the G-Men that had begun with their failure to capture the Anthracite League title, instead singing the glories of the Jim Thorpe Olympians, who remained alive in their PIAA state championship race.

Coach Phelps had decided that Kolb Memorial could be pressured into mistakes, so he decided to employ what could only be described as a tenacious full-court zone press defense against the taller opponents. It worked. Despite Coach Frank Wydo's efforts to use time-outs to settle his club, they did little good and the G-Men were up 20-8 after one quarter. The two teams played a relatively even second period and Saint Gabriel's headed to the locker room with a comfortable 41-26 lead.

When the third quarter began, the full-court pressure paid immediate dividends and Wydo was forced to call another time-out when the G-Men increased their lead to 52-29. In addition to the stifling defense, the Saints were running a fast break offense to perfection. When they were forced to set up and work the ball, they played what Coach Phelps called good, sound basketball. Once again Hoffman led the scoring parade with twenty-seven points, but he received plenty of support from Ed O'Donnell, McBrearty, and Pete O'Donnel, who scored twenty, fourteen, and twelve points respectively. Barletta played a strong game both defensively and on the boards while chipping in eight points. When the final buzzer sounded, Saint Gabriel's had won its first state title by the commanding score of 91-59.

Phelps credited his team with the win, saying that the team had become "a powerhouse in the playoffs." Ray Saul noted that the young coach had achieved something that had never been done by a Saint Gabriel's coach: winning a state championship. Saul called Phelps an inspiring leader who had a bright future in coaching. The sports editor added that a mighty roar rocked the gym when Father Joseph Conboy announced there would be no school on Monday to celebrate the G-Men and their victory.

Despite the failure to capture the league title, Phelps had probably coached the finest team Saint Gabriel's had ever sent onto a basketball court up to that time. It is worth noting that the previous year's team may have had more overall talent, but in all candor, coaching made the difference. The new coach had solid backing from the student body even if there were pockets of discord among the alumni.

Looking to the future and fresh off winning a state championship, the young coach made arrangements to meet with Tony Kinney and his parents to discuss the talented young man's future. As Kinney remembers, Phelps came to his home impeccably dressed and accompanied by some members of his championship squad. According to Kinney, Phelps didn't try to sell him on coming to Saint Gabriel's to play basketball; instead, he stressed all the small Catholic school had to offer. Phelps said Kinney had attended a small Catholic school through the ninth grade and coming to Saint Gabriel's would be an easier transition than making the move to the much larger Hazleton High.

The coach talked about the smaller class sizes and how the student body was like a close-knit family. Kinney remembers sitting there feeling "star struck" hearing from the charismatic young coach who had just won a state title. He said both his parents were very impressed with Phelps, especially "my mother." However, when push came to shove, Kinney said all his friends were going to Hazleton High, and that led to his decision to attend the larger school. Looking back, Kinney remembers, "Of course, I had no idea at the time the coaching heights he [Phelps] was going to reach."

Meanwhile Jim Thorpe carried the torch for the Anthracite League all the way to the Class C state championship game before falling to Williamsburg in the final. After winning the Anthracite League against what was arguably the finest talent in the circuit's history, the Olympians had acquitted themselves quite well in the state playoffs. Saint Gabriel's became the only eastern team to capture a state title in 1966 as the other five champions hailed from the western side of the Commonwealth. As a matter of fact, since the west had swept the state titles the year before, Saint Gabriel's was the only eastern team in the past two years to win a Pennsylvania state title. The comments made by Coach Phelps earlier in the season comparing the Anthracite to the East Penn League suddenly didn't seem so outlandish.

The close of the 1966 season also brought changes to the Anthracite League. Saint Ann's withdrew from the league; there were rumors the school was closing. Two other member schools, Foster Township and Hazle Township, did in fact close their doors. Down to seven teams, the league began looking for local schools to join the circuit.

On March 30th Father Purcell hosted a banquet at Saint Michael's to honor the state champions. Coach Phelps gave a speech at the gathering that Don Barnes reported kept "the kids spellbound with his intensity and forcefulness." Barnes added one thing he learned at the meeting was that Father Purcell and Father Deviney were cousins.

Less than a week later on the evening of April 4th, Saint Gabriel's hosted their own dinner to celebrate the state champions. The principal speaker was Army's first-year coach Bob Knight, who by all accounts did a tremendous job. Coach Phelps spoke as well, warmly thanking his first team for their effort throughout the season. Father Deviney also addressed the crowd of more than three hundred, praising Phelps, the team, the fans, but making sure to heap praise on a student body that he described as the most spirited he had ever seen. Pete O'Donnell was awarded a special trophy to honor his career scoring record. For the first time in the school's history, the team voted for a most valuable player. That trophy went to the school's sophomore standout Paul Hoffman.

While the season may have been over, the newly crowned state champs continued to be recognized. The diocese newspaper the *Catholic Light* named Paul Hoffman and Pete O'Donnell as first team members of their all-star squad. Ed O'Donnell and Ray McBrearty were picked for the second team and Tony Joe Barletta rated an honorable mention. It was the first time since 1947 that all five Saint Gabriel's starters had been named to an all-star team. Phelps was named Catholic Basketball League Coach of the Year, and Pete O'Donnell, who also had a fine senior season on the baseball diamond, was named the region's outstanding schoolboy athlete.

On Monday, May 23, 1966, the front page of the *Standard Speaker* carried news from Vietnam, a story about Robert Kennedy's criticism of former president Dwight D. Eisenhower's suggestion that the United States consider arming its European allies with nuclear weapons, and a report that Dick Van Dyke and Mary Tyler Moore had won Emmy awards for best actor and actress in a comedy series. Saint Gabriel's fans ignored the front page and turned quickly to the sports pages, where they found the confirmation of a rumor that had been circulating over the weekend.

A bold headline read "Dick Phelps of Saint Gabriel's Named Freshman Coach at Penn." The University of Pennsylvania's new coach Dick Harter had added Phelps to his staff. Phelps described it as an opportunity "I couldn't refuse." He once again took the opportunity to heap praise on the team he had piloted in his first year as a head coach and predicted, "I'm sure the winning tradition will be carried on by Saint Gabe's in the future." It topped off quite a weekend for the young coach, who had just been named Scranton Diocese Coach of the Year. Ray Saul noted, in what was probably an understatement, that Father Deviney was sorry to see him go. Saul added, "Dick had a few harpoons thrown at him during the past basketball season and it hardly need be mentioned that he is having the last laugh again."

Later that summer Phelps played in a pickup game in the small gym at Saint Gabriel's. A number of the players who would be returning were there. During a break, Phelps talked about the past year, noting that some people couldn't get over that he hadn't beaten Hazleton or West Hazleton. "Just give me half the enrollment of those two schools and let's see what happens," he remarked in his customary growl. Then he turned his attention to the future. "Wait until the new guy gets here; wait until you see him play. He'll take one step past half court and he's in range. You guys are in for it. If you thought I was tough, just wait. I'm only half Irish. The guy coming in is a hundred percent Irish."

11

HALFTIME

Jack

Junior Dennis Olexa spotted a stranger on the school grounds heading for the entrance to Saint Gabriel's. He remembers approaching the man and asking, "Are you the new basketball coach?" A quick glance was all Olexa got for an answer. It was an odd introduction for the two who would become mentor and protégé during their days at Saint Gabriel's and for the time left to them afterward.

Months earlier on June 29, 1966, the headline on the sports page of the *Standard Speaker* proclaimed that Willie Mays had clouted his 523rd career home run. Underneath the headline was a photo that showed a grinning Father Deviney shaking hands with a young man in a striped shirt with a smile that rivaled the priest's and was carried on a face that reflected a map of Ireland. The photo's caption read "Welcome to St. Gabriel's." The man with Deviney was Jack Cryan, who had been named the new head basketball coach of the defending state champions.

Cryan, like Phelps, was a graduate of Rider College. The new coach had quite a resume as a player. He had graduated as the leading scorer in Rider's history. In his senior year he had led the nation in accuracy from the foul line where he had converted 182 of 198 attempts. Cryan had been named to the United Press International Little All-American basketball team. The new coach was a Trenton, New Jersey, native who had played four sports while attending Notre Dame High School in that city. In addition to basketball, he had played baseball, soccer, and earned a spot on the track team. In his senior year he was named to New Jersey's All-State basketball team. At Rider he cut back to two sports—basketball and soccer. He suffered a broken back in a soccer game that caused him to miss a full year of college. When he returned to school he concentrated on basketball. Like his predecessor, Saint Gabriel's would be his first head coaching job.

When Father Deviney hired Cryan, the new coach was already playing professional soccer in New York and had been drafted by the Allentown Jets of the Eastern Professional Basketball League. Cryan had degrees in history and English, and in addition to taking over the physical education program at Saint Gabriel's, he was slated to teach freshman English.

There is little doubt Phelps had a hand in bringing Cryan to Hazleton. He had recommended his fellow Rider alumnus to Father Deviney. Phelps, according to some, also told Cryan about the positives the small Catholic school had to offer, praising the talent returning to the team and pointing out it was a place where he could immediately compete for a state title. Cryan had other coaching offers that would have kept him closer to home, but in the end it may have been the success that Phelps had experienced at Saint Gabriel's that lured him to the coal region to begin his coaching career. One would guess he might have been told about Paul Hoffman as well. He would soon discover a diamond in the rough in the aforementioned Dennis Olexa.

In August of 1966 Jack Cryan moved with his wife Carol and his two-month-old son John into the same house that Phelps had rented during his short stay in Hazleton. That same month he joined Phelps and Paul Hoffman at the Camp St. Andrew basketball camp in Tunkhannock. The trio were captured in a photo that appeared in the Hazleton paper. Cryan stands in the middle shaking hands with a grinning Phelps, who is described as giving the new coach some advice. Hoffman stands to Cryan's left holding a basketball and wearing a Saint Gabriel's tee shirt. A short month later Cryan started his new job, becoming Saint Gabriel's third head coach in as many years.

The new coach was just out of college and twenty-three years old when he arrived in Hazleton. He was shorter than many of his players, standing at five foot eight. A stranger seeing him in the halls might have mistaken him for a student. A wisp of brown hair would drop across his forehead waiting to be occasionally brushed back as he went about his business.

When he wasn't on or near a basketball court, it wasn't unusual to see a broad grin race across his distinctly Irish features. He seemed to enjoy being around the students, and he got to know quite a few of them personally.

Cryan continued the optional workouts started by Phelps that began in September and seemed to attract the boys who would make up the varsity basketball team. The runs to and around the parish cemetery persisted as the school body came to know their new coach. The common description that echoed through the halls, started undoubtedly by some of the boys participating in the after school runs, was that the fiery new coach was tough. To this day, that is the way many remember him. Dennis Olexa says Cryan had to be "the toughest high school coach in the country." Paul Hoffman recalls a few practices where some players exited "bloodied." John Goryl, a sophomore at the time, says he has never seen a "tougher coach." It was clear that Phelps hadn't been kidding when he said that Saint Gabriel's was getting a 100 percent Irishman.

That very September another new head coach in Pennsylvania made his debut. On September 17, 1966, Penn State defeated Maryland 15-7 in a football game played at State College. The Penn State defense recorded three safeties in the contest that marked Joe Paterno's first victory as a head coach. As it would turn out, Cryan would have a more successful initial season debut than JoePa, who finished with a record of 5-5.

Saint Gabriel's fans received welcome news that month when the PIAA ruled Paul Hoffman had two years of eligibility remaining. Hoffman had played on the varsity team at Hoban Heights when he was in the eighth grade. The ruling on Hoffman's eligibility noted that when Hoffman was in eighth grade, schools with small enrollments were permitted to play younger students in varsity contests. Though the rule had since been changed, it was not retroactive. The news article making the announcement noted that after two seasons at Saint Gabriel's, Hoffman had scored 955 career points and was on pace to set a regional scoring record. A few years down the road, the PIAA would make another eligibility ruling that would affect Saint Gabriel's basketball fortunes.

Whether or not Cryan could coach was yet to be seen, but those who had seen him work out in the school's small gym were unanimous in reporting that he sure could play. His shooting range extended beyond what anyone had ever seen locally. Just as Phelps had described, Cryan could fire jump shots from just past the half court line in the small gym and the basketball, more often than not, hit nothing but net. The new coach went to either his right or left with ease and was both fast with his feet and quick with his hands. Dennis Olexa recalled Cryan as being "the best player I had ever seen in person." Mike Heffernan echoed those remarks, adding that "we had never really seen anyone like him."

The student body was anxious for the basketball season to begin. Saint Gabriel's would be defending a state championship, but an Anthracite League title remained the goal. Paul Hoffman was now a junior and already considered the outstanding player in the region. The word was that Coach Cryan was spending considerable time working with the two big men, Tom Sock and Bill Ferry, building on the foundation that Phelps had laid. Dennis Olexa, who would start as the point guard on Cryan's first team, remembers that the new coach kept Sock and Ferry after practice in order to work with them individually. He also remembers that Cryan took an interest in him, making him work on using his weak hand and learning to go to his left. Cryan's work with Olexa didn't go unnoticed; Mike Heffernan's opinion is that it was Cryan who turned Olexa into an outstanding basketball player. Bruce Ellis takes it further, saying Olexa wanted to turn himself into a player like Jack Cryan and that he patterned his whole game after Cryan's example. Olexa himself credits his older brother Eddie with getting him started with basketball but is quick to point out that he never would have become the player he did had Jack Cryan not arrived on the scene.

On November 1st when legal practices began the players noticed other changes. Practices were well planned and drills replaced scrimmages. The new coach identified any weaknesses in his players' game and spent time working on those areas. Then there were the gimmicks the coach utilized in his quest for overall team improvement. According to Heffernan, at one practice Cryan had the players wear snow gloves as he worked on ball security with the team. Conditioning was also emphasized, and there was no time to rest during Cryan's practices. One thing the new coach was certain of: he was going to send a team onto the local courts that would not be worn down. Unless, of course, he was the one to do the wearing down.

Don Barnes, as usual, offered his early take on the coming basketball season in his sports column. He predicted another tight Anthracite League race with Weatherly and Saint Gabriel's, led by the "incomparable" Paul Hoffman, as the preseason title favorites. He noted West Hazleton would be bolstered by the addition of Dennis Mummey, and Jim Thorpe would be a contender as well. The sportswriter pointed to Freeland, Marian Catholic, and MMI as dark horse candidates. At Hazleton High Coach Fran Libonati welcomed over sixty candidates vying for a spot on his team, and the coach expected about twelve more boys to join the tryouts once the football season concluded. Once again the number of potential players the Hazleton coach had to choose from was about equal to the number of boys enrolled in the high school at Saint Gabriel's.

There was news from West Hazleton prior to the start of the season. The school announced that the Wildcats would play their home games in the gym located in the new Our Lady of Grace Parochial School. The new gym could hold twice as many people as the gym in the West Hazleton High School. The general feeling was that while the move was great for spectators, the Cats were giving up what had historically been a significant home court advantage. Overall the move was applauded as being good for both the players and the fans. With the change, West Hazleton became the fourth local high school—joining Hazleton, Saint Gabriel's, and Freeland—that had decided to move their home games out of the gym located in their high school building.

Shortly after Jack Cryan made his pro basketball debut in mid-November by scoring fifteen points in the Eastern Professional League, Ray Saul wrote his preseason preview on the '67 G-Men. He pulled no punches, saying that Paul Hoffman was to Saint Gabriel's what Jerry West was to the Los Angeles Lakers. It was his opinion that the G-Men were a title threat only because of the presence of the talented junior.

The Hazleton sportswriter, noting the losses of Pete and Ed O'Donnell as well as that of Ray McBrearty, wrote that the absence of that kind of talent would weigh heavy on any team. The only other starter to return with Hoffman was Tony Joe Barletta, who had averaged just over seven points a game on last year's state championship squad. The team would utilize a pair of six-foot-five seniors, Sock and Ferry, who would give the G-Men the tallest team they had ever sent onto a court. Saul stressed that the two had seen little varsity action, and most of that had been in mop-up duty. Saul saw Coach Cryan using senior Jimmy Rondash and junior Dennis Olexa as his outside threats. He said that the new coach hoped to develop depth off the bench using juniors Rocco Fallabel and Mike Heffernan. In his view the eight sophomores up from the freshman team would see their primary action in JV contests. The one sophomore he mentioned as possibly contributing during the varsity games was John Darraugh, whose "ability to hit from the wing has caught Cryan's eye." He noted that Cryan was new to the area and wasn't making any predictions, but Saul himself saw another year of exciting basketball for followers of the G-Men. The veteran sportswriter's prediction turned out to be right on the mark.

For three straight years Weatherly had held the league championship in its hands only to have it slip through its grasp in playoff games. The Wreckers would also have a new coach in Bill Knepper, who was replacing Skip Ebling. Knepper was inheriting a rangy and talented team led by Henry Panckeri, who at six foot two was expected to be one of the region's stars. He would be joined inside by two other six-foot-three seniors, Charles Potter and Dick Ritter, both of whom had seen plenty of varsity action in the previous season. The new Weatherly coach described his team as "hungry" and pinpointed height and experience as strengths and overall speed as a weakness. There was no doubt he expected this team to continue the tradition of contending for the league title and hopefully performing better than the three previous squads should a playoff become necessary.

Jim Thorpe was entering the new season as the defending league and PIAA Class C eastern champions. Gone from that championship squad were Joe Morgan, Bobby Brown, and Keith Miller. Coach Phil Radar candidly admitted that while his team couldn't be called preseason favorites, the Olympians still had the talent to challenge every team in the league on any given night. Though Thorpe would once again put a small club on the floor, they would have a six-foot-three junior named Clem McGinley, who would be expected to carry the load underneath. In addition, Radar was counting on Dennis Balliet to be the chief offensive threat and noted that overall team defense would be a key to his team's fortunes.

There was always West Hazleton. The Wildcats were deter-mined to regain the title they had lost to Jim Thorpe after win-ning five league championships in a row. Coach Ron Gatski's club didn't have a player taller than six foot two but were bol-stered by the addition of Dennis Mummey, who had transferred to West Hazleton after his high school in Black Creek closed its doors. Mummey had averaged twenty-three points a game in the previous season as a junior and was expected to jump-start the West Hazleton offense. Gatski's squad would return some homegrown talent as well with senior Jim Platukis and junior Dennis Karmonick expected to make solid contributions. The Wildcats expected to have deep bench strength to rest their starters when needed. Coach Gatski, perhaps remembering the two wins against the G-Men a year ago, named Weatherly and Jim Thorpe as the prime competition for the '67 title. One thing was certain: the West Hazleton coach was confident his team was going to have a voice in crowning the league champion.

Gatski's slight didn't go unnoticed in the halls of the small parochial school on South Wyoming Street, but addressing his oversight would have to wait until mid-January. In the mean-time, Coach Cryan was readying his G-Men to meet South Scranton Central Catholic in what would be the region's first high school basketball game on the day after Thanksgiving.

12

SECOND-HALF TIP-OFF

BEST EVER?

Saint Joe's gym, as had become the rule, drew a large number of fans to Saint Gabriel's first basketball game of the season. On this night it was the only game in town, and as such those in attendance included local coaches of future opponents like Hazleton High's Fran Libonati and MMI's Dave Shafer. South Scranton Central Catholic was the opponent in the 1967 opener, and their strategy was evident from the opening tip: stop Paul Hoffman. As would be the norm for much of the last two years of his career, Hoffman was double- and sometimes triple-teamed throughout the game. Gimmick defenses seldom bothered Hoffman, especially those designed to slow him down. In addition to his many other talents, he was a superb passer. He knew that when he was facing extra defensive pressure it generally meant someone else was open, and Hoffman was more than adept at finding that open man. In short, just by being on the court he made his teammates better by providing them with opportunities that would not have been available in his absence.

During the first quarter Hoffman scored eight points despite the attention he was getting. After eight minutes the G-Men were up 14-9 against the larger school from Scranton. From that point the game was dead even, and after three quarters Saint Gabriel's led by just four points. When the boys from Scranton scored the first four points in the final eight minutes, the two teams were tied at forty with a little less than five minutes to play. Coach Cryan called a time-out. Whatever was said in the huddle ignited a fire under the home team as the G-Men ran off fourteen straight points to seal a win in their opener by a final score of 54-40.

Hoffman scored eighteen for the winners, and the only other Saint Gabriel's player to hit doubles was Tom Sock, who scored eleven. Ray Saul noted that although Saint Gabriel's had turned in a strong defensive performance at this early stage of the season, this team didn't match the quality of the play exhibited by last year's state champions.

The Anthracite League had shrunk since the previous season. With the loss of Saint Ann's and Foster and Hazle Township and the addition of another school—Immaculate Heart—the Anthracite League now consisted of eight teams. As a result, Father Deviney had scheduled eight exhibition games to prep the Saints for league play. In another scheduling wrinkle, the G-Men would only meet Hazleton High once. This year's game was scheduled for December 30th.

With his team not scheduled to play again for a week, Coach Cryan used the opportunity to watch two future opponents in action. He witnessed Marian Catholic win their opener and then traveled to Berwick to watch West Hazleton in their initial contest. Even with the addition of Dennis Mummey, who led the Wildcats in scoring with fifteen, Berwick dominated the game, winning 73-57. West Hazleton couldn't deal with the much taller Bulldogs. With height of his own that he could place on the court, Cryan likely tucked that information away for future reference. Still, it was the first game of the year and most observers agreed that the Wildcats would gel as the season progressed. It seemed like they always did.

On December 2nd Weatherly opened their 1967 campaign with a 72-58 win over Northampton. The Wreckers made just 29 percent of their field goal attempts but totally controlled the boards in racking up their first win. Henry Panckeri scored twenty-five points and gathered in twenty-two rebounds for Weatherly. Panckeri was a superb player who had the ability to hit from distance or take the ball to the hole. Meanwhile, Jim Thorpe needed an overtime period to squeeze by Lehighton 74-73 on the loser's home court. Dennis Balliet, playing as predicted, scored twenty-nine for the Olympians. On the same night, the G-Men won for the second time, taking down Crestwood 79-46. The Saints showed marked improvement on the offensive side of the ball and continued to play great defense.

Paul Hoffman's twenty-two points left him five points shy of the 1,000 mark, and Dennis Olexa made his presence felt scoring twenty. Cryan knew that it was important that he get players other than Hoffman involved offensively if the Saints were going to compete for a league title, so he must have been pleased with Olexa's performance.

After getting off to a great start, Weatherly was upset by Lehighton 71-59. The loss was a stunning one for the Wreckers, who went into the game as solid favorites. Jim Thorpe, who had previously beaten Lehighton, moved to 2-0 by winning 90-78 over Slatington. The Olympians were making it known that they wouldn't relinquish their league title without a fight.

Saint Gabriel's took to the court for their third game, this time against Shenandoah Catholic, without Hoffman. The G-Men's ace was ill and didn't suit up for the game. As it turned out, it didn't matter. After a sluggish first half, the Saints erupted in the third and fourth quarters and won going away 93-54. For the first time in his career, Tony Joe Barletta took scoring honors with twenty-three, and Tom Sock was right behind him with twenty-two. Dennis Olexa scored eleven and by now had firmly established himself as the team's floor general. The easy win, coming with their star on the bench, opened some eyes around the region. It wasn't just the Saint Gabriel's student body and loyal fans who began talking about what this new coach was putting together. The G-Men were on their way to creating a bit of a buzz around town. The majority of serious fans were withholding judgment until the Hazleton game.

Hazleton High opened its season on December 9th and won easily over Palmerston, 88-72. The rangy Darrell Farkus led the Mounts with nineteen points, and Coach Libonati substituted freely throughout the game using eleven players. Tony Kinney made his varsity debut and scored the first six points in what would be an illustrious and record-setting career for the Mountaineers.

The G-Men continued to dominate their exhibition schedule when they traveled to Crestwood and handled the home team easily 84-44. The game marked the return of Hoffman to the lineup and he responded by scoring twenty-five, including the 1,000th point of his career. Tom Sock continued to make his presence felt, hitting for eighteen, while the Saints' floor leader Dennis Olexa added ten. Saint Gabriel's was now 4-0 and the wins were coming easy. While their offense had been potent, they also showed themselves to be a team that was going to be very tough to score against. Coach Cryan stressed defense just as much as his predecessor. Mike Heffernan remembers, "We never wanted to let an opponent score fifty points because when we did we knew we'd be doing a ton of running in our next practice."

They must have done some running after their next game in which they ran their record to 5-0 by beating Wilkes-Barre Saint Mary's 89-64. Tony Joe Barletta, who had been mainly seen as a role player, led the Saints in scoring by netting a career-high thirty-three points. Paul Hoffman, though his playing time was limited by foul trouble, scored twenty-four. The Wilkes-Barre team, which boasted a roster that included ten players topping six feet, was no match for Saint Gabriel's. With only two more exhibitions scheduled against teams they had already defeated soundly, Saint Gabriel's was viewed as a cinch to enter the Hazleton game with a record of 7-0. The anticipation for the Hazleton game was growing by the day among the Saints' fervent fan base.

Meanwhile, West Hazleton had bounced back from their opening night loss to win four straight. Transfer Dennis Mummey scored twenty-one in leading the Wildcats to an easy victory over Shamokin 75-58 in a game played on the Cats' new home court. Don Barnes proclaimed West Hazleton was showing every indication of reclaiming the Anthracite League title they had surrendered a year ago. As Ray Saul surveyed the coming league fight, he said it wasn't possible to pick a clear-cut favorite from Jim Thorpe, Saint Gabriel's, Weatherly, and West Hazleton. Once again, the league was seen as highly competitive.

The two other local high schools, Hazleton and West Hazleton, were scheduled to meet prior to the Hazleton playing the G-Men. Though West Hazleton was the home team, they had agreed to play the game at St. Joe's because; their new home at Mother of Grace didn't match the number of spectators that could fill St. Joe's. Hazleton was 3-1 heading into the game. The Mountaineers only loss had come by a narrow margin to the East Penn League power Bethlehem. West Hazleton was 5-2 and had showed steady improvement since their opening loss. Hazleton was considered a slight favorite in the contest scheduled for December 27th, and a huge crowd was expected.

Almost 1,700 fans showed up to witness the struggle between the two local rivals. The entire Saint Gabriel's team and Coach Cryan were on hand to scout the two teams they would meet in the near future. West Hazleton, led by Dennis Mummey, jumped to a 21-12 lead after eight minutes. In the second quarter Hazleton fought back, paced by their slick point guard Joe Marnell and the dependable Phil Andras. In the second eight minutes, the Mounts outscored the Wildcats twenty-five to fifteen to take a 37-36 lead into the halftime locker room. Darrell Farkus, who scored twenty-one in the game for Hazleton, started the second half by hitting an inside jumper. Hazleton never looked back, winning by a score of 89-75. Tony Kinney, who was seeing more and more action, scored nine points and pulled down ten rebounds. This was a good Hazleton squad that was getting better game by game. With a win over Saint Gabriel's, the Mountaineers could claim the unofficial city title.

The following night the G-Men prepped for their own encounter two days hence with the Mounts by crushing Wilkes-Barre Saint Nicholas 80-38. Hoffman scored thirty points despite playing just a little over two quarters. The only other Saint Gabriel's player to hit double figures was Sock, but seven other G-Men scored in the one-sided contest. The win left the Saints at 7-0, the only undefeated team in the region. Sports editor Ray Saul saw that all ending against Hazleton, whom he considered "a little too tough for the G-Men." Coach Cryan wasn't making any predictions, saying only, "We'll be there, I hope." The local paper's statistician Joe Kline, a big fan of the G-Men, boldly predicted "the G-Men by ten." Whatever the outcome, all agreed the game would draw an enormous crowd. As a matter of fact, Saul predicted it would be the biggest crowd of the year. The sports editor noted that the newspaper was receiving calls from out of town inquiring if tickets were still available and could be purchased at the door.

On the day of the game, the atmosphere in the halls of Saint Gabriel's High School was electric. Between classes students made their plans on getting to the contest. Many were convinced that this was the year that Hazleton could be defeated and it wouldn't be considered an upset. More than a few minds were wandering in classes that day; the good sisters had all they could handle in keeping their students on task. It goes without saying that they usually found a way to get that job done. Meanwhile, the Hazleton players were hungry for a win that would give them the unofficial city championship, but there was more at stake than that. As Tony Kinney recalled, "We knew that Saint Gabriel's had just won a state title. We also knew their players well and had competed against some of them since junior high. This was a big game; we wanted to knock them off their perch."

On the last day of 1966, the front page of the *Hazleton Standard Speaker* carried news of Britain calling for a meeting between the United States and North and South Vietnam to discuss ways of ending the war in that far off country. At the same time, fighting had broken out in Vietnam as the North Vietnamese launched a series of attacks on the eve of a New Year's truce. Scientists had also declared that a moon booster rocket had passed a test and was ready to fly. There is little doubt that most area basketball fans saved these stories for later in their rush to read the coverage of the game that had taken place the night before.

Saint Joseph's gym was filled to capacity by the time the JV game concluded with Hazleton breaking the junior G-Men's sixteen-game winning streak by a score of 58-41. Hazleton High's band was on hand, and the music added to the cheers of the spectators as the two teams took the court to warm-up. The Saint Gabriel's students were on their feet with many of them working their voices to the max. The atmosphere inside Saint Joe's had reached fever pitch before the opening tip-off.

From the start, both teams employed gimmick defenses. Hazleton played a box-in-one and concentrated on stopping Paul Hoffman. Saint Gabriel's opened with a full-court press, which they utilized throughout the game. The G-Men would settle into a triangle-and-two once Hazleton successfully worked the ball past the half court line. After one quarter, Hazleton had a 20-19 lead, and while they had successfully limited Hoffman's chances, the Saints' two guards Dennis Olexa and Jimmy Rondash picked up the scoring slack. The G-Men were finding other ways to score when Hoffman was held in check.

In the second quarter the Saint Gabriel's press forced a number of turnovers that were converted into easy scores. Hoffman picked up two fouls and was playing cautiously but still scored seven points in the period. At half Coach Cryan's team headed to the locker room with a 37-30 lead. The first half had served as a coming out party for Dennis Olexa. Not only had he scored nine points, but defensively he was everywhere, playing particularly well when defending Hazleton's backcourt ace Joe Marnell.

The intermission saw the schools' cheerleading squads take turns rousing their respective fans. The Hazleton band entertained. Some of the fans headed to the school cafeteria in search of refreshments, while others headed to the doors to smoke a cigarette before play resumed.

Early in the third period Hoffman picked up two more personal fouls and the Saints' ace headed to the bench for the remainder of the period. Tom Sock came alive and scored seven of his ten points. Finally, the Mountaineers took advantage of Hoffman's absence and scored the final seven points of the period to knot the score at forty-eight with eight minutes to play. There was a noticeable tension in the air as both teams gathered around their coaches to get their instructions prior to the final quarter.

Though the score was tied, this game had a different feeling than past Hazleton-Saint Gabriel's contests. The G-Men seemed controlled and confident, and it was the Mountaineer players who seemed to be feeling the pressure, as evidenced by the fact they turned the ball over more than twenty times in the face of Cryan's pressing defense. Hazleton took its only lead in the second half when Kinney—who along with Farkus led the Mounts in scoring with thirteen—hit the first goal of the final quarter. But Hoffman was now back on the court, and with his newfound sidekick Dennis Olexa lending a hand, the little parochial school took a 62-54 lead. Hazleton rallied to pull to within two at 62-60 with just over two and a half minutes to go, but then Olexa scored. Like his older brother Eddie, Dennis was determined to beat the Mounts.

After Hazleton made two fouls, Hoffman drove to the bucket, hit a field goal, and was fouled. He calmly sank the free throw. After a Hazleton miss, he grabbed the rebound and hit Olexa with a nifty pass that led to another Saints' score and a 69-62 lead with under a minute to go. The Saint Gabriel's student body, which had been on its feet through much of the game and the entire fourth quarter, was now in a frenzy. Hazleton scored at the buzzer to make the final 69-64.

Students rushed across the gym floor to reach Coach Cryan, who found himself on their shoulders and being carried to the locker room. Those who remained in the stands cheered and embraced. When Ray Saul entered the Saints' locker room, he was greeted with chants of "We're number one," and he wrote that Saint Gabriel's certainly was until someone could prove otherwise. Dennis Olexa, like his brother Eddie, had led the G-Men to a victory against archrival Hazleton, scoring nineteen. Hoffman was a point behind, and both Rondash and Sock had hit doubles for Saint Gabriel's. The win ranked as one of the greatest in the small school's history and set the stage for the beginning of Anthracite League play and what many hoped would be a run at the league crown.

Tony Kinney remembers a particular moment in the game very clearly and with more than a touch of modesty. "We [Hazleton] were at the line shooting a one-and-one. Hoffman and I were next to each other with Paul on the inside when the first shot went up. It missed and I went up over Paul and tapped it in. To this day I'm convinced that Paul must have thought it was a two-shot foul. I'll never forget it because I think it was the only time I ever scored going over Paul."

The new year brought with it great hopes for the Saint Gabriel's team that had gone through its exhibition schedule unscathed. Saint Gabriel's students were opening talking about an undefeated season, an Anthracite League title, and successfully defending a state championship. The first-year coach seemed to have the team running on all cylinders. Olexa was improving steadily as the year went on. Sock was a force underneath, and Ferry was adding clout off the bench. Barletta continued to make solid contributions game after game. Heffernan, Rondash, and Rocco Fallabel were contributing as well. Then there was Hoffman, who as a junior was certainly the top player in the region and, truth be told, one of the top players in the state. Even without Hoffman, this team had shown it could compete with anyone and beat many—with him they were a powerhouse. People were beginning to wonder if this was the best Saint Gabriel's basketball team in the history of the school.

The win over Hazleton definitely impressed Ray Saul, who picked the G-Men to win the first-half championship as the thirtieth Anthracite League season got underway. Saul picked West Hazleton to finish second followed by Weatherly, Jim Thorpe, Freeland, MMI, Marian, and the league's newest member, Immaculate Heart.

The night before Saint Gabriel's would open its league season at home against Jim Thorpe, the Saints' junior high team took on Shamokin Lourdes in a high-scoring affair in the little gym on Wyoming Street. Down by thirteen at half, the young Saint Gabriel's squad that included some talented eight graders fought back but fell short by a score of 95-91. Four future G-Men scored in doubles with Joe Farley netting thirty-four, Tommy Boyle scoring twenty-eight, and Jerry Fallabel and Emil Polchin hitting for sixteen and twelve respectively. All four would make important contributions during Saint Gabriel's final season of play in 1970.

More than 1,500 people were in the stands when referee Ray Scarcella tossed the ball up for the tip to start Anthracite League action for the undefeated G-Men. The Saints were without Tom Sock, who had torn tendons in his ankle during a practice session the night before. Bill Ferry started in place of Sock, who was expected to miss one or two weeks of action.

Even without Sock, the Saints had total control of the boards, and it was only the terrific shooting of Dennis Balliet that kept Jim Thorpe in the game. Balliet was so hot that the G-Men employed a box-in-one defense in the second half to slow the Olympian sharpshooter down. He still scored twenty-one in the contest, but it wasn't nearly enough as the Saints came away with a 76-61 win, their fifteenth in a row stretching back to the previous season. Once again Hoffman led the G-Men scoring twenty-eight while Olexa and Ferry both hit for fourteen. Barletta also scored in double figures with eleven.

The scheduling gods had the G-Men traveling to Weatherly in three days for a Friday night game and then returning to Saint Joe's to take on West Hazleton the following Tuesday. Don Barnes in his write-up of the game predicted that if the Saints won the next two, they could "almost walk to the first-half championship." Ray Saul gave West Hazleton the best shot of slowing down what Coach Cryan was turning into a G-Men juggernaut.

Hazleton High was also off to a strong start in the East Penn League. After beating Allentown Central Catholic 108-73, the Mounts were 3-1 and in second place. Tony Kinney, who was earning more and more playing time as a sophomore, scored twelve in the game. Hazleton's success was making the Saint Gabriel's win over the Mountaineers all the more impressive. It seemed that Coach Phelps's comments the year before relative to the quality of play in the Anthracite League closing the gap on its East Penn counterparts didn't seem so farfetched. The gap in some cases was closing at a quicker rate than Phelps had predicted.

The respect for the G-Men was more than apparent when the *Standard Speaker* installed the G-Men as a "firm favorite" to travel to Weatherly and beat the Wreckers on their home court. This prediction came in spite of Weatherly's talent and size, as well as the fact the Saints would be without the services of Sock. In the view of the local paper both squads were sending teams onto the floor that were stronger than the outstanding units who met the year before.

The game turned out to be a classic. The next day Don Barnes wrote that Weatherly star Henry Panckeri "excelled in every phase of the game last night, rebounding, offense, ball-handling, defense and general floor play. His and Hoffman's were probably the greatest performances ever seen in one game at Weatherly." Panckeri was unstoppable in the first half, scoring nineteen points and leading Weatherly to a 40-34 lead at intermission.

Coach Cryan decided to go with a gimmick defense in the final two quarters. He instructed Hoffman and Barletta to play man-to-man on Panckeri and Charlie Potter while he put his other three players in a one-one-one zone defense. Weatherly stayed hot in the third quarter, but the Saints narrowed the deficit to just two points at 61-59 with eight minutes to play. With Hoffman holding Panckeri to eight second-half points while he was scoring twenty-two in the same time frame, the G-Men finished their second-half rally winning by a score of 82-77.

Tony Joe Barletta sealed the victory with a field goal in the waning seconds. Ferry once again filled in ably for Sock, scoring seventeen points while the ever dependable Olexa added twelve while running the Saints' offense. Hoffman led all scorers in the game with thirty-one, and when he scored his thirteenth point, he became the leading scorer in Saint Gabriel's history, passing Pete O'Donnell who had held that spot for under a year. The game marked the tenth straight G-Men win of the current season and the sixteenth straight dating back to the previous year.

Meanwhile, West Hazleton, led by Mummey's thirty-seven points, had beaten MMI by a 77-70 margin, setting up next week's meeting between the two lone undefeated teams in league play. Saint Gabriel's students and fans were now anxiously awaiting the Wildcats' visit to Saint Joe's. Most were sure that this was the year the players wearing the purple and white would make the Cats pay for those heartbreaking past defeats. There remained a minority of G-Men followers who couldn't shake the feeling the West Hazleton always found a way to play at the top of their game against Saint Gabriel's. After thirteen straight losses to the Cats, they may have had the clearer heads.

The truth be told, West Hazleton hadn't managed to throw a gypsy curse or hex at the G-Men. That the Wildcats always seemed to play well against the G-Men had more to do with the importance their players and coaches put on the game. Bill Pavlick, who was the point guard on what may have been the finest team in West Hazleton history, recalls that "the Saint Gabriel's game was more important to us than our games with Hazleton. We played Saint Gabriel's twice. They were our league rivals. The games meant more since winning could decide a league championship."

On the day of the game the Hazleton paper reported that based on their performance to date, Saint Gabriel's was a solid pick to defeat West Hazleton. It sounded a note of caution pointing out history was on the side of the Wildcats and the Anthracite League was known for its upsets. Ray Saul wrote that Father Deviney could expect a big payday as the crowd of paying customers was expected to approach the 2,500 mark that had filled Saint Joe's when the G-Men met Hazleton High.

As Saul predicted, more than two thousand fans were in their seats when the buzzer ended the JV game with the Saints on top by a 63-53 score. The excitement in the crowded gym was palatable as the varsity teams went through their warm-ups. After the National Anthem and the singing of the Saint Gabriel's alma mater, the starters were introduced by Bob Farley. Then both squads huddled around their respective coaches. Coach Cryan had given the job of stopping the Wildcats ace and leading scorer, Mummey, to Jimmy Rondash.

Rondash more than did the job. With Mummey held in check the G-Men sprinted to a 19-12 first quarter lead and by the end of the first half they had extended that margin to 44-28. There was no looking back. The Saints were hitting on all cylinders. Early in the fourth quarter, they had extended their lead to 82-52. The Saint Gabriel's student body was in a frenzy whooping it up in celebration. There would be no West Hazleton players waving towels at them or rushing through the crowd to tear down signs on this night. The final score was 96-72. Coach Cryan had used ten players and nine of them scored. All five starters finished in double figures. Barletta led the way with twenty-four, Hoffman hit for seventeen, and Ferry filling in for Sock scored sixteen. Meanwhile, the two Saint Gabriel guards Olexa and Rondash hit for fourteen and thirteen respectively. Mummey scored four points for West Hazleton on a night that he was only able to attempt four shots.

In the view of Don Barnes, barring a major upset, the win sealed Saint Gabriel's as the first-half league champion. He wrote that the stock in this Saints team was "zooming by the day." Ray Saul shared his fellow sportswriter's view, writing that there should be no stopping Saint Gabriel's in their remaining first-half games. Coach Cryan said he was pleased with his team's offensive performance, but that aside from Jimmy Rondash, the defensive effort was inconsistent.

On Friday, January 13th, the G-Men traveled to Freeland to take on the Whippets at the Freeland Y. Saint Gabriel's was the heavy favorite in the game. On the same day, Adam Sieminski from Berwick was named the new football coach at Hazleton High. In less than two years Sieminski would play an influential role the final years of basketball at the parochial school.

After winning four straight big games, the Saints were due for a letdown and Freeland was a historically difficult place to play. But the game marked the return of Tom Sock to the Saint Gabriel's lineup, and the big man made his presence felt scoring twenty-one in the 57-49 win. The game was close from the start, and Freeland used a deliberate slowdown offense and a collapsing defense to keep it that way. Hoffman was held to fourteen, and the only other Saints player to hit doubles was Barletta, who netted eleven very important points. Coach Cryan could only say that a win was a win, and though ugly, this was a big one that equaled the record set by the 1947 G-Men, who had won eighteen in a row on their way to the school's first Anthracite League title.

While the Saints' varsity was setting records, the school's junior high team coached by Vince Gallagher was showing they could put points on the board. The night before the Freeland game, Coach Gallagher's club ran roughshod over Hazle Township 94-66. Joe Farley scored twenty-eight for the winners and eighth grader Tommy Boyle added thirteen. Emil Polchin and Jerry Fallabel also scored in the easy win.

Marian Catholic would be the foe to beat as Saint Gabriel's looked to break the record set by the 1947 G-Men, who won their eighteenth straight game by beating McAdoo 44-33 at Saint Gabriel's. Swish Farley led the G-Men to that victory, scoring seventeen while the teams All-Regional center Jerry Moye added seven. Mouse Marinko, currently an assistant pastor at Saint Joseph's parish in the city, scored three for the winners. The record that stood for twenty years was about to fall.

With Swish Farley in the audience, the G-Men set a new school record when they won their nineteenth straight, beating Marian 55-50. The game was much closer than expected, and Don Barnes asked why it had been so close. Answering his own question, the sportswriter pointed to sloppy play by the winners and Marian, which had only fallen to Weatherly by two points, playing up to its potential. The Saints' Rondash missed the game with a back injury, but Heffernan filled in more than adequately, scoring thirteen points. While Hoffman led the team in scoring with fifteen, he played one of his poorer games overall. The road to the first-half title was proving to be tougher than anyone expected after the win against West Hazleton. The closer than expected victories showed that no team was just going to roll over and play dead for the G-Men.

The night after his team set the school record for consecutive wins, Coach Cryan took in a Catholic Youth Organization (CYO) game and watched Saint Joseph's top Most Precious Blood 57-44. An eighth grader named Larry Walko scored twenty-two for the winners and an impression on the first-year coach. In addition to leading his team in scoring, Walko was the fastest player on the court and rebounded well. As Phelps had pursued Tony Kinney, so would Cryan pursue Walko.

Back in Saint Joe's, Saint Gabriel's stretched their winning streak to twenty straight by totally dominating the league's last place team, Immaculate Heart of Fountain Springs, 95-36. The Saints were without two starters in this one as Barletta joined Rondash on the injured list. All five Saint Gabriel's starters scored in double figures with Hoffman bouncing back from his disappointing performance at Marian to lead the way by scoring thirty-two points. The win sealed no worse than a tie for the first-half championship, and that could be clinched with a win at MMI.

Playing in the cramped confines of the MMI gym was never easy, and Coach Dave Shafer was determined to make this night anything but easy for Saint Gabriel's. From the opening tap he had his team playing a controlled deliberate game that had the Preppers on top 7-5 after eight minutes of play. Coach Cryan went with a man-to-man pressure defense in the second quarter to force an upbeat in the game's tempo, and the Saints took a 24-20 lead at half. The third quarter belonged to the Saints. Hoffman was brilliant and Olexa much the same as the G-Men drew away to lead by 45-26 heading into the final quarter.

When the final buzzer sounded, Saints Gabriel's remained undefeated and were crowned first-half Anthracite League champs after beating MMI 63-42. Hoffman had scored more than half of his team's points finishing with thirty-two, but he owed a number of those goals to Olexa, who set him up perfectly with passes that the G-Men's star converted into easy goals. The winning streak had reached twenty-one and many were already conceding that there would be no stopping Saint Gabriel's this season. The G-Men looked like a team that had it all—shooting, speed, height, depth and good coaching. It appeared that an undefeated season and a league championship was not only possible but likely.

The G-Men would open the second half a week later against West Hazleton at Mother of Grace gym. Tickets for the game went on sale at both schools the Friday before the scheduled Tuesday contest. Though West Hazleton was now playing in a larger venue, interested spectators were urged to get their tickets early or risk being turned away at the door. Despite the drubbing the G-Men had laid on the Wildcats in their first meeting, many were predicting that this one was going to be close. In the opinion of the *Standard Speaker* the G-Men had too much firepower for the Wildcats and Saint Gabriel's would have to play poorly to lose. After practice on the day before the game, Bill Ferry, who hailed from West Hazleton, implored his teammates to get this win: "It's the last chance I have to beat those guys."

By the end of the first quarter it appeared that the fans who were hoping for a close contest would be sorely disappointed.

*Richard "Digger" Phelps with the starting five on his 1966 state champi-
onship team. From L to R - Ed O'Donnell, Pete O'Donnell, Paul Hoffman,
Tony Joe Barletta and Ray McBrearty. (Courtesy of the* Hazleton Standard
Speaker*)*

The 1967 Saint Gabriel's state champions. (Courtesy of the Hazleton Standard Speaker*)*

Pete O'Donnell, described as having more moves than the Mayflower Van Lines, becomes the leading scorer in Saint Gabriel's history. (Courtesy of the Hazleton Standard Speaker*)*

The Most Valuable Player on the 1969 team John Darraugh brings the ball upcourt during a key Anthracite League game against MMI. (Courtesy of the Hazleton Standard Speaker*)*

Father Raymond Deviney welcomes new coach Jack Cryan to Saint Gabriel's. (Courtesy of the Hazleton Standard Speaker*)*

Coach Richard "Digger" Phelps with his successor at Saint Gabriel's Jack Cryan and the greatest player in the school's history Paul Hoffman. (Courtesy of the Hazleton Standard Speaker*)*

Jerry Fallabel (wearing the dark uniform) battles for a rebound during the tumultu-
ous 1970 season. (Courtesy of the Hazleton Standard Speaker*)*

Mike Heffernan, who along with Hoffman and Olexa made up Saint Gabriel's big three, scores two of his twenty-five in the 1968 win that gave the G-Men their third consecutive Scranton Diocese championship. (Courtesy of the Hazleton Standard Speaker*)*

Left: The Rev. Edward Haggarty, who made the decisions to empha-size the basketball program at the small parochial school and move the team's games to the spacious Saint Joseph's gym. Right: Francis "Chip" Kender, the Saint Gabriel's coach in the early 1960s whose 1962 team beat Hazleton High for the first time. (Courtesy of the Hazleton Standard Speaker*)*

Paul Hoffman is congratulated after breaking Pete O'Donnell's career scoring record. Pictured with the Saint Gabriel's star from L to R Fa-ther Deviney, William Hoffman (Paul's father), Coach Cryan, Assistant Coach Vince Gallagher and Saint Gabriel's fan and statistician Joe Kline. (Courtesy of the Hazleton Standard Speaker*)*

Saint Gabriel's number one fan Mr. Bill Boyle often worked as hard off the court as the players did on it. (Courtesy of the Hazleton Standard Speaker*)*

Coach Phelps addresses the crowd at the 1966 awards banquet. Seated to the right of the Saint Gabriel's coach is the event's main speaker, the young Army coach Bobby Knight. (Courtesy of the Hazleton Standard Speaker*)*

Dennis Olexa scores at Mother of Grace during the 1968 victory over West Hazleton High School. (Courtesy of the Hazleton Standard Speaker*)*

Scouting Report
Kolb Memorial High School
Masontown, Pa.

Defense: 2-3 zone no pressure, They let you shoot. Rebounds stay in their position. St. Gregory's used a 1-3-1 attack with no movement. Kolb's backmen are slow getting out to corners. If you get by wing man on baseline drive, the middle man will pick you up. This leaves postman on foul line open. Their inside men will foul, if you fake them. Backdoor plays are open also. Box them out. #54 Francgek easy to fake inside. They will react to your first move on offense. They like to block shots - leave their feet on fakes. # 42 Boskovich easy to fake inside

Press: Kolb will use a 1-2-H full court zone press, The pt. man will pressure the ball out of bounds. The middle is weak. They are slow getting back. Drop back to 2-3 zone.

Attack: Georgia Tech (colors will go). Ohio (swing) with baseline drives looking for Paul in middle.

Offense:
Against St. Gregory's 2-1-2 zone, Kolb used a 1-3-1 attack. They will throw a lot of bad crosscourt passes. # 22 Fugozzotto will play the high pt. or left wing, will go to his rt only. He doesn't like pressure. Will shoot rjs key or wing areas. They look for Boskovich # 4 in key post area. He will drive or shoot from Post. His favorite move is rjs foul line. Kolb will play a slow down against zone - looking for good shot.

Page 1 of the scouting report that was prepared by Richard "Digger" Phelps prior to meeting and defeating Kolb Memorial High School in the 1966 PCIAA Class C State Championship.

(2)

Offense Cont:

Against m-m, they set up 2-3 with Boskovich. They freelance a lot. They will work give-go's with Boskovich Say on their wing men (54,14) Boskovich will take you 1-1 when he gets ball in post area. Their total offense doesn't have many variations. Pressure then overplay and box off. St. Gregory's didn't box off and Kolb did a lot of scoring on offensive rebounds. Kolb can't handle the ball well or dribble well. <u>Pressure will hurt them.</u> They will fast break when they have it

<u>Press Offense</u>: They get the ball into Fucoggotto (22). He will try to drive all the way up the right side or look for Boskovich breaking into the middle. Kolb will try to score in their press offense.

Individuals:

Paul's man
3 or
23pts
per

38pts
St G.

#42 Frank Boskovich 6'1" - Plays high post in zone and m-m offense. Will shoot r.j's in high post foul line area will drive either side from high post, but will always shoot with his rt. hand. Good Rebounder, <u>must box him out.</u> He will force shots when pressured. He is back middle man on their zone. Easy to fake, reacts to your first move. He likes to get ball high post foul line - turn shoot r.j's Also, he will drive stop, fake, shoot r.j's. keep him off offensive board.

Page 2 of the scouting report.

Individuals Cont: ③

   #22 Sam Fugazzotto 6' Main ballhandler in zone
Ray's   Press. offense. shoots + js Keyor wing. Real slow boat,
man   avg   hothead - He's nothing. Doesn't like pressure. All
       15 pts per   right hand. Will drive from pt or wing stop, rjs
       19 pts   Good foul shooter, offensive Rebounder. Pressures
       5t. G   ball on press (#1 man on pt 1-2-1) Top man on zone
       def. Poor def player - foul trouble.

Pete's   #14 John Pisula 6'2" lean not aggressive shoots
man   avg   left hand js rt corner. goes to boards on
       12 pts per   offense. Floater to either corner in zone off.
       6 pts + G.   Wing man in m-m off. goes away from board on
       off reb' shot.

Tony's   #54 Dan Francgek 6'3" 190 lbs deep man on press
man   slow, will play wing in zone or m-m offense.
       worked give go with post man. rjs; rebounder.

my   #44 Dennis DeNardo 5'10" Guard, dribbles either-hand,
man   slow - no shooter, shoots 2 hand set. Not a scorer,
(Eddie)   will choke under pressure. Top man on zone

   Key: This is not a sound ball club. They are only as
   good as you want them to be. Do your job; you'll
   win. Be aggressive, hustle, box out, run. They can't
   handle the ball under pressure. Fake them; they
   will foul. Use defensive fakes, be tough help each
   other. Do your Best! plus, ...

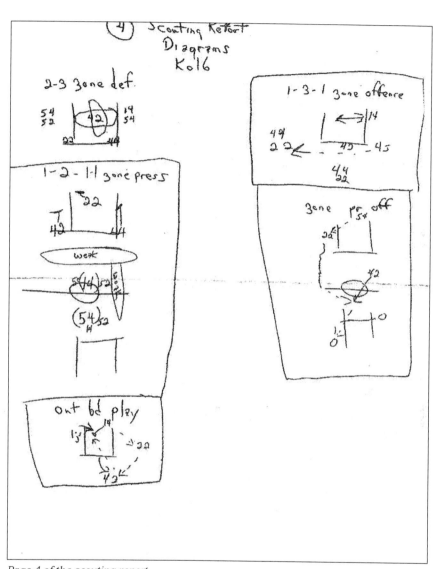

4) Scouting Report
Diagrams
Ko16

2-3 zone def.

1-3-1 zone offense

1-2-1-1 zone press

weak

zone press off

out bd play

The Saints' Larry Walko battles Hazleton High's Ed Parsons for a rebound in 1969. To their right Hazleton star Tony Kinney looks to get in on the action. (Courtesy of the Hazleton Standard Speaker*)*

Just before fans rush the court in a near riot Father Deviney attempts to break up a fight that broke out between Dennis Olexa and Mike Gallagher during a 1968 contest against West Hazleton. (Courtesy of the Hazleton Standard Speaker)

Joe Farley sends the first of his three last minute goals towards the hoop during the Saints "miraculous" 57-56 win over Saint Nicholas of Wilkes Barre in 1970. (Courtesy of the Hazleton Standard Speaker)

John "Swish" Farley connects from the foul line for the 1947 G-Men. This is one of the few surviving photos that show the Saint Gabriel's team in action on the floor located in their high school. In the mid 1950s the team began playing their home games in the spacious gym at Saint Joseph's.

The Rev. Paul Purcell was a popular priest who as Moderator of Athletics administered the Saint Gabriel's basketball program in the early 1960s and established the school's biddy basketball program. (Courtesy of the Hazleton Standard Speaker)

The 1969 Pine Street playground team. First row (L to R) Joe Farley, Jimmy Munley, Larry Walko, Tommy Boyle. Standing Coach Bruce Ellis, Chico Evans, Joe Curry, Jerry Fallabel, Mike DeCosmo, John McGheehan. (Courtesy of Bruce Ellis)

The last high school team to take the court for Saint Gabriel's and the 1970 PCIAA state champions. (The author sits in the front row wearing number 13).(Courtesy of the Hazleton Standard Speaker)

After West Hazleton opened the scoring, the G-Men scored six-teen unanswered points, and after eight minutes of play the score was 22-5. At that point Coach Ron Gatski decided to press the Saints. The boys in the purple and white began to turn the ball over, a feat they would repeat twenty-six times before the game ended. But even with the full-court press taking its toll, Saint Gabriel's still held an eleven-point advantage at the half, 34-23.

In the third quarter, the Cats caught fire and after three periods it was all square at forty-seven. The deadlock didn't re-sult from a Saint Gabriel's collapse but from consistent play displayed by their opponents. West Hazleton had bounced back from their poor start and were playing one of their best games of the season. With the G-Men leading by a score of 53-52, Sock fouled West Hazleton's Tucker Schneider, who converted both tries to give West Hazleton the lead. With just three minutes left, Mummey hit two more fouls, and the Wildcats led by three.

At this point in the game West Hazleton went into a stall. Saint Gabriel's was forced to foul. The underdogs made good on those free throws and when the buzzer sounded, the twenty-one-game win streak had ended by a score of 60-58. The Saint Gabriel's defeat broke the Anthracite League second-half race wide open, and celebrations broke out in both Weatherly and Jim Thorpe when the news of the game reached those vicinities. Coach Ron Gatski was described as jubilant after the game and credited his team for fighting back after the first quarter thrash-ing. If Coach Cryan had a reaction to his first loss, it wasn't shared with anyone but his team. If Bill Ferry was going to get another chance to beat West Hazleton, it was going to be in a playoff game.

Losing to West Hazleton always stung, and this loss hurt more than most. The Saint Gabriel's student body saw the win string end, and to make matters worse the defeat had come at the hands of the Wildcats. The halls of Saint Gabriel's High school were significantly quieter the next day. There was what could only be described as a stunned silence.

Three nights after losing to West Hazleton the Saints squared off against the Freeland team that had given the Saints all they could handle in the first half. But this game was at Saint Joseph's gym where the Saints seldom had an off night. Coach Cryan had put his team through two challenging practices since their lone defeat. He had left little doubt in their minds that losing left a bad taste in his mouth.

Freeland stuck with the G-Men for a half, though they still trailed by a 34-27 score after sixteen minutes of play. In the third quarter the Saints played the kind of basketball they were capable of, outscoring the Whippets by a 39-5 margin in those eight minutes on the way to a convincing 96-47 victory. Ferry had a career night, scoring twenty-nine, while Hoffman added twenty-six. Meanwhile, West Hazleton picked up another big win when they went on the road and beat Jim Thorpe 61-59 in overtime. Weatherly also remained undefeated in second-half play by sneaking past MMI 61-59. Saint Gabriel's fans had been pulling for Thorpe against West Hazleton since the G-Men would face the Olympians in the last game of the regular season, and someone was going to have to knock off the Wildcats if the Saints were going to have any shot at even a tie for the second-half crown.

On Sunday, February 6, 1967, a number of members of the Saint Gabriel's varsity were on hand to watch the Saint Gabriel's junior high squad take on the undefeated Mother of Grace team. The junior G-Men gave the Gracemen quite a scare before fading late in the contest to come out on the short end of a 77-63 score. Ed Parsons scored twenty-nine for the winners, who also got twenty-six from Tom Cherasaro. Joe Farley scored twenty-three for Vince Gallagher's Saint Gabriel's squad in their last game of the season. Though Farley didn't know it at the time, it wasn't yet time for him to hang up his sneakers for the year.

A big February snowstorm shuffled up the Anthracite League schedule in the month's second week. All Tuesday games were cancelled and Saint Gabriel's versus MMI was the only one played the following night. Once again, Coach Dave Shafer decided to play a slowdown offense against the G-Men. It worked for a short while, but by halftime the Saints were leading 31-15. Shafer continued to play a slowdown game in the second half even though the strategy had no chance of success, and while it held down the final score, it didn't change the result. The Saints improved their record to 17-1 by a 57-34 margin.

After the game, Coach Cryan voiced his displeasure about the slowdown tactics used against his talented squad, though he admitted that it afforded some opponents their only chance to keep games close. He also noted that Jimmy Rondash, who had been out of action with a bad back, remained sidelined and that his return to health would make the G-Men even tougher in the remaining games on the schedule.

Rondash wasn't needed when Saint Gabriel's faced Immaculate Heart a few days later. The Golden Falcons were the weakest team in the league, and the Saints made short work of them winning 102-43. While nine G-Men saw action, a hundred of the points came from the five starters. Olexa led the way scoring twenty-seven, while Hoffman, who was now playing a guard position in place of the injured Rondash, scored twenty-five. Barletta and Sock added nineteen each, and Ferry hit for ten. Rocco Fallabel was responsible for the only field goal not scored by the starters.

Elsewhere in the league Weatherly remained undefeated in second half play when they came back from a thirteen-point deficit to beat Jim Thorpe 59-57 in a classic Anthracite League battle. Weatherly's rally was led by Henry Panckeri, who scored eleven points in the last twelve minutes of the game and also came up with several key steals. But the real big news came out of Hometown where the Marian Colts held West Hazleton without a point in the final 4:44 of play while upsetting the Wildcats by a score of 54-51. The West Hazleton loss left Weatherly as the only undefeated team in the second-half race. The Wreckers would face both West Hazleton and Saint Gabriel's the following week, and wins in those contests would set up a playoff with the G-Men for the league title. A G-Men win over Weatherly would vault them back into a tie in the second-half race.

While the Anthracite race had certainly heated up, two fellows associated with Saint Gabriel's found their way back into the local news. Former Saint Gabriel's star Pete O'Donnell was now playing for the Saint Joseph's University freshman team. In the latest game with his team down by one, O'Donnell had secured a rebound, taken the ball the length of the floor and tossed in the winning field goal to beat the University of Penn freshman. Penn, of course, was being coached by O'Donnell's mentor from the previous year, Dick Phelps.

While the Anthracite League race was getting lots of local attention, Hazleton High continued its march toward a good, though not great, championship season. On the night before Weatherly would take on West Hazleton, the Mountaineers defeated Allentown Central Catholic 84-71. Hazleton was led to victory by sophomore Tony Kinney, who scored twenty-nine points. As the year had progressed, the young Kinney had moved into the starting lineup and become a key player for Coach Libonati.

The Weatherly-West Hazleton game had become a must-win for the Wildcats. After stumbling against Marian Catholic, another loss would eliminate then from the league's title chase. Meanwhile, that Marian team would be looking to pull off another upset against Saint Gabriel's on the Saints' home court.

Marian arrived at Saint Joe's very much alive in the race for the second-half crown. If they could pull off another rabbit out of their hat, not only would they knock the G-Men out of the race but they would be right in the thick of it with West Hazleton, Weatherly, or both, depending on how things shook out at Mother of Grace gym. Coach Wink Gallagher's Colts had a lot on the line and they played like it. At half, the two teams were neck and neck as Saint Gabriel's had a very slim 32-31 lead.

Whatever Coach Cryan told his team at halftime worked like magic. In the first four minutes of the third quarter, the G-Men outscored the Colts by a 20-4 margin. After three full periods the score was 59-39 and the contest, which ended 82-59, wasn't in doubt. This was yet another game where all five Saint Gabriel's starters scored in double figures, Hoffman leading the way with twenty-two. Hoffman was still the team's go-to man, but those who had doubted his supporting cast had learned that this Saint Gabriel's team had plenty of other weapons. Jimmy Rondash got some playing time, though he was still bothered by back problems. After the game Saint Gabriel's fans had one thing on their minds. What had happened at Mother of Grace between Weatherly and West Hazleton?

Bill Ferry wasn't going to get his chance at revenge for the Saints' lone defeat of the season. West Hazleton, forced to go without Dennis Mummey, who was down with a virus, was no match for Weatherly. The Wreckers shot a blistering 58 percent from the floor and controlled both boards on the way to a 63-43 victory on the Wildcats' home floor. The Saint Gabriel's-Weatherly game scheduled to be played in three nights was now the biggest game in the region. Weatherly could wrap up the second-half crown with a win. A victory by the G-Men would almost certainly mean that the two teams would meet at least once and maybe twice in a playoff.

On the morning of the Weatherly game Saint Gabriel's fans reading the local paper found that the G-Men had been made the favorite to defeat the Wreckers and move into a tie for the second-half title. Ray Saul noted in his column that Weatherly fans were confident that their team was much improved, and a different club lost a first-half game on their home court to this same Saint Gabriel's squad 82-77. One prediction sure to come true was the game would draw a capacity crowd, and those who wanted a choice seat had better get to Saint Joe's early.

With Saint Gabriel's junior high season in the books, freshman Joe Farley had every intention of getting to the game early. With the JV game set for a 6:30 p.m. start, he walked into the gym at six and no sooner had he ascended the ramp leading to the gym's playing floor he heard, "Joey, come over here." Nobody but Coach Cryan called him Joey. Farley immediately ran across the court to where the coach was waiting. Before the youngster could say a word, Cryan said, "Can you get your parents to drop your sneakers off? I want you to dress with the JV team for the rest of the season." Farley's heart was racing as he formed some sort of affirmative answer then turned and ran to the payphone at the entrance to the gym. As he waited for his parents to arrive, he was thinking, *I wonder if Pete O'Donnell felt like this.*

When the two JV teams took the court to warm-up, a good portion of the more than two thousand fans who would fill Saint Joe's were already in their seats. The Saint Gabriel's student section was filled and reacted to Farley's appearance with cheers several times as the news spread from class section to class section that a freshman was on the floor. The Saint Gabriel's JV team had had quite a season of their own with a record of 17-3 as they prepared for the game against Weatherly.

When the first game began, Farley found a seat on the bench. He certainly didn't expect to see any action—after all, he had never practiced with the JV squad and didn't even know the offense. With about four minutes left and the junior G-Men up by double figures, he heard, "Joey." He quickly rose and took a seat next to Coach Cryan, who said, "Go in for Gallagher."

When Farley took the court, the student section erupted with cheers. A minute later he found himself with the ball as part of a Saint Gabriel's fast break. He heard Cryan yell, "Shoot." He let the ball go from around fifteen feet. The ball hit the front of the rim, bounced to the back, and then rolled in. Based on the sound within the gym, you would have thought it a game winner, and the varsity game at that. The freshman added two foul shots that hit nothing but net before the game ended with Saint Gabriel's winning 74-57. Afterwards, Farley hurried to shower and dress in order not to miss a second of the varsity game. At the top of the steps leading from the locker stood his uncle Francis "Snapper" O'Donnell. He stopped his nephew, smiled, and said, "Good job on those fouls shots—they made up for that cheap field goal."

The varsity game was over after sixteen minutes. The G-Men headed to the locker room with a 39-23 halftime lead. The Saints were playing a tight aggressive defense and were controlling both boards. Weatherly was hurt by the fact that Henry Panckeri was in early foul trouble. He fouled out with less than a minute to play in the third quarter. The Weatherly star scored just two points in the game. Meanwhile, Sock had a great outing for Saint Gabriel's, scoring twenty-five. Barletta added eighteen, and Hoffman hit for fifteen while going over the 1,400-point career total in the second quarter. A Saint Gabriel's win over Jim Thorpe in their final league game would set up a playoff for the second-half championship with this same Weatherly team. The Saints' followers left Saint Joe's confident that they had just watched the Anthracite League champions in action. Weatherly fans were shocked by the 77-60 loss.

Saint Gabriel's still had one more hill to climb taking on Jim Thorpe on the Olympians home floor before they could claim their share of the second-half crown. Few expected the Saints to have any problem at all in picking up their twenty-first win of the season. As it turned out, Thorpe gave the G-Men everything they could handle. After three quarters the G-Men were clinging to a slim 40-38 lead and with two and a half minutes left the score was tied at fifty-one. Hoffman scored to put Saint Gabriel's ahead by two, but the Olympians responded with a goal to draw even yet again. On the next possession, Barletta was fouled, and he went to the line and calmly sank both ends of a one-and-one to make the score 55-53. Thorpe then ran the clock down to twenty seconds when Mike Tessitore attempted a shot that Hoffman deflected into the arms of Sock. Sock passed the ball to Olexa who was immediately fouled by Jim Thorpe's Dennis Balliet. Olexa missed the foul try, but Hoffman tied up Tessitore in a fight for the rebound. The G-Men's star easily controlled the tap, and Saint Gabriel's finished its finest regular season with a record of 21-1.

Hoffman led the Saints scoring with twenty-three, but more importantly he scored eleven in the final eight minutes. Coach Cryan credited his team's defense and Hoffman for the win. Thorpe's Pip Radar had high praise for Hoffman as well and openly wondered if any team would be able to stop him the following year. Don Barnes covering the game for the *Standard Speaker* wrote that both teams had played good basketball and looked like Class A and not Class C teams in the contest.

The following night Weatherly defeated Freeland 74-47 to tie the G-Men for the second-half title. The playoff game was set for two nights later at Marian Catholic. It would be Saint Gabriel's chance to get the albatross off their backs and bring home that elusive league crown.

13

SHOOTING ONE-AND-ONE

THE AGONY AND THE ECSTASY

On the day before the playoff game with Weatherly, Saint Gabriel's held a practice session on the court in Marian High School. As the Saint Gabriel's players were warming up shooting at the multiple baskets in the gym, Marian students, including members of their basketball team, watched from the stands. Freshman Joe Farley along with the other members of the JV squad were still practicing with the varsity though their season was over. Jerry Gallagher, looking at the students in the stands, said, "I hope they get out of here." Farley asked him why they mattered. "Cryan will show off for them if they stay to watch. He'll run us like crazy."

Sure enough, as soon as practice began Coach Cryan lined his team up on one end of the court and told them to start running. They did back and forth on the Marian gym floor while the coach took a seat in the stands and began reading a newspaper glancing up occasionally to make sure no one was loafing. It went for a full half hour before the coach called the workout to a halt. If Cryan's goal was to make an impression on the students who were observing the practice, it worked. Spread by word of mouth, the story of how the practice began found its way onto the sports pages of the local paper serving Allentown. One of the Marian students had told his dad about the start of the practice, and the dad worked for the Allentown paper.

As for the Saint Gabriel's team, there was an air of confidence around them. They had already defeated Weatherly twice and had won the most recent contest handily. The team itself had come a long way. Four players had finished the regular season averaging in double figures. The investment of time Coach Phelps had put into Sock and Ferry certainly paid off for Coach Cryan. They had both developed into offensive inside threats and consistent rebounders. Olexa had improved tremendously at the point guard position under Cryan's guidance. As for Olexa, he loved his coach. Looking back, he says Cryan was "beyond words," adding, "There's not a week in my life that goes by that I don't think about Jack Cryan." As Mike Heffernan recalled, "Cryan made Dennis so good, they were very much alike." Heffernan as well as Rocco Fallabel also provided Coach Cryan with options coming off the bench. The '67 G-Men had grown deeper and more talented as the year progressed.

The Saints' student body and their many fans could only be described as overconfident. They viewed the lone loss to West Hazleton as a fluke that, while making a playoff game necessary, wasn't going to change the ultimate result. The fact the game was being played at Marian was viewed as an advantage. The G-Men, who played their home games at Saint Joe's, were used to spacious surroundings, quite unlike the Wreckers, whose home court was small enough to qualify for the bandbox designation used to describe many of the older gyms in the area. Finally, the G-Men were led by Hoffman, who was widely considered to be the finest ball player in the area. There was a feeling that no matter what happened, Hoffman would find a way to win.

The *Hazleton Standard Speaker* picked Saint Gabriel's as slight favorites on the morning of the game. Despite having dominated the Wreckers in their last encounter, the paper noted that Weatherly star Henry Panckeri was in foul trouble throughout that contest and scored only two points. Panckeri was one of the area's leading scorers, and few believed he wouldn't be a major factor in this playoff game. Weatherly also had the size to deal with the Saints inside. Charlie Potter and Dick Ritter could hold their own against Saint Gabriel's tall duo of Sock and Ferry, plus Weatherly had an excellent outside player in John Hartz. Local radio station WAZL announced they would cover the game, which was sure to be a sellout.

Marian Catholic was packed a good half hour prior to tip-off. Based on the advanced ticket sales, more seating had been added on the school's stage to handle what turned out to be an overflow crowd. The paying customers got their money's worth as they witnessed what Don Barnes described as a game that would take its place among the greatest Anthracite League contests ever played in the circuit's storied history.

The teams felt each other out in the early going, but with Hoffman leading the way, the G-Men took a 15-10 lead after eight minutes of play. The two teams played an almost dead even second quarter, but Weatherly had no answer for Hoffman, who scored twenty first-half points in leading the Saints to a 33-26 advantage at half. Both Hartz and Panckeri shouldered the offensive load for the Wreckers but even with the superb play of their inside and outside men, Weatherly appeared to be overmatched. The G-Men appeared poised to capture their first league title since 1960.

The 1,900 thousand fans were seeing a good one, but it appeared that Hoffman and company had too much firepower to be denied. Both teams played tough defense, and the referees allowed them to play a physical game. After three quarters, the G-Men still led by four 44-40. Every time Weatherly made a run, Saint Gabriel's seemed answer with one of their own.

With just twenty-eight ticks left on the clock in the final quarter, the G-Men led by a score of 61-55. Weatherly inbounded the ball after using a time-out, and the Saint Gabriel's fans were on the feet cheering on their championship squad. A six-point lead seemed insurmountable with so little time left, especially against a team as talented as the Saints. Hartz took the ball down court and scored. Weatherly regained possession after Saint Gabriel's missed a shot when they could have held the ball and forced the Wreckers to foul. With eight seconds to go, Panckeri scored making it 61-59. It was then that Jack Cryan made what many would consider to be the biggest mistake of his young coaching career. He signaled for and his team called time-out with six seconds showing on the clock. The clock would have continued to run had the Saints not stopped it. Now they would have to put the ball in play against the Weatherly defense.

Cryan ordered Olexa to make the inbounds pass and sent every player but Hoffman to the far end of the court. The referee handed the ball to Olexa and when the whistle blew Hoffman attempted to move away from Henry Panckeri, who was guarding him closely. Olexa's pass to Hoffman was intercepted by Panckeri, who immediately lofted a shot from the side. As described by Don Barnes, "The ball hit the far edge of the basket rim, bounced high, came down on the support at the back of the basket, bounced up again—and down through the netting for the tying points." The Weatherly fans in the crowded gym exploded; it sounded like a cannon blast. The Saint Gabriel's followers stood in stunned silence, the life sucked out of them. The shot sucked the life out of the G-Men as well. They were outscored 4-2 in the overtime, and Weatherly emerged as the league's second-half champion by a score of 65-63. Hartz and Panckeri had combined to score fifty-four of Weatherly's sixty-five points. Hoffman led the G-Men with twenty-eight.

Weatherly coach Bill Knepper was literally beaming after the game. He praised his team's resilience, saying, "They never panicked when they might have." A despondent Cryan said his team had been out-hustled. It is hard to argue that Coach Cryan's decision to call a time-out wasn't a mistake. The team *behind* in that situation should call a time-out, stopping the clock and forcing the inbounds play. However, to this day Dennis Olexa says he was responsible for the defeat. Looking back, Olexa mused, "All I had to do was heave the ball the length of the court. Even if it's intercepted, they'd have been in no position to get a decent shot. That loss is all on me." Whoever was responsible, the outcome meant the same two teams would meet on the same court three nights later.

On the morning after the game, the Saint Gabriel's team arrived early for a practice at Saint Joe's. The mood was somber, the gym quiet except for the sound of basketballs hitting the floor as the players shot while waiting for practice to begin. There was virtually no conversation as Coach Cryan began practice by having the team take a seat on the gym floor in front of him. If any of the players hadn't read the morning papers, it was clear that Cryan had as he talked about calling the time-out the night before.

"They can say the time-out was a mistake, but that didn't cost us the game. We shouldn't have put ourselves in that position, and we should be able to make an inbounds pass." With that said, he talked a little about the need to let the game go and concentrate on the job that needed to be done on Monday. Then practice started, but the sense of gloom and quiet remained.

On the Sunday before the championship tilt, the Public Parochial Junior High League held their awards banquet. Coach Neil Cusat of Mother of Grace accepted his third league championship trophy in the past four years. The coaches, including Saint Gabriel's Vince Gallagher, were introduced. These same coaches had voted to name the league's five outstanding players. A number of the players honored would have a definite impact on the fortunes of Saint Gabriel's basketball in the next few years, including Ed Parsons from Mother of Grace, Laverne Mummey from Rock Glen, and Saint Gabriel's Joe Farley.

That Monday the *Standard Speaker* carried its preview of the championship game. The paper noted that the teams would be hard pressed to match the excitement Friday's game had generated. Rubbing salt in Coach Cryan's wounds, the article branded the time-out with six seconds to play the key call in the game. This time the paper didn't pick a favorite but simply predicted a scoring duel between Hoffman and Panckeri as well as an outstanding game.

That night Marian's gym was once again filled to capacity. A few minutes into the game one thing was obvious to Saint Gabriel's fans: they had never seen their team play like this all year long. The only thing keeping the G-Men in this championship game was the fact that they were playing tough defense. The team wearing purple and white missed their first seventeen shots from the field. They trailed at halftime by a score of 23-15. The fifteen points was by far the lowest they had put up on a scoreboard all year long. As a matter of fact, the Saints fans were hard pressed to remember the last time one of their teams had played so poorly on offense. It was almost like someone had put a lid on their basket. It wasn't that the shots weren't there or that the shot selection was poor—it seemed that for a half, the G-Men had lost the ability to shoot.

Weatherly made a free throw to start the scoring in the second half, but then the G-Men seemed to spring to life. They ran off eleven straight points capped off by a driving layup by Dennis Olexa, and all of a sudden after that horrible start, they were on top 26-24. That lead was short-lived as Weatherly star Henry Panckeri answered with a long jump shot, and after a Saint Gabriel's turnover, John Hartz put the Wreckers on top by two when he scored on a driving layup. The two teams played a relatively even game for the rest of the period, and the score after three quarters was 35-32 with Weatherly clinging to the advantage.

When the fourth quarter began, the Saints assumed control once again, scoring nine straight points to take a 41-35 lead before Weatherly coach Bill Knepper signaled for a time-out. Whatever he said calmed the Wreckers down, and they quickly scored seven straight to retake the lead 42-41. With three minutes to play Hoffman drove to the basket and scored, but Weatherly quickly responded with a field goal. A minute later Dick Ritter scored again for Weatherly, but Tony Joe Barletta responded for the Saints. With a minute and a half to play, it was a one-point ballgame.

Then Ritter, who had scored Weatherly's last two field goals, canned another and the G-Men trailed by three. Hoffman's short jumper rolled just off the rim and after a scramble for the rebound, the ball was knocked out of bounds. All eyes were on referee Joe Barletta, who awarded the ball to Weatherly. With the Saints applying intense defensive pressure, Hartz was called for traveling and the G-Men regained possession with just forty-two seconds to play. Once again they worked the ball to Hoffman, who went up for a shot only to have it partially blocked as a result of a tremendous defensive play by Henry Panckeri. The ball landed in the arms of Hartz, who was immediately fouled. The Weatherly guard made both shots, and those proved to be the last points scored in the game. When the buzzer sounded Weatherly had won its first Anthracite League title by a score of 50-45. Weatherly fans, cheerleaders, and coaches joined their players on the floor in a wild celebration. The G-Men headed quietly to their locker while their followers stood stunned and silent in the stands.

The G-Men had come up empty, shooting nineteen of sixty-two from the field—a dismal performance from so talented a team. Hoffman had scored eighteen on an off night, and Olexa had played his heart out while putting fifteen on the board. The Saints had gone with five players the whole way, and the other three starters had managed just twelve points between them. A dejected Jack Cryan shook his head after the contest and commented, "What can you say when you lose." While he may not have said it, he probably thought it's even tougher when you lost one you didn't have to play because you gave the other one away. Ray Saul, noting the splendid support both teams had received from their followers, wrote that it was too bad that someone had to lose. He also wished both teams luck in their post-season playoffs.

At the close of the league season, Coach Cryan had much to be proud of as his team had come a long way. When the season began, the common observation about the G-Men was that they would go as far as Hoffman took them. There is no denying that Hoffman was the key to the squad. For the third straight year, he had led the team in scoring, and this year he had showed his versatility by moving to an outside guard position when Cryan put both his big men, Sock and Ferry, on the court at the same time. But Cryan had developed a true team as evidenced by the fact five of the G-Men averaged in double figures in league play. In addition, Olexa had shown marked improvement in his overall play as the season progressed, largely due to the work the coach had put in with his point guard.

Despite the great season, coming so close to the league title only to fall short again left a bad taste in the mouths of the Saints' loyal followers. In their minds, there was no doubt that a championship had been given away. The players felt the same way. As mentioned earlier, Olexa blamed himself for the first playoff loss, and Hoffman harbored similar thoughts. After the season was over, Hoffman and Joe Farley went to St. Joe's to take in a game in the St. Joseph's amateur tournament held on a yearly basis. In talking about the playoff loss, Hoffman said, "I should have gotten more open on that play, and I shouldn't have let Panckeri get off that shot." Time hasn't dimmed the star's thoughts on that contest. He still points to the Weatherly defeat as one of the biggest disappointments of his storied high school career.

The league season now complete, the Saints could focus on post-season play. For the G-Men, the playoff path would be much easier in terms of games this year. Because of the number of teams that had qualified for the state playoffs in the east, Saint Gabriel's as the defending state champion would receive two byes before they found out who their next opponent would be, and they would play that team for the eastern half of the state title. This year one win would put them back into a title game. After the two consecutive losses, there were doubts among the G-Men faithful that their team would be successful in retaining the state championship.

The night after Saint Gabriel's let another Anthracite League title slip through their fingers, West Hazleton met East Penn

League Champion Allentown Dieruff in a District 11 playoff game. West Hazleton took a 14-8 record into the game as the representative of the Anthracite League. While the team from Allentown prevailed by a score of 90-77, Ray Saul wrote that the Wildcats had gained a lot of respect. The game provided a little more evidence to support Digger Phelps's argument that the quality of play in the two respective leagues was indeed narrowing. Dennis Mummey scored seventeen points in the contest and finished his outstanding high school career with 1,882 points.

On March 9th, Saint Gabriel's finally found out the identity of their initial opponent in the state title race. Scranton Holy Rosary earned the right to face the G-Men when they defeated Plymouth Saint Vincent's 50-48. The game with Holy Rosary would be played at Abington Heights High School, and a large crowd of Saint Gabriel's followers made the trip north to see if their team could bounce back from what was to most two devastating defeats at the hands of Weatherly.

Holy Rosary promised to be a formidable foe as they would carry a record of 24-1 into the contest. The record was all the more remarkable by the fact that the Scranton team would start five underclassmen. A win would give the G-Men their twenty-second win of the season, which would tie the mark set by Danny Gregoria's 1960 team that went 22-4.

Saint Gabriel's hadn't played a game in two weeks when they took the court to take on the aptly nicknamed Beads. Coach Cryan had decided to go big from the opening whistle, so he started both Sock and Ferry. He also decided he was going to press from the beginning of the game. He had scouted Holy Rosary, and in his view they were a disciplined team who wanted to slow the ball down and control the tempo of the game. Cryan ordered his team to press and to run, using a fast break offense whenever possible.

The two teams played a relatively close first quarter, but the teams were setting a pace that fit Cryan's game plan. With Holy Rosary playing a collapsing defense to offset the Saint Gabriel's height advantage, Cryan sent Mike Heffernan, an outstanding outside shooter, into the game toward the end of the first quarter that found the G-Men on top 18-12.

Heffernan made his presence felt in the second eight minutes by hitting five shots while the Beads' defenders sought to cut off the Saints' inside game. With their big men controlling the boards and Olexa engineering fast break scores, Saint Gabriel's stretched its lead to 41-24 at the half. While the teams headed to their lockers, Holy Rosary fans were wondering aloud how this team thrashing them lost three games in the past season.

The third quarter was played relatively even, which didn't help the Scranton team at all. With eight minutes to play the G-Men were winning by a score of 58-39. Midway through the final quarter, one play did bring the Saints fans to their feet. Olexa hit Hoffman with a pass that he caught about two feet outside the top of the key. The Beads' defender didn't challenge Hoffman, who let go with a long jumper that hit nothing but net. It was his twenty-third point in the game, and it gave him an even 1,500 in his three-year career. Shortly after, Cryan took him out of the game to a tremendous ovation from the supporters of both teams.

The final score left little doubt as to the superior team. Saint Gabriel's throttled the previously once-beaten Beads by a final of 81-58. In addition to Hoffman, three other Saints scored in double figures. Heffernan came off the bench to score seventeen, Barletta played his usual steady game and added fourteen, while the two big men, Sock and Ferry, contributed eleven and ten points respectively. Coach Cryan praised his team's control of the boards and defense after the win but added he was still concerned with his team's tendency to turn the ball over needlessly. Perhaps he was thinking back to the two playoff losses to Weatherly. There were two surprise visitors at the game. Father Purcell made the trip from Saint Michael's to take in the action, and Dick "Digger" Phelps was also on hand. Phelps visited the G-Men locker room after the game to congratulate Coach Cryan and his team.

The state title game was scheduled to be played at Gannon College in Erie. Many G-Men fans began making their plans to get to the game once the contest with Holy Rosary was no longer in doubt. The opponent for the state title would be North East Saint Gregory's. Saint Gregory's was located about fifteen miles from the championship site, so the match was shaping up as a home game for the team from the west.

On the same page as the newspaper story covering the Saint Gabriel's victory over Holy Rosary, there appeared a three-paragraph story on a game played the previous Sunday. In a CYO

All-Star game, the Hazleton team had defeated Freeland by a score of 62-59. The Hazleton team was led by a Saint Joseph's eighth grader Larry Walko, who scored nineteen. Walko was soon going to have to decide where to attend high school. One of the interested spectators who took in the game was Jack Cryan.

In what many G-Men fans considered a good omen, the state championship game would be played on Saint Patrick's Day, March 17, 1967. Saint Gabriel's was attempting to do something that no regional team had done since the late 1920s when Hazleton High won back to back state titles. The G-Men were considered the slight favorite going into the game based on the fact that the Saints were the taller team and, of course, they had Paul Hoffman.

It appears that Saint Gregory's didn't get the word that the G-Men were the favorites. From the opening tip, they shot to the lead. They also found a way to negate Saint Gabriel's supposed height advantage by simply not missing very many shots. After eight minutes of play the Crusaders enjoyed a 14-11 advantage. The second quarter mimicked the first as Saint Gregory's continued to control the pace of the game. The game was beginning to resemble the second playoff loss to Weatherly, and the Saints headed to the locker room at half trailing by a score of 28-23.

Saint Gabriel's didn't look like the same team that had run Holy Rosary off the court in the game played a week earlier. Paul Hoffman remembers that he thought the team played slow and said he himself felt "leg heavy." The third quarter went much like the previous two and after three quarters Saint Gregory's led 50-46.

With two minutes gone in the final period of play, the G-Men trailed 50-46. Barletta drove through the Crusader defenders for a score. Rondash made good on one of two foul tries, and then Hoffman turned a steal into a field goal that gave the Saints their first lead since the early going 51-50. Hoffman was fouled on the play by Gary Lipnickey, who was Saint Gregory's key man underneath. It was his fifth foul and it sent him to the bench.

Though Hoffman missed the foul shot he more than made up for it by scoring on the next two Saint Gabriel's possessions after rebounding Saint Gregory missed attempts. With two and a half minutes left, Olexa scored, giving the G-Men a 61-54 lead. Saint Gregory's took a time-out, and Coach Cryan advised his team to begin holding the ball and taking time off the clock. The Crusaders were forced to foul to get the ball, and the G-Men made enough of them to win by eight, 68-60.

The Saints won their second consecutive state title, and in doing so set a new school record for wins, finishing the season with a record of 23-3. Hoffman paced the G-Men scoring thirty-one, including seventeen in the final period when he forgot about his "heavy legs" and put the team on his shoulders and carried them to victory. Barletta, playing his last game for Saint Gabriel's, hit for seventeen.

After the game, the Saint Gabriel's fans on hand for the victory celebrated both the win and Saint Patrick's Day. Cookie Dolan led the festivities dressed as a leprechaun. Coach Cryan heaped more praise on the losing team than he did on his own. He said hustle and determination had kept Saint Gregory's in the game. Father Deviney received numerous telegrams congratulating the team on their win, and a good-sized crowd greeted the G-Men upon their return to Hazleton. Coach Cryan was named "Coach of the Week" by the Reading newspaper. Few who knew the young coach doubted he had anything on his mind but the following season, and even fewer doubted that he meant to capture that league title that so many, including the coach himself, thought should have been won in 1967.

14

ON THE LINE FOR TWO

PREDICTION PERFECTION

In the summer between the 1967 and 1968 season, the small gym in Saint Gabriel's High School was a busy one. On rainy days, the players would find a way into the school or the door would be opened by Father Deviney or Coach Cryan to let the boys play. Some said that both Hoffman and Olexa had keys to the school so that they could access the court at any time. Often present were young players from the grade schools who were invited to join the regular Saint Gabriel's students as they played and practiced.

One of the visitors that summer was Ed Parsons, who had led Mother of Grace to the junior high Public Parochial League title. There was no doubt that Coach Cryan wanted Parsons to continue his schooling at Saint Gabriel's. Parsons recalled the doors were locked on one of the nights, as they always were if Coach Cryan was present. According to Parsons, before anybody started playing, Coach Cryan told all those in the gym, "If there's a knock on the door, drop the ball and start kicking it—you're playing soccer."

When the boys weren't in the gym, you could generally find them on the playgrounds. South Side playground had long been home to the Saint Gabriel's players in the off season. That was beginning to change. If you wanted to find Dennis Olexa, John Darraugh, Joe Farley, or Paul Hoffman, your best bet was Pine Street playground where Bruce Ellis coached the summer league team. Ellis was a student of the game who loved sports, and he also had his own vehicle. It wasn't unusual for Ellis to load five players from Pine Street into his car and set off in search of games against rival teams who favored the playground courts located at D. A. Harmon, Lahm Avenue, or James Street. In a few years, Ellis would play a major role in the development of the last team to wear the purple and white.

Toward the end of the summer, a number of Saint Gabriel's students were gathered in the gym when Jack Cryan showed up and the doors were locked. Teams were selected and games began, with the winners keeping the court. In between one of the games, an incident took place involving Coach Cryan and Joe Farley. Farley had refused to follow a directive the coach had given him between games. What started as a discussion ended in an argument. An angry Farley left the gym with choice words from the coach still ringing in his ears.

With Labor Day and the start of school approaching, Farley joined Paul Hoffman for a weekend with Hoffman's parents at Saint Michael's. The two played a lot of basketball that Saturday, and it became obvious that Hoffman was as popular at Saint Mike's as he was back at Saint Gabriel's. On Sunday the two boarded a bus and headed back to Hazleton. The talk turned to basketball and the playground championship Pine Street had won with Hoffman leading the way.

Then the Saint Gabriel's star began talking about his senior year. He thought the 1968 team would be the best he had played on at Saint Gabriel's. He pointed out that Olexa had improved a lot under Cryan's tutelage. He spoke of Mike Heffernan's abilities as well, saying that all three were capable of scoring in the twenties in every game. Then he said, "And I don't care what Jack [Cryan] says about Darraugh's defense—the way he shoots, you can't keep him out of the lineup." He ended by saying to Farley, "And you are going to see an awful lot of playing time."

Farley didn't reply except to agree, but he didn't share what he was thinking, which was *I'm not even sure I'm going to play.* On November 1, 1967, when the Saint Gabriel's team gathered to begin the first official practice session for the coming season, Farley was not among them.

On November 22nd, two days before their season was to begin, the *Standard Speaker* selected Saint Gabriel's as the favorite to win the Anthracite League title. Coach Cryan went further, declaring, "We expect to go undefeated." It was unheard of for a coach to predict an undefeated season. The paper stated Cryan said it and he meant it. It was a far cry from a year earlier when the first-year coach refused to hazard a guess as to how his team would do. If the coach wanted a target on his team's back, he had painted it himself. That said, Coach Cryan had a few things going for him and as the paper pointed out, not the least of which was the return of a "six-one senior answering to the name of Paul Hoffman."

Hoffman's resume was impressive to say the least. For three straight years he had led the G-Men in scoring, and the year before he had been the leading scorer in the Anthracite League. After three years he had accounted for 1,531 career points and been the top rebounder on a team that had won back-to-back state titles. Since his freshman year he had improved every facet of his game. He had developed a jump shot and could handle the ball with the best in the region. Offensively, he was a threat facing or with his back to the basket, and ever since his freshman year he had been regarded as the best defensive player on the team. The only thing missing on Hoffman's sparkling resume was the failure of the previous three Saint Gabriel's squads to win a league title. In two of those three years they had lost the title in a playoff. Needless to say, although the paper did, Hoffman, the G-Men, and their fans were hungry and the goal was obvious.

The Saints were going to get their oppositions' best shot every night as opposing coaches agreed they were the team to beat, and it wasn't just because of Hoffman. Olexa had grown an inch or two over the summer—and about six inches since his sophomore year—and had vastly improved his skills. He was the acknowledged floor leader of the club, and those who had played with and against him on the Hazleton playgrounds over the summer months fully expected he was going to do far better than the 11.4 points he had averaged as a junior. Not holding back, Cryan called Olexa "the best outside man in the region."

Mike Heffernan had shown flashes of brilliance the year before and would now be counted on to deliver on a consistent basis. Heffernan was considered by many to be the most outstanding outside shooter on the squad, but others would say that honor belonged to junior John Darraugh, who would play the guard position opposite Olexa. If anyone could match Heffernan's ability to hit from the outside, it was Darraugh. Coach Cryan couldn't lose no matter which player came out on top. One thing Darraugh did bring to the table was a will to win. Looking back, Olexa said of Darraugh, "He was a fierce competitor. I never played with anyone who hated losing as much as Johnny. He couldn't even stand losing a playground game."

Another junior, Pat Curry, was expected to round out the starting lineup at the center position. Curry was a muscular six foot three and would be a role player much like Barletta had been for the Saints. Aside from Rocco Fallabel, there wasn't a lot of varsity experience on the bench but Cryan said he expected that depth to develop. The coach saw Jerry Gallagher and John Goryl eventually filling that role. Goryl was a junior at the time, and he remembers Cryan driving him home on occasion. "To get to my house we had to drive past a few stripping holes. I remember Coach Cryan shaking his head, saying that if they ever sent someone to bomb this area they'd fly right on by figuring somebody beat them to it."

In terms of the style of play fans could expect, Cryan believed this team would prove to be better from the outside offensively and better overall defensively than last year's state champions. He also noted making individual achievements secondary to the team's achievements would be the key to the Saints' success. Chief obstacles in terms of the elusive league title, according to Cryan, were Freeland, Jim Thorpe, and the always dangerous West Hazleton. Ray Saul ended his article by saying it looked like a great season lay ahead for the "enthusiastic" G-Men followers. He also noted Father Deviney wasn't making any predictions on how the year would go, though he sensed Deviney couldn't wait for the season to begin.

Saint Gabriel's was the first team in the region to play a game at the beginning of the 1968 season. The foe, West Scranton Saint Patrick's, was expected to give the G-Men a true test. Saint Patrick's had a star in Gerald Jones, who at six foot five would be the tallest player on the court. There was no doubt the area's coaches would join the Saint Gabriel's fans to watch the opener. This was their chance to get an idea of exactly what this Saints squad had to offer.

The G-Men took the court before what was described as a "good-sized crowd" just minutes after the Saint Gabriel's JV team won their opener in impressive fashion 74-38. After Bob Farley, the "Voice of the G-Men," announced the starting lineups, the two teams took the floor. From the opening tip Coach Cryan's game plan was obvious: the Saints would utilize a full-court zone press and would fast break at every opportunity. Though the press did force a number of turnovers, John Darraugh picked up three quick personal fouls playing the aggressive defense. When Rocco Fallabel was sent into the game as a sub, Bob Farley announced that Darraugh had picked up his third foul. In a second, Assistant Coach Vince Gallagher was in Farley's ear. "Don't announce the number of fouls—they may not be tracking it." The Voice of the G-Men got the message; it was the last such announcement of the year. After one period, the G-Men were up 26-17. The Scranton team would get no closer. After three quarters it was 76-40, and only Cryan's insertion of the reserves kept the Saints from hitting the century mark. When the final game ended, Saint Patrick's was on the short end of a 95-56 score.

Hoffman got his senior season off to a great start scoring thirty-three, and Olexa didn't disappoint with his twenty-three points. Heffernan also hit double figures with fourteen, and Darraugh just missed with nine. Pat Curry only scored five points, but he did his part in helping the Saints dominate the boards against the taller visitors. Coach Cryan was pleased. His team had scored at will both inside and from distance. Defensively they created turnovers and made their opponent work for good shots or take bad ones. Most importantly, they played with the sole purpose of winning as a unit. Saint Gabriel's had lived up to the preseason hype.

Ray Saul took note of the coaches of future G-Men opponents who took in the game, mentioning Fran Libonati of Hazleton and Pip Radar of Jim Thorpe. He noted they had to be impressed by what they had witnessed. If it were possible for Hoffman to get better, he sure looked it, dominating every facet of the game. Still, Saul said those in attendance had to be awed by the general overall improvement in the Saints' play. The sportswriter singled out Olexa, who was described as having "cat hands" that would result in more than his share of steals this season. He also noticed Olexa had added a hook shot to his offensive arsenal and was more of a threat to score than he had been a season ago.

Two days after the varsity opener, the Saint Gabriel's freshman team issued a warning of their own when they beat Saint Michael's of Hoban Heights 102-81. Jerry Fallabel scored thirty-nine points in the win, and Larry Walko, who had decided to attend Saint Gabriel's, added twenty-two.

A few days later, Freeland MMI opened its season losing to Plymouth Saint Vincent's 70-56. The score was a little misleading in that MMI was without Steve Makuta, who was expected to be one of their top scorers and a force on the boards. Makuta missed the game due to illness. Two sophomores, John Lamberson and Jerry Hludzik, both scored in double figures for the Preppers and served notice that MMI would improve as the year went on, though most believed the team was a year away from contending for the league title.

Hazleton High wouldn't begin their season until later in December. Once again the number of boys trying out for the Hazleton team nearly equaled the total enrollment of boys at Saint Gabriel's. The late start gave those who participated on the football team time to adjust to the basketball court. Coach Libonati saw his team as having a chance to win the East Penn League. Darrell Farkus, now a senior and standing at six foot five, was expected to be a force on the inside. Tony Kinney was also expected to provide the Mountaineers with some offensive punch after averaging in double figures as a sophomore. Robert Farnell and Joe Duda were solid outside threats. Filmore Williams would be a valuable sixth man for Libonati, who saw the junior as a player who could help on both ends of the court. Two talented sophomores, Ed Parsons, who had decided to go to Hazleton despite Coach Cryan's efforts to get him to Saint Gabriel's, and Tony Manfredi Jr., were also expected to help off the bench as the season went on. The Mounts would meet the G-Men at Saint Joe's on December 29th looking to avenge their loss to the Saints a year earlier.

The G-Men faced the always pesky Crestwood in their second outing of the year. The Saints unleashed an offensive assault from the opening whistle and after eight minutes led by a score of 35-5. Things didn't improve for the visitors from there as after three quarters the score stood at 94-20. All five of the Saints' starters scored in double figures with Heffernan leading the way with twenty-five. Olexa hit for twenty, Darraugh was a shade behind with nineteen, and Curry scored thirteen. Hoffman played less than a half and scored twenty-one. The final score was 111-34, and the Hazleton paper was referring to the Saint Gabriel's offense as a blitzkrieg. One local writer, Don Garber from the *Weatherly Herald*, cautioned Coach Cryan against booking a banquet hall to celebrate a championship based on the early contests. He predicted that "the Saints would take their share of lumps."

West Hazleton stumbled out of the gate losing to Berwick at Mother of Grace, and Jim Thorpe fell to Lehighton by two. Saint Gabriel's was scheduled to meet Lehighton as part of their exhibition schedule. While West Hazleton and Jim Thorpe opened their seasons with losses, Freeland hammered Wilkes-Barre Township 102-50. Four Freeland players hit double figures led by Jimmy Titus who scored twenty-four. Based on these early outings, it appeared that aside from Saint Gabriel's, some of the usual heavyweights in the Anthracite League might not be as strong as in years past.

The next foe for Saint Gabriel's was the highly regarded Kingston Catholic team. Not only was the Kingston outfit noted for being tough out in the Wilkes-Barre area, they had some players from Swoyersville transfer after that school was swallowed by the jointure that became known as Wyoming Valley West. Quite a few local observers were anxious to see how the G-Men would fare against the Queensmen.

Kingston Catholic started fast and held the lead in the early going, but then the G-Men went to work. Trailing 13-9 the Saints scored eight straight and led 17-13 when the first quarter came to an end. Once again, Coach Cryan used a full-court press from the get-go and it took its toll on the visitors. By halftime the Queensmen were trailing by a 42-27 margin. At the start of the final quarter, the score stood at 58-40. The Saints ran off thirteen straight points and the lead ballooned to thirty-one. The final score was 86-55, and people began to wonder aloud that this Saint Gabriel's squad just might be a very special team.

The big three—Hoffman, Olexa, and Heffernan—accounted for the bulk of the Saint Gabriel's offense, scoring twenty-six, twenty-five, and twenty-three points, respectively. Don Barnes, who covered the game for the *Standard Speaker*, wrote that while it was still early in the season, "with more experience under actual fire the defending PCIAA state champs could shape into the kind of outfit that will make fans forget about last year." The paper was also beginning to follow Hoffman's rising career point totals. A separate story described a jump shot from about fourteen feet that dropped through the net making the score 50-34. The story said the basket was significant because it raised the Saint Gabriel's star career points to 1,601. The countdown to two thousand had begun.

On the same night, Hazleton High School traveled to Berwick and defeated the same Bulldog squad that had handled West Hazleton easily. Tony Kinney led the Mounts to a 59-56 win by scoring nineteen points and hauling down fifteen rebounds. While the Saints and Mountaineers meeting was still three weeks away, there was no doubt players on both teams were having thoughts about that game. It was up to their respective coaches to keep their teams' minds focused on the matters at hand.

The halls at Saint Gabriel's had been filled with excitement during previous basketball seasons, but this year was different. There was an air of invincibility about this team. Many were going to games not wondering about whether they'd be leaving after cheering for the winning team, but thinking, *I wonder how bad we'll beat these guys tonight?* Next up for the Saints was the Lehighton team that was undefeated and had already beaten Jim Thorpe. Since Thorpe was considered a contender for the Anthracite crown, many viewed the game as a measuring stick that could be used to compare the G-Men and the Olympians.

A large noisy crowd gathered inside the gym at Saint Joseph's to watch the G-Men JV team win their tenth straight 94-40. It was a fitting prelude to the varsity match. Previous opponents had found Saint Gabriel's potent offense impossible to defend, and this night was no different. After one quarter, the Saints led 21-12. When the second period began, the Saints really turned it, on scoring sixteen unanswered points to make the score 37-12 on the way to a 56-29 lead at halftime. Thirteen Saint Gabriel's players took the court in the game; twelve of them scored. The final score was 102-69, and there was little doubt that the G-Men had made a statement that may have even reached the ears of a certain sportswriter who lifted his pen for the *Weatherly Herald*.

The Saint Gabriel's offense was putting points on the board in numbers that had never been witnessed before in the region. After four games the Saints had scored 394 points, or 98.5 per game. The big three were all averaging more than twenty points a game with Hoffman leading the way at 26.0. Olexa was a close second, putting up 24.3 a game, while Heffernan was contributing at a 20.4 clip. Heffernan remembers that teams came out "trying to stop Dennis and Paul, but not only was that not working, the attention they were drawing left me open, and I was playing with a team that would get the ball to the open man." Anyone who had ever played with Heffernan knew that given the opportunity he was deadly from the outside, and opposing teams were learning it quickly and the hard way. To this day, Bruce Ellis points to Heffernan as the Saint Gabriel's player who would have benefited the most had a three-point line been in existence at the time. Had Saint Gabriel's teams handed down nicknames, Heffernan probably would have been given John Farley's moniker "Swish."

Hazleton High won their second straight when they went on the road and easily handled the Palmerston Bombers 83-61. Farkus turned in an impressive performance for the Mounts, scoring twenty-three and hauling down nineteen rebounds. Kinney also made his presence felt, rimming fourteen points and pulling down seventeen boards. Ray Saul was hoping both the G-Men and the Mountaineers would head into their December 29th meeting undefeated. Should that happen, the veteran sportswriter wrote, "a shoe horn might be needed to get all the fans into Saint Joe's" for the game.

Saul's column on December 11th contained the comment that "Father Joseph Conboy, assistant pastor at Saint Gabriel's Church, made a comeback as a basketball coach yesterday and may retire with a perfect record (1-0). His Saint Gabriel's High Sophomore team defeated St. Gabriel's Freshman 70-55." That game was an in-school contest played before the student body. Future teammates, Joe Farley scored eighteen for the sophomores while Larry Walko was top gun for the freshman with twenty. Saint Gabriel's outstanding freshman team would lose only one other game that season.

Any hope that both local teams would be undefeated when they met in late December ended when Allentown Allen came to town and defeated Hazleton 71-62. The Mountaineers played a horrendous first half that found them behind by a 41-19 margin. Numerous turnovers and a bad shooting night plagued Hazleton who, to their credit, tried to claw back in the second half.

On the same night the Saint Gabriel's bandwagon showed no signs of slowing as the G-Men beat Crestwood for the second time 107-38. Once again the G-Men were impossible to stop as all five starters finished in double figures. The Saints defense was also drawing attention. Ray Saul wrote that if there was an area team with a defensive press as effective as Saint Gabriel's, they had yet to show it.

With Saint Gabriel's taking the night off, Hazleton High bounced back in convincing fashion to beat Bethlehem Catholic 88-74. Bob Farnell scored thirty-one points for the Mounts. Considering the fact that he made fourteen of seventeen shots from the field makes his performance was all the more impressive. Farkus continued to be a force underneath, scoring twenty-seven for Fran Libonati's club. Kinney and Joe Duda also hit doubles for Hazleton, scoring eleven. Both Jack Cryan and Father Deviney used the night off to get a look at the Mountaineers in action. On the same evening, Freeland took down Plains by a 112-76 margin, and Ray Saul christened the Whippets as the "only Anthracite League team that has the stuff to give Saint Gabriel's a run."

Though the season was still young, honors and acknowledgements were coming Hoffman's way. The *Harrisburg Patriot News* named the Saint Gabriel's star to their Big 33 All-Star squad. Hoffman was also fielding numerous scholarship offers from colleges throughout the country. Before the season was over, more than a hundred institutions of higher learning would make a bid for his services.

Saint Gabriel's next win was controversial for all the wrong reasons. The G-Men easily dispatched Shenandoah Catholic 120-45 and set a few records in doing so. The 120 points were the most any Saint Gabriel's basketball team had scored in a game. Olexa scored forty-seven, which tied the school's individual scoring record established by Jerry Moye twenty years before. The controversy swirled around the amount of playing time Coach Cryan gave his starters in the rout. The five starters scored 114 of the Saints 120 points, and Olexa tied the individual mark when he sank two foul shots with just six seconds left on the clock.

Don Barnes began his story covering the game by writing, "Saint Gabriel's probably didn't win a lot of friends but did influence a lot of people, especially Shenandoah Catholic fans, with a 120-45 rout of the Mighty Atoms at St. Joe's gym last night." Ray Saul commented on the game in his column, saying that he counted Jack Cryan among his best friends in the coaching fraternity "but I can't go along with Jack's failure to substitute more freely in one-sided games." Saul also wrote that he didn't have an individual picture of Dennis Olexa but that he hoped to remedy that within a couple of days. Olexa's photo would play an interesting part in a future Saint Gabriel's game against an archrival.

On the day following the game, a rumor made its way through the halls at Saint Gabriel's High School. The story went that when the two coaches met to shake hands after the game, the Shenandoah Catholic coach said, "I hope you don't win another game all year." Coach Cryan responded, "I know you won't win one."

Hazleton High continued their winning ways when they traveled to Allentown and beat Bethlehem Catholic 68-64. Once again, Farnell led the Mounts in scoring with twenty-two. Kinney not only scored seventeen points but hauled down twenty-two rebounds and made four important foul shots late in the victory. Hazleton would stay close to home the following week when they would meet their local rivals Saint Gabriel's and West Hazleton.

The G-Men were preparing to travel to take on Scranton South Catholic, a team that had just disposed of its most recent foe, Scranton Tech, by thirty-seven points. South Catholic would carry a record of 5-0 into the contest with Saint Gabriel's. Several of South Catholic's wins had been by convincing margins over Class A schools. The Scranton club was deep and experienced and, playing at home, they were a definite threat to take down Saint Gabriel's.

The game began in front of what Don Barnes described as "a wall-to-wall" crowd. South Scranton showed quickly they were a team to be reckoned with when they scored the first six points of the game. Led by Hoffman, Saint Gabriel's fought back and after eight minutes of play they trailed by one, 14-13.

The second quarter found fans on both teams on their feet as the crowd witnessed what Barnes called "magnificent basketball." During the second eight minutes, the lead changed hands an incredible twelve times. When the buzzer blew signaling halftime the score was knotted at thirty.

Hoffman seized control of the game in the third quarter when he scored the first five points after intermission. With just two minutes to play in the period, the Saints led 53-41 but South Scranton scored six straight points to make it 53-47 after three quarters. Led by Hoffman and Olexa, the Saints widened that lead to 65-56 with a minute left to play. South Scranton scored the last five points to make the final 65-61.

Hoffman scored twenty-two, followed by Olexa with eighteen and Curry's very important twelve points in the victory that kept alive Cryan's prediction of an undefeated season. The jubilant coach called it "a big win," saying that the G-Men had just beaten the best team they had faced in his two years as coach. While Cryan was talking about Hoffman's talents, someone yelled out, "And what about Olexa?" Without missing a beat, the coach shouted back, "Best backcourt man in the east." Don Barnes needed no further convincing, writing that he doubted that either Saint Gabriel's or South Catholic would lose another game all season. After the big win, the G-Men would celebrate Christmas before facing Hazleton High just one week later.

Christmas fell on a Monday in 1967, and sports-wise Christmas week would feature the three city schools in Hazleton vie for the unofficial city championship. On Wednesday, Hazleton would meet West Hazleton, and two nights later Saint Gabriel's would put its undefeated season on the line while attempting to do something that had never been done in the history of the school: beat Hazleton two years in succession. The Feeley Theater was advertising the opening of the film *Cool Hand Luke* starring Paul Newman all week long, but the hottest ticket in town was Hazleton versus Saint Gabriel's.

Hazleton entered the game with West Hazleton as the solid choice, and they didn't disappoint, coming away with a 71-62 win. Farkus once again led Hazleton in scoring with twenty-six while Kinney and Farnell scored sixteen each. Gary Marsch led the Wildcats with twenty-one. The day after the game, Ray Saul installed the Saints as favorites to beat Hazleton mainly because of Hoffman, though the sportswriter added that having Olexa around wasn't exactly a problem. Saul wrote there were followers of the G-Men who were willing to give fifteen points and take the Saints in the matchup, but he cautioned that betting a game involving these types of rivals was never smart. The *Standard Speaker* naming Saint Gabriel's the favorite was noteworthy in that it would be the only time in the history of the series that the G-Men would carry that tag into the game.

Beating Hazleton was always big for the little parochial school on Hazleton's south side. Olexa remembers beating

Hazleton as eclipsing the thrill of winning a state title. Likewise, Hoffman recalls beating Hazleton as one of the highlights of his legendary high school career. The opposition had similar feelings. Looking back, Kinney says, "We knew all about the state titles. It [Hazleton versus Saint Gabriel's] was a chance to prove something. It was really one of the most important games on our schedule." Eddie Parsons had similar thoughts. "We were always up to play Saint Gabe's and West Hazleton. Those were big games against kids we had played against for years back on the playgrounds. Losing to those teams could ruin your season."

The game played on December 29th, 1967, was big for both teams. Hazleton was 5-1 and the Saints were undefeated. What was unusual was the fact that most Saint Gabriel's fans expected a win. The game took place over Christmas break, which was undoubtedly a positive thing for the students at both institutions, for their minds would have been on little else. The advanced ticket sale was brisk, and the *Standard Speaker* reported that if any tickets were still available they would be sold at the door until the supply was exhausted.

On the day of the game, Don Barnes devoted his sports column While the Cat's Away to the fast approaching tilt. He noted that the first points scored by Hoffman would put him over 1,700 for his career on his march to the two thousand mark, which would place him in very select company that included players like Wilt Chamberlain. Barnes wrote that Hoffman was much more than a scorer; he had developed into a team leader on the floor and an excellent ball handler who probably also held the regional record for rebounding. While no such records existed, Barnes pointed to the Saints' last game in which Hoffman pulled down twenty-seven off the boards to go along with his twenty-two points. The sportswriter noted this Saint Gabriel's team had a lot more going for it than just Hoffman, saying that working hand in glove with Olexa, the two formed a one-two punch as effective as any ever seen "in these parts." As far as the game itself, Barnes saw this one as different from years past in that it was Hazleton High that had everything to gain and nothing to lose against the G-Men.

Parking around Saint Joseph's was at a premium on game night. Local residents who had dug out of the twelve inches of snow that had fallen the night before used lawn chairs and garbage cans to protect the spaces they had cleared for their vehicles. Lack of parking failed to hold down the capacity crowd that exceeded 2,500 to watch the two local teams in action.

When the game started, it was obvious that Coach Libonati had prepared his team for Cryan's full-court zone press. Sharp passes beat the G-Men defensive pressure and resulted in easy scores as reflected by Hazleton's first-half shooting statistics that saw the Mounts hitting on fourteen of twenty-four attempts. Despite their excellent play, the Mountaineers carried a slim 35-33 lead with them to the locker room.

At halftime Coach Cryan made some adjustments. He stayed with the press but went straight man-for-man. It had the desired effect. With Olexa and Darraugh pressuring, the Hazleton backcourt men had trouble getting the ball past half court. When they did, they were forced to set up their offense rather than have the opportunity for an easy score after beating the press. With 5:35 left to play in the third quarter, Heffernan hit a long set shot giving the Saints a 41-40 lead—the first time the G-Men had been on top since early in the game. John Darraugh followed with two quick jumpers, and all of a sudden Saint Gabriel's led by five. After Hazleton converted a foul shot, Hoffman scored five consecutive points to make it 50-41. The Saint Gabriel's ace wasn't finished as he added two more field goals before the period ended with his team on top 56-44.

In the final period Cryan had the G-Men play a semi-possession game working for clear uncontested shots. Farkus, who scored sixteen for the Mounts, fouled out with a minute to go, but by then the game was long decided. At the final gun, Saint Gabriel's had scored a convincing 69-55 win over their archrivals. The win was satisfying for all Saint Gabriel's fans—except those who had bet their team would win by fifteen points.

After the game, a smiling Jack Cryan told Ray Saul, "This was a big win for us." Saul acknowledged as much, saying any time a school the size of Saint Gabriel's could defeat a big Class A school it was a big win, especially when it was as convincing as this one had been. Saul also wrote that Hoffman had solidified his credentials for an all-state selection with his play.

A picture of a radiantly smiling Father Deviney taken immediately after the win said more than a thousand words. The G-Men had won eight straight exhibition games to prepare them for league play. For three years, the G-Men had been thwarted in their quest for the Anthracite League title. First it was West

Hazleton then Jim Thorpe and finally Weatherly. Was this the year that Saint Gabriel's would finally get the monkey off their backs? Would the G-Men make good on Coach Cryan's prediction of an undefeated season? The Saint Gabriel's student body and their many fans certainly expected that to be the case—not to mention the only thing going to keep that smile on the good father's face was a league championship.

15

THE FAST BREAK

Feast and Famine

Getting ready to head back to school after Christmas break, Saint Gabriel's students and fans who picked up the morning paper were stunned to see a small, bold-lettered blurb at the top of the sports page. The headline read "Olexa Is No Longer with St. Gabe's Squad." According to the story, school officials confirmed that Olexa hadn't attended practice over the weekend and was no longer with the team. The G-Men were scheduled to open their Anthracite League season the next day against Freeland, the team most were pointing to as their chief competition for the league title. The question on everyone's lips was what the heck happened?

It appears that Saint Gabriel's had supplied the *Standard Speaker* with incorrect statistics on two occasions. The paper then printed the stats, which had Olexa averaging fewer points per game than was the case. After the initial publication, Olexa's father had contacted both the newspaper and Saint Gabriel's officials to let them know a mistake had been made. When it was repeated a second time, Edward Olexa (Dennis's father) no longer viewed the matter as a simple mistake, and he told his son that he wasn't attending any practice until the matter was settled. Despite the reports in the Hazleton paper that Olexa was no longer with the team, the memories of those involved at the time indicate this may have not been the case.

As Hoffman remembers, Olexa was suspended for missing a practice but was never officially separated from the team. Heffernan recalls that Coach Cryan told him that he was going to have to pick up some of the offensive burden in Olexa's absence but never indicated that the talented backcourt player had been dismissed or quit the squad. In terms of the offensive load, Cryan probably had a similar conversation with John Darraugh. On the day before Saint Gabriel's opened their quest for the league title, Ray Saul reported that Edward Olexa had told him that his son did not quit the team but he had instructed him not to attend practice. Olexa himself says that he never quit the team he simply wasn't about to disobey his dad. While much was murky, the one thing that appeared clear was that Saint Gabriel's would face a talented Freeland squad without Olexa. The Saints' point guard wasn't mentioned in the newspapers preview of the contest.

Another large crowd gathered within Saint Joseph's as the G-Men took on the Whippets. What had already been considered a key contest in the league's first half race became even more pivotal because of Olexa's absence. When the game began, the Saints' point guard was with his father in the stands. Rocco Fallabel started in Olexa's place and only one other Saint Gabriel's player, Jerry Gallagher, would see action for the G-Men. The Saints took control early and led by eight 18-10 after the first quarter and stretched that to a 34-23 lead at half. It appeared, at least for tonight, that Saint Gabriel's was going to get the job done without their star backcourt player.

In the third quarter, Freeland went on a run and Cryan called a time-out when the Saints lead was cut to two at 35-33. At this point, Olexa turned to his father and said, "Won't you let me play?" His dad said he could ask Father Deviney. Olexa approached Deviney, who basically said his playing tonight was not possible and his status couldn't be decided at the moment. In the meantime, led by Hoffman and Heffernan, the G-Men went on a slight run of their own to take a lead of 47-38 after three periods. The two teams played an even final quarter and Saint Gabriel's emerged with what many viewed as an unimpressive 69-60 victory.

Freeland actually had one more field goal in the game than Saint Gabriel's, but the Saints had won it at the foul line by converting twenty-seven shots from the free throw line compared to sixteen for the visitors. Hoffman scored twenty-six, Heffernan hit for sixteen (including twelve of fourteen fouls), and Curry added twelve in the victory. Many who had viewed Saint Gabriel's as being the de facto league champs began to harbor doubts. Minus Olexa, this was a different team. If Freeland had hung with the Saints at Saint Joe's, many felt their chances of taking the G-Men down on their home court in the second half was a distinct possibility.

Don Barnes still saw the G-Men as the heavy favorites to win the league title. He pointed out that adjustments were going to have to be made in the backcourt, but he fully expected Coach Cryan was up to getting that job done. Saint Gabriel's fans, on the other hand, were a little concerned, and to put it bluntly, they wanted Olexa back on the court. MMI was up next for the Saints, and everyone wondered if the star guard would be back in uniform.

After the game with Freeland, Cryan, Father Deviney and Mr. Edward Olexa got together for a meeting to discuss how to move forward. The matter was resolved to everyone's satisfaction as evidenced by the fact that Dennis Olexa was once again wearing purple and white as the G-Men took the floor for warm-ups before taking on the Preppers. Coach Cryan may have been making a public statement on team discipline when he kept his backcourt ace on the bench at the start of the game.

MMI had won six straight games heading into this one, but most observers thought the team was a year away from legitimately contending for the league title. The Preppers only had one senior on their team and were off to a very promising start with a squad dominated by underclassmen. A junior, Jim Kennedy, was given the job of guarding Hoffman by MMI coach Dave Shafer. Kennedy did a nice job holding Hoffman to a single first-half field goal, though the Saint Gabriel's star hit nine foul shots. Coach Cryan didn't wait long to insert Olexa into the lineup; he sent him into the game midway in the first quarter. At halftime the Saints held a slim 38-36 lead. MMI had taken everything the G-Men had thrown at them and answered back.

In the third quarter Saint Gabriel's began to put some distance between them and their visiting rivals. Led by Hoffman and Olexa, they stretched their lead to a 57-43 lead on the way to a 79-63 win. Hoffman scored twenty-seven for Saint Gabriel's, and Olexa, who played a flawless floor game, scored twenty. Darraugh and Heffernan also hit doubles with thirteen and eleven points respectively. Steve Makuta scored twenty-one for the Preppers, and sophomore John Lamberson hit for fourteen despite being slowed by an ankle injury. By the end of the night, only Saint Gabriel's and West Hazleton remained undefeated in the first half of league play.

As Ray Saul had promised, his sports column of January 13, 1969, included a picture of Dennis Olexa, who had tied Jerry Moye's 1947 single game scoring record two weeks earlier. That day's paper also carried the story of Saint Gabriel's crushing defeat of Immaculate Heart of Fountain Springs 89-47. All five G-Men starters hit doubles in the win. West Hazleton kept pace with the Saints, bringing their league record to 3-0 by beating Marian Catholic 65-56. Saint Gabriel's wouldn't meet West Hazleton for two more weeks, but locals already pointed to that game as the one that would decide the league's first half. Since the game was going to be played at Mother of Grace, it was also being viewed as the game most likely to ruin Saint Gabriel's undefeated season. Nobody had any idea just how wild that game would be or the part Olexa's picture in the paper would play in it.

That Sunday, the second Super Bowl was played before a sellout crowd in Miami's Orange Bowl. The game itself didn't turn out to be so super as the Green Bay Packers scored the first three times they touched the ball on their way to an easy 33-14 victory over the Oakland Raiders. On the same day that you could read about the Packer win, Ray Saul reported that the *Scranton Sunday Times* still rated Saint Gabriel's as the area's second best team behind Scranton Cathedral.

On the night before Saint Gabriel's would meet Marian Catholic in their next league outing, the Saints' freshmen team showed just how tough they were by beating Weatherly 73-41 despite the fact that three starters missed the game due to illness. With Larry Walko, Jerry Fallabel, and Robby Marusak unable to play, Tommy Boyle picked up the slack and scored seventeen in the win. These freshmen were the best unit Coach Vince Gallagher had ever sent onto a court and in all probability were the single most talented class in the history of the school. Coach Cryan had to be pleased with the players heading his way. After all, he had recruited several of them.

The Saint Gabriel's varsity took no prisoners against Marian winning by a 97-58 margin. Five G-Men scored in double figures with Hoffman leading the way with twenty-two. Olexa was close behind with nineteen and, as the Saints' playmaker, set up his teammates for numerous scores. Heffernan hit for seventeen.

Darraugh scored eleven, as did Jerry Gallagher, who got his coming off the bench. Marian's Tom Andregic was the top scorer for Coach Wink Gallagher's Colts netting twenty-four, but he could have scored twice that many and it wouldn't have made any difference. To this day Andregic looks back on that game with pride, pointing out, "I outscored Hoffman."

Don Barnes, who covered the game, wrote that "it's a shame" Anthracite League teams couldn't even seem to make this year's G-Men work hard for their wins. The sportswriter was beginning to wonder just how good this team was. In his view, opponents would have to play at the top of their game just to give the Saints a few anxious moments, much less beat them.

Next up for Saint Gabriel's was the league's defending champions, the Weatherly Wreckers. But this was a far different team than the one that had claimed the championship by upsetting the G-Men in two late season playoff contests a season ago. Weatherly had been hard hit by graduation losses and was winless in four league contests heading into the game. With Saint Gabriel's having a score to settle, few gave the Wreckers any chance in the game to be played in Saint Joe's gym.

It was over from the moment it started as the Saints jumped out to a 13-0 lead on the way to a 94-55 win. There was no stopping Saint Gabriel's big three as Hoffman, Olexa, and Heffernan combined for seventy-one points. The G-Men dominated the boards and Weatherly couldn't handle the defensive pressure the Saints exerted. Dale Bachart scored twenty-five for the Wreckers in the defeat. Meanwhile, MMI beat West Hazleton 67-60, which left the G-Men atop the league standings as the lone undefeated team. Now the Wildcats would have to beat Freeland and upset the high scoring Saint Gabriel's squad just to earn the possibility of a tie for the first-half title.

The win by MMI kept the Preppers within a game of the G-Men as well. Ron Gerlach, the very successful CYO coach at Freeland Saint Mary's, was a big MMI supporter and had begun to urge Joe Farley to consider a transfer to the private Freeland school. Gerlach was of the opinion that Farley could team up with John Lamberson to give MMI a strong backcourt on a team sure to be a solid contender for the league crown in 1969. Gerlach, like the rest of the local coaching community with the possible exception of West Hazleton's Ron Gatski, didn't see anyone stopping the G-Men in the current season.

Farley, who was playing most of his basketball at the local Y, gave the transfer serious thought. Little did he know there was a transfer in his future, and it wouldn't be voluntary.

As the end of January approached, Saint Gabriel's remained the only undefeated team in the Greater Hazleton area. The G-Men squad included three of the top ten scorers in the area. Hoffman was having an outstanding senior year scoring 25.5 points per game. Olexa was ripping the nets for a 22.8 average, and Heffernan was adding 16.3 each contest. These three would lead Coach Cryan's team into their final two first-half games versus Jim Thorpe and then against one of their archrivals, West Hazleton. The Saints would be favored in both and could wrap up the first-half title with wins.

The G-Men were solid favorites when they headed to Jim Thorpe to take on the Olympians. Thorpe had won only two games in twelve tries, while the Saints were going for their fourteenth straight this season. The question on the minds of most of the Saints' fans was how many will we win by tonight. Though the game wasn't close, those on hand got their money's worth.

At halftime Saint Gabriel's had raced to a 54-27 lead. What had the attention of the paying customers was Paul Hoffman: he had scored thirty-one points in the first sixteen minutes. What they didn't know was that Coach Cryan was telling him to keep shooting, and according to Hoffman, the coach wasn't making a suggestion. "He told me if I didn't keep shooting, he'd take me out of the game" is the way Hoffman remembers the conversation. Most players wouldn't require such an order to keep scoring, but Cryan knew Hoffman's habit of passing off to other players once a game was well in hand.

In the third quarter, Hoffman scored seven to bring his point total to thirty-eight, and in the fourth he went on a rampage, scoring nineteen on what the local paper described as "a glittering assortment of shots." The Saint Gabriel's star finished with fifty-seven points, which not only broke the school's single game record held by Jerry Moye and Dennis Olexa, it also topped the league and regional mark.

The only thing that didn't go right for Hoffman and the G-Men on this night was the fact that Coach Cryan was ejected from the contest when he argued Referee Sam Esposito's judgment call late in the fourth quarter. Joe Barletta, the second ref, felt that Cryan overstepped his bounds, and he was the one who ejected the Saint Gabriel's mentor. On the very night that Hoffman set his mark, Tony Kinney established a new individual scoring record for Hazleton High when he scored thirty-seven points in Hazleton's 83-60 win over Easton. Kinney scored thirty of his points in the second half.

In the Anthracite League, both West Hazleton and MMI came away with victories to stay one game behind the G-Men with one game left to be played in the first half. The West Hazleton win set up the pivotal contest with Saint Gabriel's at Mother of Grace. West Hazleton had been the thorn in the Saints' side too often to count. It was only a year ago that the Wildcats had handed Saint Gabriel's their only regular season loss—a loss that cost them a league championship and what would have been an undefeated season. There was no doubt in anyone's mind that tensions would be running high when the Saints and Cats took the floor. Nobody knew just how high.

On January 26, 1968, Hazleton's Feeley Theater was showing a film starring James Coburn titled *The Presidents Analyst.* Meanwhile, the Grand was advertising the exclusive limited engagement showing of *Valley of the Dolls.* The Grand's newspaper ad noted that the film was "For Mature Audiences." Based on the early sale of tickets to the Saints-Wildcats game, it was clear that the Grand's management wasn't going to have to worry about turning away students from either school at the theater box office.

It was standing room only at Mother of Grace by the time the West Hazleton JV team left the floor with a 61-43 win in the preliminary contest. There was literally no room to move in the building as the two teams took the floor for pregame warm-ups. Both fan bases were loud and vocal. Sitting in the bleachers, one got the feeling of sitting on a powder keg ready to blow.

From the opening tip-off it was clear that Coach Gatski had instructed his Wildcats to play a physical game. Before the night was over, the G-Men would shoot forty-four free throws. While free throws were being shot, fans noticed the odd behavior of West Hazleton's Mike Gallagher. Gallagher had been given the difficult task of guarding Dennis Olexa. During those breaks in the action, Gallagher would approach Olexa and, while holding his hands in front of his face as if something were in them, say something to Saint Gabriel's star backcourt player. Olexa remembers that "he was pretending to hold a camera and he kept saying that he was taking my picture because Hoffman and I liked to get our pictures in the paper." During time-outs, Gallagher would leave the West Hazleton players gathered around their coach and move toward the Saint Gabriel's players who were listening to Coach Cryan's instructions. It appeared that Gatski had decided that he wasn't going to beat these G-Men with a gimmick defense—he was going to change the pace of the game with the rough play and try to get into the heads of the opposing players and their young coach.

At the end of the first eight minutes, the G-Men held a 19-14 lead. Both fan bases were cheering wildly every time their team scored and, as the local paper later reported, the atmosphere inside the gym was tense. West Hazleton, perhaps feeding off last year's upset or enjoying the physical nature of the contest, continued to hang tight through the second quarter. At half, the underdog Wildcats trailed by eight, 34-26.

The play on the court grew even rougher in the third quarter and referees Jack Shema and Vince Rosata began calling it close in an attempt to get the game under control. Saint Gabriel's—led by Hoffman, Olexa, and Heffernan—maintained a steady lead, but they couldn't shake West Hazleton. Meanwhile, Mike Gallagher kept taking his imaginary pictures. By the midway through the third quarter he must have been on his fourth role of film.

Late in the third period, Hoffman made a move to the basket and was in the air when the Wildcats' Dennis Karmonick committed what the referees deemed a flagrant foul that sent the Saints' star crashing to the floor. After the whistle blew Hoffman didn't get up and Coach Cryan and Vince Gallagher rushed to his side. Hoffman was on the floor for what seemed like hours to the G-Men followers. After several minutes he was helped to his feet and, looking around the court, asked, "Who did it?" Karmonick had already been ejected as a result of the foul. Hoffman stayed in the contest and sunk both fouls. After three periods the Saints had extended their lead to 52-40.

In the final quarter, the G-Men began to pull away and with about three minutes left, Hoffman was fouled again. As he was going to the line, Mike Gallagher pulled out his imaginary camera. Coach Cryan called time-out. With his team gathered around him, Cryan said, "Somebody has to take care of that guy." He'd evidently had enough of Gallagher's antics. As Dennis Olexa recalls it, Cryan decided that Mike Heffernan should do it, but Olexa said he interrupted the coach and said he'd do it. It was then that the G-Men set up their play. Cryan said that between the two foul shots, Olexa was going to let Gallagher have it.

Hoffman made the initial shot, and as the referee was getting set to hand him the ball for his second effort, Gallagher raised his arms to take a picture. He didn't get to click the imaginary camera before Olexa caught him with a solid right. In a flash, Olexa and Gallagher were exchanging swings and grappling at half court as Father Deviney raced onto the floor, only to be sent flying over the two players in one direction while his glasses went in another. Both benches quickly emptied and numerous fans spilled onto the floor to exchange blows. Big Neil Darrough, who years before had sunk some key shots to help a Hazleton High team beat Saint Gabriel's, grabbed Paul Hoffman and pulled him away from the action. With Darrough standing in the way, nobody approached the Saint Gabriel's star. It took more than ten minutes for school personnel and police to get things under control. Both Olexa and Gallagher were ejected from the game.

The final score was 81-62, and Saint Gabriel's remained undefeated, winning the first-half crown in a convincing fashion. The two teams were dead even from the field, both netting twenty-four field goals, but the G-Men made thirty-three fouls compared to fourteen for West Hazleton. Wildcat coach Ron Gatski's only comment was, "They're better than we thought they were." In the Saint Gabriel's locker room, Father Deviney, who had retrieved his spectacles, told Dennis Olexa, "You're walking with me as we leave the gym and get on the bus."

Don Barnes writing the next day criticized both fan bases for the near riot. He noted that the gym was overcrowded and speculated the number of spectators contributed to the incident. He criticized West Hazleton fans for booing Paul Hoffman when he was taken out of the game, writing that such a display was totally uncalled for since watching a player with Hoffman's talent was a rare privilege. He also noted the newspaper had received calls from fans of both teams complaining about the other's display of poor sportsmanship. In the sportswriter's view there was plenty of blame to go around, and since these same two teams would meet again in just eleven days, it was in everyone's best interest to calm down and "bury the matter."

By the start of second-half play Saint Gabriel's was the number one team in the region as rated by the *Scranton Times*. The Saints had seven regular season games to play and most observers saw no way of stopping them. Coach Cryan was on the verge of making good on his preseason prediction that this team would go undefeated.

Weatherly was the first opponent for the Saints, and they made short work of the defending league champions, dispatching the Wreckers by a score of 96-58. It was the sixteenth straight win of the season for what Don Barnes coined the "Saint Gabriel's basketball juggernaut." Hoffman scored thirty-five in the win, bringing his career total to 1,986 points. Olexa scored twenty and the sharp-shooting Heffernan added eighteen. Playing with Hoffman and Olexa, Heffernan's significant contributions to the success of the team was often overlooked, though there was no doubt he was having an outstanding senior season. Looking back on those days, Heffernan modestly credits his teammates for much of his success: "Other teams were so busy trying to stop Hoffman and Olexa they left me open and I was getting a lot of open looks and time to shoot."

Ray Saul paid homage to Hoffman in his daily column, writing that more than two thousand people would be on hand the following Tuesday to watch Hoffman score his two thousandth point. According to Saul, Hoffman was a shoe-in to reach that milestone unless Ron Gatski employed a triangle-and-two defense with both the triangle and the two guarding the Saint Gabriel's senior star. It was almost like the outcome of the game wasn't in doubt and the only question was how long it would take Hoffman to reach that summit. Considering the fact that the Saints' opponent was West Hazleton, the lack of excitement about the game's outcome was remarkable.

So it was that in the second week of the second half of the season Saint Gabriel's would face West Hazleton at Saint Joe's and Freeland on the road. Win those two and the only team that realistically stood between them and a league championship as well as an undefeated season was MMI. The Saints' student body and many fans were enjoying the ride. Going back to last year's state title run, the team had won eighteen straight and nobody saw that streak ending anytime soon.

On the day of the West Hazleton game the *Standard Speaker* installed the G-Men as overwhelming favorites and opined that

Coach Gatski might be forced to go to a slowdown game to even stay in the contest. Over the years, Gatski had pulled more than one rabbit out of his hat against the G-Men, but few expected any magic in 1968.

As the two teams went through their pregame warm-ups the referees, Sam Esposito and Gabe Flintosh, gathered both teams' captains to center court. They let the players know in no uncertain terms that they wanted no repeat of the behavior that had led to the melee at Mother of Grace less than two weeks earlier. The Saint Gabriel's student body had draped a banner across the upper deck. It read, "The Cats are Dead."

It didn't take long before the banner appeared to be more a prophecy than a taunt. Three minutes into the game, the Saints were up 17-3 despite two Wildcat time-outs called by Coach Gatski to slow the momentum. Hoffman scored thirteen points in the first period, giving him a career total of 1,999 as the second eight minutes of play began. Two minutes into the second period with the ball in his able hands, Hoffman worked himself loose inside and scored on an easy layup. As Don Barnes reported, bedlam broke loose as "a legend in his own time, has broken the two thousand-point barrier and the ovation reverberates, assaulting the ears in wave after repeated wave." Play was stopped and Hoffman was presented with the game ball that he held as he posed for photos with Coach Cryan and Vince Gallagher. Then it was back to business.

There were no imaginary cameras present in this game, but West Hazleton continued with the physical style of play as evidenced by the fact that the G-Men shot forty-eight fouls before the game was over. When it was, Saint Gabriel's was on top 99-76 and Hoffman had scored thirty-nine points. Barnes noted that Hoffman could have added to his point total had he not passed up many opportunities to score in the second half. As was his custom Hoffman looked to keep his teammates involved once the game had been decided. Coach Gatski and his Wildcats simply had no answers for this year's G-Men.

There was one bright spot for West Hazleton. George Petrylak, a six-foot-three-inch sophomore, scored twenty-seven points for the losers. Petrylak had improved significantly as the year progressed, and he was sure to be a major force in the Anthracite League in the years to come.

On the day after Saint Gabriel's beat West Hazleton, D. A. Harman beat Panther Valley clinching the Anthracite Junior High League championship. Wally Kisthardt scored thirty points in the victory and Charlie Liott added nine. The two freshmen would be moving on to Hazleton High in the coming year, and both would play important parts against Saint Gabriel's at Saint Joe's and on the city playgrounds in the last two years of the parochial high school's existence.

For the G-Men a trip to Freeland was next on the schedule. The Whippets had hung tough with the Saints when they met in the first half, losing by nine at Saint Joe's. Freeland High played their home games at the Freeland Y, and they were known to be very tough on their home court. Still, Olexa would be in the lineup this time, and that more than made up for any advantage Freeland might get from not having to travel. The Saint Gabriel's offense was the most potent anyone had ever seen in the area, and few believed that Freeland could score enough to keep pace.

The Freeland court, once considered a mecca, was one of the smallest in the league by the 1960s. Though the cramped conditions may have slowed the G-Men down, it didn't stop them in a game where they never trailed. The final score of 72-51 was a little deceiving as the Whippets had stayed within ten points most of the way. Midway through the fourth quarter, Coach Cryan went into a freeze, and Freeland was forced to foul to get the ball. The Saints hit their foul shots, which accounted for the final margin of victory.

Once again Hoffman, Olexa, and Heffernan were all in double figures with twenty-six, twenty, and eleven points respectively. Darraugh just missed with nine. For Freeland, Jim Titus led the way, scoring eighteen. Freeland was another young club that would lose only one starter to graduation. Come next year, they would certainly have a say in the Anthracite title chase. As for Saint Gabriel's, it would have been difficult to find a local resident who didn't share the opinion that this was the finest squad ever to wear the purple and white.

By the time Saint Gabriel's was scheduled to play Marian Catholic on February 13th, 1968, the Hazleton paper was referring to Hoffman, Olexa, and Heffernan as the most potent 1-2-3 combination ever "seen in these parts." The distinction was well earned as these three often outscored the opposition without the help of their teammates. The Saints had already beaten Marian by thirty-nine in their first half meeting, and most felt that if Coach Wink Gallagher's Colts could come within thirty of the high-flying G-Men in their second meeting, they would have done well.

Wink Gallagher had been coaching for decades. He had seen many good and some great teams over his legendary career. He was not known for being prone to exaggeration or for handing out excessive praise. Therefore, his comments after Saint Gabriel's beat his Marian Colts 89-48 made more news than the game itself. "That's probably the best team in the state, Class A, B or C" was Gallagher's assessment after the game. When asked if he was talking about teams who participated in PCIAA ranks, he wasted not a moment in adding, "I mean PCIAA, PIAA, or what have you." The coach wasn't finished. "I've seen a lot of teams and we played Shamokin Lourdes, but I haven't seen anything like St. Gabriel's." Once again, Hoffman was outstanding for the Saints, scoring thirty points in three quarters of play. The other two members of the big three also turned in strong performances, putting nineteen (Olexa) and eighteen (Heffernan) on the board for Saint Gabriel's. Only one Marian player hit doubles with Jack Pieracini scoring twelve. Junior Tom Andregic, who hit for twenty-four against the Saints in the first-half game, came close with nine.

Father Deviney released the PCIAA schedule the G-Men would have to traverse to win their third state championship. Scranton Holy Rosary would provide the opposition in a first round game. The winner of that contest would meet Plymouth Saint Vincent's. The eastern final would follow against Saint Francis Prep of Spring Grove and the state championship game would be played on March 16th against an opponent to be determined in the Harrisburg area. Few if any doubted that the Saints would be making the trip to Harrisburg and returning with their third consecutive PCIAA Class C state title.

The G-Men had three opponents to face before they could complete an undefeated season. Immaculate Heart of Fountain Springs provided little resistance before falling to the G-Men 89-42. It was the twentieth win of the season, and it continued a winning streak that dated back to February 23, 1966, when it came to games being played at Saint Joe's. Coach Bob Gilbride of the Holy Rosary Beads, whom the G-Men would face in the opening round of the state playoffs, brought his whole team to Hazleton to see the game. Gilbride said he thought the Saints were a fine team, but he thought his team could play with them if they could control the pace of the game. He said his team this year was far better than the one the Saints had beaten 81-58 a year before. The coach added, "If we can beat their press and get the ball up-court it should be a real nice ballgame."

On February 19th Ray Saul wrote that the chances were good that Saint Gabriel's would participate in the prestigious Alhambra basketball tournament held in the Washington, D.C., area late in March. Saul added that Coach Cryan and his team would concentrate on the state playoffs first.

The very next day the headline leading off the *Standard Speaker's* sport pages said it all: "St. Gabriel's Will Face Last Major Obstacle at MMI Tonight." The story detailed the fact that a win would virtually wrap up an undefeated season for the G-Men. The Preppers, it was thought, were capable of giving the Saints a game if they put together one of their better efforts. There was no doubt that Saint Gabriel's had the edge in talent and experience, but this game was being played at MMI, and stranger things at happened in that small gym.

One very interested spectator would be Saint Gabriel's student Joe Farley, who had recently taken the entrance examination for acceptance at the prep school. Farley, like everyone else, had no idea about the changes that were to occur at Saint Gabriel's in the next few months. Those coming events would keep Farley at Saint Gabriel's for the next year.

If there was any doubt in anyone's mind about the outcome, the G-Men erased them early when they shot off to a 19-5 lead on the way to a convincing 86-48 victory. Don Barnes summed it up, writing that "St. Gabriel's crushed MMI like a bug last night." MMI coach Dave Shafer was subdued after the game. "What can you say? They're a good ball team and we didn't have it tonight." Paul Hoffman set another school record when he scored twenty-nine, making his senior season total 613. That number surpassed the school single-season scoring record previously held by Chico Ferdinand, who scored 605 points in twenty-four games back in 1956.

In a radio interview after the game, Coach Cryan said he never worried about the outcome of this contest but was worried about facing Jim Thorpe in the final game of the regular season. He pointed out that in their last six games, the Olympians had been allowing only fifty-six points per game. Some thought Cryan's comments were an attempt to boost ticket sales.

It was senior day at Saint Joe's gym the night that Saint Gabriel's looked to complete the first undefeated basketball season in the school's history. It would also mark the last home court appearance for four players. Rocco Fallabel, who had played the role of sixth man perfectly, would take his final bow. It would be the final appearance for Mike Heffernan, who would have been the star on other area teams. Dennis Olexa, who may well have been in the discussion for All-State honors on other squads, would display his wares before a home crowd for the last time. All three players received a tremendous ovation when they were introduced prior to the game by the Voice of the G-Men Bob Farley, who was also a senior performing his duties for the last time. When Farley introduced Hoffman, the ovation was deafening. Even the visitors from Jim Thorpe joined in to acknowledge the senior who was the greatest basketball player ever produced by the Hazleton area. The senior cheerleaders were also honored, and before the game began, the senior class song *Words* by the Bee Gees was played through the gym's loudspeakers.

Thorpe decided to play a semi slowdown game in an attempt to stay with the G-Men. After eight minutes the strategy appeared to have some success as the Saints led by a mere five points 16-11. Of more concern to Saint Gabriel's fans was a leg injury suffered by Paul Hoffman in those first eight minutes. The Saints star had gone flying hard into a wall chasing a loose ball. Hoffman continued to play but was obviously hobbled. After the game he was examined at Saint Joseph's hospital, where it was revealed that he had suffered a severe contusion of the leg complicated by internal bleeding and would keep him sidelined for at least a week. Fortunately, the Saints would have a week off before beginning the defense of their state title.

Hoffman still scored seventeen in the game, but it was Olexa who picked up the slack, netting twenty-seven in leading Saint Gabriel's to a 74-37 win and the first undefeated season in the school's history. Olexa, singled out for criticism by Coach Cryan for his performance in the previous game against MMI, was flawless. He scored outside and inside, on jump shots and hook shots, and he even used the behind-the-back dribble to leave a Thorpe defender flat-footed on his way to an easy layup. Hoffman's career point total now stood at 2,161, which placed him eighth all time in Pennsylvania history. Among those who had scored more career points in their high school days were Wilt Chamberlain and Tom Gola, and both would be within Hoffman's reach in the post season.

On the very evening the Saint Gabriel's student body and fans celebrated the unprecedented season, Father Deviney announced the school had accepted an invitation to compete in the Alhambra tournament, which would host eight of the top-rated Catholic schools in a five-state area. But before they could even think about Alhambra, the G-Men had to face another highly rated team, Scranton Holy Rosary, in the first round of the state playoffs.

Coach Cryan and his team had made good on his preseason prediction that the team would go undefeated. While the Saints fans were in the midst of wild celebrations, one thought remained on the minds of many of them: How badly was Hoffman hurt and would he be able to play?

If Cryan had really been concerned about the outcome of the Jim Thorpe game, he would have been unaware of the celebration that fans had planned for the team after the contest. According to Ray Saul, the Saints players, official athletic staff, parents of the players, and ardent followers of the G-Men gathered at the local Elks club to celebrate the league championship and the undefeated season. The celebration included a "wonderful buffet dinner," a toastmaster, and prepared remarks from multiple speakers. Father Deviney and Hoffman arrived late to the celebration since they came via a visit to the hospital.

With less than a week to go before starting the defense of their state title, the word on Hoffman's health was not encouraging. It was being reported that the region's leading scorer would be hampered and limited by the injury if he was able to play at all. Considering the fact the Scranton Holy Rosary Beads were considered the toughest test the Saints would face in the playoffs, the news created apprehension among the Saints' faithful fans. Within the halls of Saint Gabriel's students were reassuring each other that Hoffman would be ready to go. Whether that was the case was difficult to tell: some of the rumors said the injury was far more serious than anyone was admitting, while others were saying he was healing quickly and was going to play at 100 percent.

On the day of the first playoff game, the *Standard Speaker* had Hoffman listed as probable to start that night. What was concerning was the fact that The G-Men's star had missed a full week of practice and had only engaged in what was called a light workout the day before the game. Coach Cryan had scouted Holy Rosary and said he was impressed with their team offense, but he gave his team the edge defensively. While the paper declared Saint Gabriel's as the favorite, it added that it might be necessary "to pull out all the stops against the Beads."

When the G-Men took the floor to warm-up one thing was obvious to the more than two thousand fans gathered at the Scranton CYC. Paul Hoffman's right leg was heavily taped from below the knee to the hip. The tape job was performed by the Hazleton High School football coach Adam Sieminski. The Hazleton coach had been attending an Army Reserve meeting in West Pittston, after which he hurried to Scranton to give Hoffman a professional tape job. Even taped Hoffman's discomfort was obvious; he grimaced in pain every time he came down on his right foot.

Once the game started it was clear that Hoffman was playing at 50 percent at best. To make matters worse for the G-Men, Olexa was having an off night from the outside. The talented guard couldn't find the net. Holy Rosary was playing a compact zone, so the shots were there–they just weren't falling. At half the score was knotted at twenty-seven, and it was clear that this game was going down to the wire.

With two minutes to go in the third period the G-Men were leading 34-30 and had the ball. Cryan ordered his team to hold the ball, hoping to get Holy Rosary to abandon their zone defense. The Beads stubbornly refused to change defenses, and the G-Men held the ball to the buzzer, when John Darraugh hit a long jumper to make it 36-30 after three periods.

At the beginning of the final quarter, Saint Gabriel's controlled the tap and went right back into their freeze. Holy Rosary stayed in their zone and waited for the Saints to make a mistake. Two minutes later, the G-Men turned the ball over and Bob Walsh hit form distance for the Beads to make it 36-32. On the next possession Mike Heffernan made one of his few mistakes of the night and threw an errant pass out of bounds.

Walsh scored again and it was 36-34. With just over a minute to go and trailing by two, Holy Rosary finally abandoned the zone and went to a man-to-man defense. John Darraugh got careless with a pass and after the steal, Holy Rosary called time-out. When play resumed, the Beads got the ball to their top scorer Jim Casey, who faked left and drove right before dropping in the tying goal.

The G-Men had the ball and were working to get a good shot when Heffernan was tied up with thirty seconds to go. After a contested jump ball and a scramble for possession, the Saints gained control and got the ball to Olexa, who drove to the basket and let go a shot that hit the rear of the rim and rolled almost completely around the iron before dropping through just as the referee blew his whistle. Olexa was called for an offensive foul that occurred after the ball had left his hands. The bucket counted, putting Saint Gabriel's in front 38-36, but Casey was heading to the line for Holy Rosary with six seconds left to play. Casey's shot bounced off the rim into the hands of the Saints' Pat Curry, who was tied up by the much shorter Tom Crofton with four seconds to play. Easily controlling the jump ball, Curry batted the basketball deep down court, and time ran out before the Beads could get off a shot. The Saints had survived by the skin of their teeth.

Though Olexa had scored the winning basket, it was Mike Heffernan's first-half play that had kept Saint Gabriel's in the contest. The sharpshooter, who was the Saints' high scorer, hit all thirteen of his points in the first sixteen minutes of play. The only other Saint Gabriel's player to hit doubles was the hobbled Hoffman, who scored ten. Darraugh came close with nine. For the Beads, Jim Casey, who Hoffman remembers as one of the finest high school players he ever faced, scored eighteen.

For probably the first time since he had taken the reins from Digger Phelps, Jack Cryan was being criticized by some Saint Gabriel's fans. In particular, they were upset about a team averaging ninety points a game going to a freeze with twelve minutes still to play in a game. In Cryan's defense, he certainly knew more than the fans about the seriousness of Hoffman's injury and the strain his star was putting on his leg. The hope at this point was that Hoffman's atrophied thigh muscles would start to strengthen. Plymouth Saint Vincent's was up next for the G-Men and though they weren't as highly regarded as Holy

Rosary, they were still dangerous—especially if Saint Gabriel's didn't play better ball than they had against the Beads.

By the day Saint Gabriel's was to face Saint Vincent's on March 8, 1968, the reports were that Hoffman was feeling much better and was expected to operate at about 80 percent. The Vinnies had lost only four games all year, and two of those were to a good Class B team, Saint Mary's of Wilkes-Barre. The final loss to Saint Mary's by a score of 61-54 decided the Catholic League title. Saint Vincent's also owned two wins over MMI by margins of fourteen and twenty-one points. The word on Saint Vincent's was that they were a team that liked to run. Playing at a brisk pace was seen to favor Saint Gabriel's. If Hoffman was indeed healthy, the Saints were a solid choice to bring home a victory.

Once the game began, Hoffman looked much improved. In front of two thousand fans at the Wilkes-Barre Coughlin gym the G-Men dashed out to a 24-11 first half lead. The two teams played an even second quarter, but starting the second half the Saints scored six straight points to take a 45-26 lead, and they didn't look back on their way to a 78-59 win. Hoffman once again led the Saints in scoring with twenty-six, and Heffernan, who played a near perfect game, was a shade behind with twenty-five. Tom Kennedy scored thirty-two for the losers but didn't get the support he needed from his supporting cast to stay in the game. Though Coach Cryan was upset over the number of turnovers his team committed, he was happy with his team's defensive effort and rebounding.

Ray Saul took particular notice of Heffernan's play in the game, writing that the Saint Gabriel's senior was "one of the most under-rated players in the region." Saul pointed out that Heffernan had been a key component in the Saints' last two victories. The Saints were now two games away from a third straight state championship and they would travel to York, Pennsylvania, to meet their next foe, Saint Francis Prep of Spring Grove. Father Deviney announced tickets to the eastern final would be on sale at the school and buses would depart the school at 4:30 for fans interested in making the trip.

In Saint Gabriel's final practice before the game, Hoffman twisted his injured leg in a workout. Coach Cryan reported that while his star suffered some pain and discomfort, he seemed to bounce back okay. Though the Saints were the heavy favorites heading into the contest, Saint Francis was said to be an out-standing shooting team that had the ability to give any team trouble.

By halftime, the G-Men were clearly in trouble. They entered the locker room trailing 29-23. Father Deviney entered the room and headed right for Hoffman and asked if his leg was all right. Before the Saints' star could answer, Coach Cryan stormed in and headed to a portable chalkboard that had been wheeled into the locker room. Cryan never reached for a piece of chalk or an eraser—instead, he reared back and delivered a sharp right, cracking the board. Heffernan remembers that the punch got the team's attention. "We had seen him break clipboards during games but never a chalkboard." The punch apparently got Father Deviney's attention as well, though he kept quiet at the time.

The G-Men were still trailing after three quarters 41-37 but scored the first eight points of the final period to take a 45-41 lead. The Saint Francis coach Lou Sabler called a time-out and steadied his team. They responded by knotting the score at forty-five. With time running out, the G-Men were trailing by a point. Dennis Olexa inbounded the ball under his own basket. When no Saint Gabriel's player broke free, Olexa threw the ball in, hitting a Saint Francis player on the back. After the ball hit the floor Olexa jumped inbounds, grabbed it, and laid it in to put the G-Men up by a point.

With the Saints leading 55-54 and time running out, Frankies' Jerry Gagnon threw up a contested shot from the right wing. That shot wasn't even close, and two G-Men along with Kevin O'Flaherty for Saint Francis went up for the air ball. O'Flaherty got there first and sent the ball heading toward the rim with a one hand flip. It tickled the twine as the final buzzer sounded, and Saint Gabriel's was beaten for the first time since the previous season. A twenty-six-game winning streak was over and with it any chance for a third straight state championship.

After the game Coach Cryan didn't use Hoffman's injury as an excuse. He simply said that his star player had an off night. Hoffman scored twelve points in the game while being constantly double teamed. Looking back, Hoffman says, "They really didn't have to double team me. I couldn't put my full weight on the right leg. I really couldn't move at all." He also remembers the game as the toughest defeat of his high school career for another reason: "It didn't matter that I was hurt. We were the better team. We should have won."

The other two members of the big three felt similarly. Olexa played brilliantly in the game, leading all scorers with twenty-five points. After all these years he recalls the defeat as the one hardest to take during his time at Saint Gabriel's. "To this day it's hard for me to believe we lost that game." Heffernan scored eleven in the game and maintains that the G-Men were by far the better team and should never have lost that night. He says, "I can still see that last shot going in. I'll never forget how I felt."

Coach Cryan had gone all the way with five players and pointed to turnovers as the main reason for the defeat. He was quick to add that he remained proud of the team and all they had accomplished during the course of the season.

On the day after the game, Olexa was sitting in class when he was told to report to Coach Cryan's office. All the way down the halls and then the stairs, Olexa was wondering, *What did I do now?* He was sure he was in some kind of trouble. A somber coach greeted Olexa, who took a seat. Coach Cryan said that he was going to tell him something in confidence. What he said caught his backcourt ace totally by surprise. The coach said he had just come from a meeting with Father Deviney and that he had been informed that he wouldn't be back as coach the following year. He told Olexa that Father Deviney thought he had been a bad influence on the boys.

A few days later, Saint Gabriel's officials announced Hoffman would not play in the upcoming Alhambra tournament. Hoffman, the officials said, had played in constant pain throughout the state playoffs and that the leg injury wasn't healing as expected. Fearing that playing in the tournament could make matters worse, the decision had been reached to hold him out of the competition. Father Deviney said the decision to play Hoffman in the state playoffs had been a mistake, and he would blame himself if it ended up costing Hoffman a spot on the All-State team. Hoffman needed just fourteen point to pass Wilt Chamberlain's career point total and wasn't going to get the chance. Without Hoffman, the G-Men made the trip but came out on the short end in three straight games. The greatest basketball season in the history of the school was over, and so was the Hoffman era.

16

THE THIRD QUARTER

JERRY

The fact that Coach Cryan was not going to return for the 1969 season was known to few. After sharing the news with Olexa, the coach sat down with the rest of his seniors and told them, though he requested they keep the information to themselves. The circle of those in the know included Monsignor Maher and Father Deviney but extended no further. As far as the vast majority of Saint Gabriel's students knew, Jack Cryan was the coach and he would continue in that position.

The Hazleton Area School Board was behind the first coaching change in the area. On March 21, 1968, the board voted to dismiss the entire coaching staff at Hazleton High. By a 6-2 margin with one abstention, Fran Libonati was removed as the head basketball coach. The announcement included notice that applications were being accepted to fill the position. Ray Saul was critical of the action taken by the board. He noted that Libonati had a winning record and was an excellent teacher and role model for the boys he coached. Saul also predicted that Libonati would be the first coach at the as yet non-existent though long rumored Hazleton central Catholic high school.

A day later, the first of several post-season honors was bestowed on Paul Hoffman. The region's leading scorer was named to the United Press International Little All-State first team. Others named to the team included Tom McMillan from Mansfield and Dave Twardzik, who played his high school ball at Middletown.

Within a week the Associated Press All-State team was announced, and Hoffman also secured a spot on that first team.

Hoffman had finished his career as the fourth highest scorer in Pennsylvania high school history. He trailed only Ron Krick, Larry Miller, and Wilt Chamberlain. More awards were sure to come Hoffman's way at a series of post-season banquets planned to honor the G-Men. The big question was at which college Hoffman would decide to continue his basketball career.

In an interview with Ray Saul, the G-Men's star said he was considering St. Bonaventure, Brigham Young, Kansas, Oregon State, and Kings. Saul's story also included quotes from some notables about the young phenom. Stan Watts, the head coach at Brigham Young, said, "We consider Hoffman the brightest young prospect in the eastern United States." Ed Donohue, the head man at Kings, said if he could land Hoffman, he would build his team around him. Father Deviney called Hoffman the most unselfish kid he had ever known, adding, "He is the perfect example of what a young man should be." In the end, Hoffman decided to attend St. Bonaventure.

Though less than a month had passed since the end of the 1968 high school basketball season, Don Barnes was already looking ahead to next year. On April 16th the Anthracite League held their league banquet where, as the sportswriter noted, the Saint Gabriel's delegation would accept the championship trophy after dominating the league in a manner seldom seen. Barnes wrote that Freeland, MMI, and West Hazleton already had designs on next year's title, and they all had the stuff to bring it home. Saint Gabriel's wouldn't part with the championship easily, which only added to the forthcoming drama. He said that the league in 1969 "bears the early promise of being the merriest race since Jack beat Fee-Fi-Fo-Fum down the beanstalk." Then Barnes dropped a morsel, writing that after two excellent years, Jack Cryan might be too hot a property to stick around for a third. Had Barnes gotten wind of what had transpired between Deviney and his coach?

While the high school season was over, there was still some basketball being played. The seventh and eighth graders of Freeland Saint Mary's coached by Ron Gerlach won their third straight Diocesan title and the Pennsylvania-New Jersey championship by beating Saint Elias of Carteret, New Jersey, 77-72 in overtime. All five Saint Mary's starters scored in double figures, including Joe Feno with twelve. Feno would play a major role on a MMI state championship team in just a few years.

On Wednesday, April 24, 1968, the *Standard Speaker* reported the voting results from the primary elections held the day before. Of far more interest to area sports fans was the headline on page twenty-four boldly announcing that "Jack Cryan Won't Return as St. Gabriel's Coach in 1968-69." It appeared Don Barnes had some solid information when he had ventured the opinion just a few days earlier that Cryan's days with the G-Men were numbered.

The announcement stunned the vast majority of the Saints' followers. Cryan was arguably the most successful coach in the school's history. In two years he had won both a league and a state title. His regular season record was an amazing 43-1 and he was 47-7 overall. He had a record of 5-1 against Hazleton and West Hazleton. His was going to be a very difficult act to follow.

Commenting on his resignation, Cryan said, "I will certainly miss my association with the athletes at Saint Gabriel's. The boys gave it everything they had in every game and cooperated with me to the fullest extent of their capabilities. What we achieved was the result of hard work by everyone directly involved."

What was puzzling to many was the fact that Cryan hadn't resigned to accept another job. As a matter of fact, he said that at present he didn't have any definite plans in mind but was in the process of negotiating with several schools. Ray Saul was of the opinion that Cryan would be leaving Saint Gabriel's but not the local area. Saul's prediction proved true when Cryan accepted the position as freshman coach at King's College in Wilkes-Barre. The contrast between Cryan and his predecessor Richard "Digger" Phelps was striking. When Phelps announced his resignation, it was to take a job offer he said was too good to pass up, while Cryan, at the time he announced his exit, had no solid plan.

There were rumors as to the reason for the decision. Some were saying that with Hoffman gone, he was losing his meal ticket and getting out while the getting was good. Truth be told, Saint Gabriel's was losing a lot more than Hoffman. The other members of the big three, Olexa and Heffernan, would also be graduating, as would last season's dependable sixth man Rocco Fallabel. Opposing teams' fans were saying that Cryan didn't want to stick around and take the licks that were awaiting him in the coming season. Few who had ever come into contact with Jack Cryan bought this explanation. They knew his competitive nature would have welcomed the chance to show that he could be successful with his returning squad.

In retrospect, it should have been obvious that Cryan didn't leave Saint Gabriel's of his own accord. While it was true the school would be hit hard by graduation, two starters, John Darraugh and Pat Curry, would return from the undefeated '68 squad. In addition, the Saints' JV team had an outstanding year, and players like Jimmy Brown and Jerry Gallagher were more than ready for varsity action. Perhaps most telling was the fact that the most talented freshman class in the history of the school would be moving up to compete on the next level. Cryan had been active in recruiting some of the key components of that freshman unit, including Larry Walko and Robby Marusak. The resignation didn't add up under even a cursory examination. Even with the significant losses to graduation, the G-Men would remain a prime contender for next year's league title. If he was planning on jumping ship when Hoffman left, why would he have been building for the future? The answer, of course, is that he had been left no choice. Father Deviney had made the decision for him.

In many ways Father Deviney took a hands-on approach as the school's moderator of athletics. Certainly he was far more involved in the day-to-day operations of the basketball team than his predecessors. In Mike Heffernan's view, he was a "micromanager" before the term became common. What had tipped the scales in Deviney's mind regarding the young coach he had hired? Perhaps it was the fight at West Hazleton. Maybe it was breaking the chalkboard at halftime of the Saint Francis Prep game. It could well have been a combination of factors, some of which are known to but a few people to this day. The bottom line remained the same: Father Deviney would be searching for the fourth coach to take the reins at Saint Gabriel's since his arrival just a few years earlier. Though few knew it at the time, Deviney's next hire would also be the last head high school basketball coach in Saint Gabriel's history.

In early May, Digger Phelps was announced as the main speaker at the Saint Gabriel's championship banquet scheduled for May 8th at Stan Genetti's Pennsylvania Room. Phelps was coming off a fine 18-5 season coaching the University of

Penn freshmen. Those who would also deliver remarks included Monsignor Maher, Father Deviney, Father Conboy, Coach
Cryan, and Ray Saul.

The banquet served as the final chance to pay tribute to Paul
Hoffman, who left loaded down with honors. Ray Saul presented him with his All-State trophy and Father Deviney awarded
him the team's most valuable player award. His uniforms were
retired and a life-sized painting of Hoffman in action by Katie
Mackenzie, a Saint Gabriel's student artist, was displayed. That
painting would be hung in the school gymnasium flanked by
the two state championship banners. Jack Cryan received two
standing ovations—the first after his speech, and the second
coming at the end of the program when his players presented
him with gifts. The other major announcement made during the
festivities was that Saint Gabriel's veteran junior high and assistant coach Vince Gallagher had resigned. Gallagher was going out on top having just won the Public Parochial Junior High
Championship. He had been involved with the Saint Gabriel's
basketball program for thirty years and no Saint Gabriel's
coach would ever mentor more players who were members of
the school's state championship teams than Gallagher.

Hazleton High beat Saint Gabriel's to the punch when they
announced their new head basketball coach, Gene Evans, on
June 3rd. Evans was chosen over twenty other applicants for
the position. Hazleton's new man had experience at both the
high school and college level having been the head coach at
Carlisle High School and Bucknell University. Hazleton, perhaps following the example set by Father Deviney, went outside
the local area to hire their head man. As far as Hazleton High
School basketball went, this was a first. A day after the announcement, Evans was at his new high school meeting with
over sixty perspective candidates who intended to try out for his
first team.

By mid-June Saint Gabriel's students and fans were wondering when their new coach would be named. There were rumors. Some said Fran Libonati recently let go by Hazleton was
interested. Other rumors involved an unnamed coach from New
Jersey. Some folks were saying you never could tell with Deviney
as to who or how far he would go in his search for a head man.
Saint Gabriel's wasn't out of the area's sporting news as Paul
Hoffman was chosen as the winner of the Scotty Roman award

as the region's outstanding high school athlete. Hoffman joined fellow G-Man Pete O'Donnell as a Roman award winner. Saints' players had earned the honor in two of the last three years.

As the summer progressed so did play in the Hazleton playground basketball league. Pine Street, instead of South Side, continued to be the home away from home chosen by the G-Men. By the summer of 1968 Dennis Olexa, John Darraugh, Joe Farley, and Jerry Fallabel were all on the Pine Street team that on July 24th beat South Side by a score of 114-31. Just three days later, the news came that those four and the rest of Saint Gabriel's parish and sports fans in the area had been waiting for.

The headline read simply "St. Gabriel's Hires Coach." Underneath was a picture of Father Deviney shaking the hand of a smiling Jerry Anderson, the new basketball and baseball coach chosen to replace Jack Cryan. Anderson remembers Deviney as "a wonderful man." He said Deviney hired him largely because he was recommended by Hazleton High's football coach Adam Sieminski. Anderson served in a national guard unit with Sieminski and the two had become friends. According to Anderson, it all fit together nicely: "They were looking for a coach, and I was looking for a job."

The new coach was a graduate of Berwick High School and East Carolina College. Though he played basketball at Berwick, his strongest sport was football, where he became the first player from Berwick to be named to Pennsylvania's Big 33 team. Anderson was newly married like his predecessors, but unlike Phelps and Cryan he was not new to the area. Speaking to the local paper, he said that he planned to stress defense and hoped to put a balanced club on the floor. In what might have been considered a prophecy, he said he wanted to have eight players that he could consider starters. By the end of his first year, at least that many players would appear in a Saint Gabriel's starting lineup. The paper concluded by saying that with all of Saint Gabriel's recent successes, the new coach faced a challenging assignment in his first job. This would be his first head coaching job, and he couldn't have picked a tougher situation. In the last three years Saint Gabriel's had won two state titles and a league championship and the fans and followers of the G-Men expected that winning to continue.

Father Deviney was following the path that had led him to success with his first two hires by finding a young coach eager to make his mark. In many ways Anderson was more like Phelps than Cryan. He certainly didn't have Cryan's playing ability, and he would have been the first to tell you that in terms of his own abilities basketball was not his top sport. After a football injury ended his college playing career he served as an assistant coach at East Carolina in their basketball program. Now the square-jawed, short-haired, amiable young man was following the most successful coach in the school's history. Looking back, Anderson said he didn't feel intimidated by following two coaches who had won state titles, saying, "I didn't know them from Adam—I just wanted to coach."

In late August the city playground championship was played at the James Street playground. As would become the norm for the next few years the title game pitted Pine Street against D. A. Harman. Jerry Fallabel led Pine Street to a 56-41 win before a large crowd who either brought lawn chairs or found standing room around the court. Jimmy Munley, Joe Curry, and Joe Farley joined Fallabel in the victory celebration afterwards. Pete Gentile scored ten for the visitors from the north side of town.

The summer faded and school began as more than 12,000 area students headed back to the classrooms. Parents complained about overcrowding at a few local elementary schools. At Saint Gabriel's many of the students were anxious to eye up the new basketball coach who would be teaching history. The Hoffman era may have ended but expectations remained high.

No sooner had the Saint Gabriel's students settled into a routine then a major announcement was made. Both Father Deviney and Father Conboy were being transferred to other parishes. The priests bid farewell to the students at an assembly. Both were greeted with applause, but Deviney's speech surprised some when he went out of his way to apologize to those students who felt he had slighted them during his time at Saint Gabriel's. He didn't dwell on his accomplishments, which were many. As athletic moderator, he had guided Saint Gabriel's basketball through the most successful period in the school's history. His decision to bring coaches in from outside the local area had affected the style of play throughout the region, especially in terms of the focus on defense. Offensively, Jack Cryan had, by his own example, increased the shooting range of local athletes. Having seen the coach shoot from distances considered outside the range of most local players, many experimented and found they could be successful as well. Coaches seeing the success their players were having shooting from the increased distances were more lenient in judging the shooting range of some of their players.

Filling Deviney's shoes wasn't going to be easy. His successor was Father Wayne Doherty, another young priest with an easygoing manner who took a much softer approach than his predecessor. Doherty seldom attended a practice and was the furthest thing from a micromanager one could imagine. He seemed determined to let Coach Anderson do the coaching while he applied himself to the administrative duties as athletic moderator. His attention to detail would play an important role in bringing another championship to the school now in its final two years of existence.

17

INBOUNDS PLAY

ANOTHER YEAR, ANOTHER PLAYOFF

On November 1, 1968, Jerry Anderson addressed his Saint Gabriel's team for the first time. The players sat in the first couple rows in the small Saint Gabriel's gym. Two state championship banners hung on the rear walls with a life-sized painting of Paul Hoffman completing a layup between them. Standing before the group Anderson began, "Today I'm addressing the defending Anthracite League champions. I expect to stand right here a year from now and say the exact same thing." The coach's introduction then moved on to what he expected: a team in excellent condition able to go full tilt for four quarters. He stressed defense and talked about how he expected everyone to contribute. The goal was winning, winning would take work, and that work would start today. Then practice began.

Anderson had clearly laid out the goal, but getting there wasn't going to be easy. There was definitely no dominant team in the Anthracite League heading into the new season. MMI was going to be talented and experienced. Freeland would suit up its best team in a decade. West Hazleton wasn't going to take a back seat, though the Wildcats would rely on younger players. Saint Gabriel's would contend even after losing the big three to graduation. Jim Thorpe and Marian wouldn't be pushovers. It was going to be a long and wild ride.

Saint Gabriel's returned two starters from last year's squad. John Darraugh would be expected to give the Saints outside scoring power while Pat Curry would be a stabilizing force close to the basket. Those two seniors were joined by classmates Jerry

Gallagher, Jimmy Brown, John Ammon, and John Goryl as the most experienced players on the squad. There were four juniors on the team: John Ferry, John Breslin, Emil Polchin and Joe Farley. Farley had returned from a year away from organized ball, after deciding against a transfer. There was major talent coming from the current sophomore class with Larry Walko, Jerry Fallabel, Joe Curry, and Jimmy Munley all expected to see some action with the varsity.

The G-Men were facing a tough exhibition schedule to get them ready them for league play that promised to be just as difficult. First up would be the Scranton South Catholic team that had taken the Saints to the wire a year earlier. Two days before the opener, Coach Anderson received some bad news. Pat Curry was ill and likely unable to play against the Dons.

With or without Curry, the G-Men were going to be a team short on varsity experience. In preseason scrimmages, it was obvious that the team leaned heavily on John Darraugh, especially on the offensive side of the court. He had emerged as the leader on this team, though by example more than by words. If he had something to say to another player, he did so in private. Darraugh was a solid basketball player, a competent ball handler with an outstanding outside shot and a quick release. On the basketball court he cared about one thing: winning.

On Friday, November 28th, the stands at Saint Joe's were filled with fans anxious to see the latest edition of G-Men. The Saints' JV team got things started by beating the Scranton team 52-47. When the varsity appeared, they were the first Saint Gabriel's team since 1964 to take the floor without Hoffman. From the opening tip, it was obvious this was going to be a close one. After one quarter, the Dons had a 17-16 lead. It was also evident the Saints were playing an aggressive defense that sent the Scranton team to the foul line more than Coach Anderson would have liked. In the second quarter, Saint Gabriel's shots couldn't find the basket and the G-Men headed to the locker room trailing 31-22.

John Darraugh put the Saints on his back in the third period. His field goal from the top of the key tied the score at thirty-seven. South Scranton called a time-out and then staged a small run of their own to take a 46-41 lead into the last eight minutes of play. The Saints scored the first six points of the final period to take a 47-46 lead. The Dons answered when Paul Steinmetz, who would go twelve for twelve from the foul line, hit two of them to regain the advantage. With under a minute to play, another goal by Darraugh pulled the Saints within one at 54-53. South Scranton went into a stall, and the Saints fouled going for the ball. The Dons converted their fouls, and when the buzzer sounded they had erased any chance for another undefeated Saint Gabriel's season by a score of 57-53.

The Saints had lost this one at the foul line, where they converted five of nine attempts while South Scranton was hitting twenty-seven of thirty-six. In the absence of Pat Curry, the visitors had also controlled the boards. John Darraugh had scored thirty of the Saints' fifty-three points, hitting on fifteen of thirty shots from the field. It was obvious the G-Men had to give him some help offensively if this season was going to be successful. Even with the loss, nobody was pushing the panic button. After all, the Saints went without Curry and had played a number of young, inexperienced players. Most Saint Gabriel's fans still had a wait-and-see attitude when it came to this team. Meanwhile, supporters of opposition teams were anxious to avenge the recent losses to the little school whose basketball team had dominated the region for two straight years.

Though a number of local teams like Saint Gabriel's began their season in late November, the first week of December was when the local high school basketball season really got rolling. Between then and the end of the year, fans could expect games every Tuesday and Friday. On Tuesday, December 3rd, virtually all the local teams saw action.

MMI made its first start of the season against Blue Mountain. A year before, the Preppers had lost their first three games before finishing with a record of 14-8. MMI had only lost one starter to graduation and, led by Steve Makuta and Jimmy Kennedy, they had their sights set on a league title. Hazleton High played its first game under new coach Gene Evans against a very strong Bethlehem Freedom club. West Hazleton, which had opened its season with a decisive win over Berwick, headed to Ashland to take on the North Schuylkill Spartans. Freeland, which already had two wins over Crestwood under its belt, hit the road against Southern Area. The Whippets were anxious to continue what many believed would be the best season the school had enjoyed in a long, long time. Saint Gabriel's looked to get back on track against Crestwood. Cardinal Brennan, Jim Thorpe, Marian, and Weatherly were also scheduled to see action.

The Saints took the floor at Saint Joe's determined to get back into the win column. Crestwood did their best to hang on but after eight minutes trailed 19-11. In the second quarter the G-Men caught fire, outscoring the Comets twenty-six to one on the way to an impressive 87-32 win. Saint Gabriel's played an aggressive, stifling defense and was never seriously threatened. Fourteen players wearing the purple and white saw action in Coach Anderson's first win, and twelve of them scored. Joe Farley, who was scoreless in his varsity debut, led the way with fifteen, while Jerry Gallagher, Jimmy Brown, and John Goryl also hit doubles with thirteen, twelve, and ten respectively. Anderson was going to use every chance to get his younger players varsity experience. Grumbling began among the upperclassmen about playing time.

In other games, MMI led by Steve Makuta's twenty-nine points beat Blue Mountain easily. West Hazleton, relying on a lineup consisting primarily of juniors, stayed unbeaten with a 61-47 win over North Schuylkill. Freeland also won easily, as did Jim Thorpe by beating Lehighton. All of a sudden, the Olympians looked like contenders for the league crown. More and more it appeared that the Anthracite League race was going to be wide open.

Hazleton High got off to a rough start, losing to Bethlehem Freedom 61-50 despite an eighteen-point performance by Tony Kinney. Hazleton's new coach Gene Evans wasn't very happy about his team's performance in their first game under his guidance. He pointed to poor shooting, turnovers, and defensive lapses as areas where the Mounts would have to improve to have a successful season. Several Hazleton players, including Wally Kisthardt, Charlie Liott, and Tony Manfredi Jr. were unavailable since they had just joined the team after the completed football season. All three were expected to provide significant contributions on the court as the year progressed.

Next up for the G-Men in what the *Standard Speaker* was referring to as the Hoffman-less era was West Scranton Catholic. The Saints would be on the road for the first time and were considered favorites in the game. Most local observers would stay close to home to catch either West Hazleton take on a fine Shikeillamy team at Mother of Grace or Hazleton against Allentown Allen at Saint Joe's.

West Scranton and the Saints went at it toe to toe in what did seem like a boxing match. At half the G-Men held a slim 48-47 lead. Jerry Gallagher scored nineteen points in those two quarters, but when the second half started he was sitting on the Saint Gabriel's bench. Anderson remembers the game and exactly why he made the move: "We were getting killed underneath, and I felt that I needed to go with a taller lineup in the second half." After three periods the Saints stretched their lead to thirteen on the way to a 90-70 win.

Don Barnes summed the game up writing, "This was undoubtedly the roughest game the G-Men have been engaged in since some of those fabled blood baths over at Freeland St. Ann's. It was downright dirty at times. The onus of roughness lay more on the losers. Down by nineteen points with nineteen seconds remaining in the game, they were still committing intentional fouls with gusto."

John Darraugh, who played from start to finish, led the Saints in scoring with twenty. Gallagher, as mentioned, had nineteen, though he didn't get back on the court after the half-time break. The pleasant surprise for Anderson and the Saints' fans was the play of sophomore Larry Walko, who scored seventeen. Barnes called Walko a player to watch, writing that he was destined to tear the Anthracite League apart in the coming years. Barnes also commented on the depth of the Saint Gabriel's team, saying that the G-Men didn't have to take a backseat to anyone in that department. That depth proved to be both a blessing and a curse as the season wore on.

While the Saints won their bout, Freeland knocked out Central Columbia by a final of 95-49. Five of Coach Casimir Lasecki's Whippets scored in double figures, with Joe Carisa leading the way by hitting for twenty-two. To date nobody had come within twenty points of Freeland, but they would face a stern test against Nanticoke in their next contest. West Hazleton, MMI, and Jim Thorpe also continued their winning ways.

Hazleton High found themselves behind Allentown Allen 66-46 after three periods at Saint Joe's. The Mountaineers roared back in the final eight minutes and actually took a 77-76 lead with forty seconds to play. Allen scored to regain the advantage with eleven ticks left, and a last second Hazleton shot rolled off the rim as the buzzer sounded. The comeback was for naught. Tony Kinney led the Mounts with twenty and Ed Parsons was a shade behind with nineteen. Despite the loss, Coach Evans felt his team was heading in the right direction.

Next up for Saint Gabriel's was Lehighton at Lehighton. This would be the first time these two schools had ever met. The Saints were considered slight favorites going into the game. The two teams played an even first half, but in the final sixteen minutes the G-Men pulled ahead to win by a 59-48 margin. Coach Anderson continued to make liberal use of his bench as ten players saw action. Once again, John Darraugh led Saint Gabriel's in scoring with sixteen. Pat Curry, finally back to full health, scored twelve and pulled down fifteen rebounds. The G-Men had now won three straight after their opening loss and appeared headed in the right direction. Still, there was a restlessness growing among the seniors. John Goryl remembers, "We felt it was our year and Anderson was playing all these underclassmen. We just didn't like it."

Meanwhile, Hazleton High beat Phillipsburg 83-61 for their first win of the season. Ed Parsons scored nineteen while Tony Kinney and Joe Duda hit for seventeen. Tony Manfredi Jr., fresh off the football team, came off the bench and scored eleven. The big news was carried in a headline that draped the second page of sports news in the local paper. It read, "Freeland, West Hazleton and MMI Suffer Initial Cage Defeats." Now the only undefeated Anthracite League team was Jim Thorpe.

The G-Men were off for a week, but other local teams saw action. Hazleton High evened its record at 2-2 by beating Easton 68-53. Once again Tony Kinney led the way for Coach Gene Evans, scoring sixteen while hitting on six of eight shots from the field. West Hazleton turned around and beat the Shamokin team they had lost to three nights earlier. Steve Makuta scored forty-one points to lead MMI to a win over Plymouth St. Vincent's. The victory on the road gave Dave Shafer's club a record of 3-1 as they prepared for league play.

After a week off, Saint Gabriel's traveled to Crestwood and once again easily beat the Comets 81-54 for their fourth straight win. Coach Anderson used fourteen players in the game and ten of them scored. The Saints took another week off before participating in the Kingston West Side Holiday tournament scheduled to begin on December 26th. At this point in the young season, those who thought the significant graduation losses would be too much for Saint Gabriel's to overcome appeared to have been mistaken. The Saints had only suffered one defeat and that was by a narrow margin in their first game without one of their key inside men.

While the G-Men prepared for the holiday tournament, Hazleton went on the road and defeated a tough Allentown Central Catholic team 76-70 in overtime. Filmore Williams played his finest basketball of the year scoring seventeen, and sophomore guard Wally Kisthardt scored ten important points. Elsewhere, Freeland beat Lehighton by twenty and showcased a balanced attack with five players hitting double figures in the win. Jim Thorpe remained undefeated, getting by East Stroudsburg in a tight contest while West Hazleton was beaten by Nanticoke. The Wildcats, now 4-3, would face Hazleton in their last exhibition game.

The solid defense Saint Gabriel's played in the early part of the season was nowhere to be found on the day after Christmas. The opponents from Ashley basically outlasted the Saints and came away with a 104-101 win despite a forty-one-point performance from John Darraugh. The score was tied eight times in the final period, but the G-Men missed a few shots in the final minute that proved the difference. Despite putting 101 points on the board, all the Saints had earned was a spot in the consolation game scheduled for two days later. The night before that contest, Hazleton and West Hazleton would meet in a game sure to fill every seat at Mother of Grace.

Sure enough, fans were turned away at the door on the night of the game between the Mountaineers and the Wildcats. Those lucky enough to get a ticket saw a game to remember, if not one that was flawlessly played. Hazleton was the more experienced team and had a truly outstanding player in Tony Kinney. Coach Ron Gatski's Wildcats relied on a stellar but inexperienced group of juniors that included Tommy Smith, Billy Pavlick, George Petrylak, Laverne Mummey, and Dave Scripko. Hazleton jumped to an early lead and maintained a six-to-eight-point margin for the first three quarters. With eight minutes to play, the Mounts were seemingly in control leading 51-43. According to Ray Saul, the West Hazleton fans, who had been subdued to the point of being quiet, finally came alive in the final period.

Mike Gallagher, a senior, came off the West Hazleton bench and sparked a comeback with several steals that led to quick Wildcat scores. With four minutes to play Hazleton still led 61-56 when Gallagher scored to narrow the margin to three. Hazleton answered with Ed Parsons hitting two fouls with just over two minutes to play, and Hazleton again led by five. At this point Petrylak tapped in a missed shot for the Cats. Gallagher came up with a timely steal that he turned into points when he hit Petrylak with a nifty pass for an easy score. Just like that, Hazleton's lead was cut to one at 63-62.

With a minute and a half remaining, the Cats' Tommy Smith committed his fifth personal and took a seat on the bench with Coach Gatski. Tony Manfredi converted both foul shots for the Mounts. Gallagher responded by hitting a field goal with forty-eight seconds to play, and in a scramble for a loose ball, the Cats' Laverne Mummey was fouled. He hit one of two and the game was tied. Joe Duda missed a shot for Hazleton and then Hazleton coach Gene Evans drew a technical foul when he left his seat on the bench to avert a brewing fight between Ed Parsons and one of the Wildcats. Dave Scripko, who was a tremendous pure shooter, hit the foul shot to give West Hazleton a one-point lead.

Sophomore Wally Kisthardt scored for Hazleton, but Gallagher came right back and scored for the Cats putting them up 68-67 with twenty-three seconds to go. Gallagher stole the ball again and was fouled and made one of two shots to make it 69-67. Hazleton worked the ball inside to Tony Kinney, who made a terrific move and sent the ball toward the rim. As the ball fell through the net, referee Dan Dura blew his whistle and ruled that Kinney had been fouled in the act of shooting. With three seconds left, Hazleton's star calmly walked to the foul line and converted a pressure-filled shot to put Hazleton ahead 70-69. A desperation heave by West Hazleton wasn't close, and the Mountaineers escaped with a narrow win.

Next up for Hazleton would be the G-Men in three days. The Saints were preoccupied with their preparations to play Dallas in the holiday tournament game scheduled for the next evening.

Saint Gabriel's trailed the entire way in the tournament's consolation game and were down by as many as ten points in the last quarter. A late run narrowed that margin to two, and even that was erased when John Darraugh scored to tie the score at sixty-two with twelve seconds to play. After a time-out, Dallas put the ball in play and Charlie LaBerge let go a shot with just three seconds to play. It hit the mark, and the G-Men lost for the second time in three nights. Having lost two tournament games by a total of five points, the mood in the Saint Gabriel's locker was somber. The team was down and with the Hazleton game looming, it couldn't have come at a worse time.

The local paper declared the Mountaineers to be solid favorites to avenge losses to the Saints in the previous two years. Both teams were 4-3, but Hazleton was on a bit of a roll while the G-Men were coming off two close losses and playing their third game in less than a week.

Close to two thousand fans were on hand to watch the two local teams go at it at Saint Joe's. Saint Gabriel's started strong, racing to a quick 8-3 lead, but then the Mounts got on track. After one quarter Hazleton was on top 16-10. On a night when the G-Men needed John Darraugh to have a hot hand, he was coming up empty. In addition, Saint Gabriel's was playing like a team that was tired. They were a step slow defensively and were being badly beaten off the boards. The score at half was 34-19.

The final sixteen minutes was much of the same. Saint Gabriel's was getting good shots but few were dropping. Hazleton, on the other hand, was having one of the better shooting games as a team. Sophomore Wally Kisthardt had the best game of his young career, scoring eighteen in the Mounts' 72-48 win. A sophomore also led Saint Gabriel's—Walko scored seventeen. Curry was the only other player in double figures for the Saints with ten. Darraugh and Farley scored six each for the losers. Hazleton's coach Gene Evans summed things up saying, "St. Gabriel's was working its offense well and we know they have some real fine shooters, but they weren't going in tonight. I think they might have been tired after three games in five nights." Coach Anderson gave Hazleton credit for the way they controlled the boards, and he noted his club had a lot of young talent, adding, "Don't count us out yet."

Clearly the Saint Gabriel's coach was referring to the Anthracite League and a key opening game against West Hazleton later in the week. Looking ahead to that game, Ray Saul wrote, "On the basis of comparative scores West Hazleton would be a shoo-in against the G-Men Friday night, but we certainly don't think anything of the kind. We're looking for a rugged ball game, one that will be close all the way. It's a spectacular way to open what should be one of the finest races in the league's history."

Saint Gabriel's fans were not used to losing three games in a row. As a matter of fact, in the previous two years the Saints didn't lose that many in the regular season. They were letting their feelings be known as evidenced by remarks contained in Ray Saul's January 2, 1969, column. Saul wrote that Saint Gabriel's fans "of long standing" were upset with Coach Jerry Anderson's use of relatively inexperienced underclassmen in tight situations. The morale of the seniors on the team was said to be low. Saul said he seldom published complaints of this kind, but the opinion had been expressed by so many people that it had become newsworthy.

Looking back John Goryl, a senior at the time, remembers the seniors "were upset about the playing time we were getting." He adds that Anderson may not have been given a fair shake. "He was so different than Jack Cryan, some of us decided we just didn't like him." Joe Farley remembers the discontent among the seniors as well. "The anger and frustration was hanging over the team like a dark cloud. Some of the players were voicing their complaints in public, and I think that's what led to the newspaper coverage. I didn't realize it at the time, but Coach Anderson had been put in a very tough situation. As a team we felt we had lost games we should have won, but we all didn't agree on the reasons." Whatever the problems, with West Hazleton being the next opponent they were going to have to be addressed quickly.

Whether Anderson had read the papers or decided to take a new approach with the start of league play was an open question after the game. Only seven players saw action for the G-Men, and of the seven only three were underclassmen—Walko, Farley, and Jimmy Munley. Before over 1,600 fans, the Wildcats started strong and raced to a 12-3 lead, forcing Anderson to call a time-out in order to stem the tide. After the time-out, the Saints settled down and the score after one quarter of play was West Hazleton 17, Saint Gabriel's 14. The second quarter was dominated by defense as neither team seized control. When the buzzer sounded ending the second quarter, the Wildcats had a 26-20 lead.

At the beginning of the second half West Hazleton scored six points while blanking the G-Men. The Cats sat on top of a

32-20 lead with just twelve minutes to play, and it looked like the rout was on. It was at this point that someone hit the Saints' "on" switch. Jim Brown scored and Curry followed with a quick field goal. The G-Men went to a full-court press and it rattled the visitors. With about a minute to play in the third quarter, the Cats' Mike Gallagher hit a foul shot to put his team on top by three. Saint Gabriel's answered with what Don Barnes called "a brilliant drive and a layup by Joe Farley" followed by a foul shot from Larry Walko, which left the teams tied at thirty-five heading into the last quarter.

The G-Men had their hands on the reins, and they weren't about to let go. Goals by Darraugh and Brown started the fourth quarter, and even a time-out by Ron Gatski couldn't change the momentum. Saint Gabriel's had seized control of the game. Playing solid offense coupled with a stifling defense for a quarter and a half, they played their best ball of the season. The final score was Saint Gabriel's 51, West Hazleton 41. In the final twelve minutes the Saints had outscored West Hazleton 31-9 and had roared back from an apparent defeat to a very big win.

An ecstatic Coach Anderson said, "I think they gelled out there tonight. If we get past Freeland on Tuesday, we're going to be a mighty tough team the rest of the way." Freeland had opened league play with an impressive 64-49 victory over Jim Thorpe on the Olympians' court. Riding high, the Whippets would get Saint Gabriel's at the Freeland YMCA, always a tough venue for visitors.

Local interest in the league race was higher than normal, or at least seemed that way. A year ago Saint Gabriel's had totally dominated the league. This year as many as five teams had championship aspirations. Those five included charter members Freeland and MMI, who hadn't contended in quite some time. Tickets to some of the games played in the smaller gyms were hard to come by. There was an electricity in the air. John Goryl remembers the intensity of those games: "The bedlam, the heat, the excitement—there was nothing like it."

The *Standard Speaker* billed the G-Men-Freeland game as the night's "Anthracite Biggie." Freeland was 8-1 led by one of the best players in the league, Jim Titus. The Whippets were expected to control the boards and feel more at home on a small court than the visitors from Hazleton. The paper picked the home team to prevail on the scoreboard. In other league action, Jim Thorpe was at West Hazleton in what was viewed as a must-win game for both teams. MMI, which also sported an 8-1 record, was a heavy favorite to win their ninth against a struggling Weatherly team.

While the G-Men certainly preferred the spacious court at Saint Joe's, they had handled the limited space afforded by the Freeland Y well over the years. As a matter of fact, the Saints hadn't lost a game at Freeland since February 14, 1961, and they hadn't gone quietly in that one, losing 75-72. Coach Anderson decided to stick with what worked against West Hazleton, going with the same seven players who saw action against the Wildcats.

The first quarter was evenly played, and after eight minutes the Saints led 14-12. In the second quarter the Whippets went to a full-court press, and it rattled the G-Men. Before they knew what had hit them, Freeland had dashed to a 28-15 lead. Anderson signaled for a time-out. The Saints fought back to get to within seven at half, 34-27. In the locker room, Coach Anderson was imploring his team to get the ball inside against the Freeland defense.

Freeland opened the second half scoring with two quick buckets courtesy of Titus and John Machella, putting the Whippets ahead 38-27. Once again the Saints seemed to wake up, fighting back behind Curry to close it to 47-45 after three periods. The final eight minutes were hard fought as both teams looked to gain the momentum. The score was tied four times, the first at fifty-one and the last at sixty-three. It was at this point with just over a minute to go that Freeland's Dan Myers attempted to drive to the basket when he collided with a Saint Gabriel's player. Referee Carl Duser blew his whistle and cupped his hand on the back of his head, signaling an offensive foul. Upset with the call, Myers sent the basketball sailing towards the gym's ceiling. Duser then called a technical foul, which John Darraugh converted, giving the Saints a one-point lead.

Awarded the ball after the technical, the G-Men went into a four-corner stall and Titus fouled the Saints' Jim Munley going for a steal. The steady sophomore hit both ends of the one-and-one and Saint Gabriel's led by three. After a Freeland miss, the Whippets fouled Darraugh, who hit one of two shots to make it 67-63 with twenty-three seconds to go. Machella scored quickly for Freeland, but then the Saints beat the Whippets' full-court press and got the ball to Curry for an easy score, and he was fouled in the act of shooting. After he made the foul shot, a Freeland player grabbed the ball and threw it at the backboard drawing a second technical foul that Darraugh converted to make the final score 71-65.

Coach Anderson had quieted the critics for now, and the G-Men, led by Curry's twenty-six points, were in the driver's seat for the first half title. Coming off three losses in five days to beat quality title contenders West Hazleton and Freeland in succession has to rank as one of the most unexpected turn-arounds in the school's basketball history.

West Hazleton, led by a fast-improving junior Tommy Smith, knocked Jim Thorpe out of the first-half race by registering a convincing 88-56 win. In the meantime, MMI struggled to get by Weatherly 64-63. The Preppers were without the services of Jimmy Kennedy, who was expected to miss several games with an injury, but the margin of victory was a major surprise. With the win MMI maintained pace with Saint Gabriel's, as did Wink Gallagher's Marian Colts, who improved their first-half record to 2-0 with a win over the league's newest member, Cardinal Brennan. Marian would be the next test for the G-Men, who Ray Saul was now touting for comeback-of-the-season honors.

In other important sports news of the day, Joe Paterno announced that he was staying at Penn State. He had informed the owner of the Pittsburgh Steelers, Art Rooney, that he had decided to turn down what he called a "very generous offer" to become coach of that professional team. Paterno added that his decision was based on his love for Penn State University and the community in which he and his family lived. The Steelers ended up hiring Chuck Noll.

On the Friday before the 1969 Super Bowl where Joe Namath would lead the eighteen-point underdog New York Jets against the Baltimore Colts, the G-Men headed to Marian Catholic in a battle of Anthracite League undefeated teams. Those who opted out of one of the local basketball games had the option of checking out the film *Paper Lion* starring Alan Alda and co-starring, according to the ad being run by the Feeley Theatre, "the Real Detroit Lions." One thing was certain—few Saint Gabriel's fans would be purchasing movie tickets in the midst of a heated first-half title race.

The G-Men jumped on the Colts early and looked every bit the part of defending league champions, grabbing a 28-16

first-quarter lead on the way to an 81-61 win. All five starters scored in double figures for the Saints, who went without
a flu-stricken Jerry Gallagher. Brown and Farley led the way
with thirteen each while Curry, Walko, and Darraugh each netted twelve. Goryl came off the bench and scored seven in the
balanced attack. Marian got seventeen points from talented
sophomore John Teprovich, and another underclassmen Ed
Stulginsky hit for sixteen. Tom Andregic just missed doubles
with nine. The win left Saint Gabriel's and MMI, who crushed
Jim Thorpe 90-63, as the only teams without a loss in first-half
league play. The Saints looked to continue their winning streak
against a Cardinal Brennan team still searching for its first
league win, while the Preppers would take on the tough task of
playing crosstown rival Freeland.

That Monday, everybody was talking about Joe Namath and
the New York Jets. Namath had made good on his prediction
that the Jets would beat the Colts in the Super Bowl. The win
obviously impressed Ray Saul, who wrote that while Namath
"may be a flake, he's not a fluke."

MMI players didn't have time to dwell on Namath's heroics
as they were facing one of the biggest weeks in basketball the
school had experienced in years. Tuesday night they would take
on Freeland, and Friday they would welcome Saint Gabriel's to
the MMI gym which historically had proved a tough venue for
visitors.

In previewing the week's early games, the *Standard Speaker*
referenced Sunday's Super Bowl, noting that in light of that
event you had to give Cardinal Brennan a chance against Saint
Gabriel's while making the prediction that the game shouldn't be
close. Freeland was viewed as the slight favorite at home against
MMI. The game was a must-win for Freeland since a loss would
all but eliminate the Whippets from the first-half race.

Cardinal Brennan was unable to duplicate the Jets upset,
falling to the G-Men by a score of 84-58. The win all but assured
the Saints of no worse than a tie for the first-half title. Coach
Anderson used eleven players in the game and they all scored.
Darraugh hit for twenty-two in three quarters of play, and Curry
added thirteen. Polchin, a six-foot-three junior, had the best
game of his career to date, scoring eleven, while Walko added
ten. Farley just missed being the fifth G-Man to hit doubles with

eight. For the time being, winning quieted Coach Anderson's critics.

Meanwhile, the fans who were fortunate enough to get into the Freeland Y saw a game Don Barnes described as having "more turning points than the old Broad Mountain highway." The game was close all the way, and the lead kept changing hands. Neither team led by more than six through the entire contest, which is precisely the lead Freeland had, 54-48, with five minutes to play. At this point, Steve Makuta scored for MMI, and his teammate John Terri followed with another field goal after a Freeland miss. The Whippets turned the ball over on a traveling violation, and Bob Buchman scored for the Preppers to tie things up.

MMI then went up by a point on a foul shot by Frank Herring. Dan Myers put Freeland back in the lead when he hit two from the charity stripe, but Buchman answered with another field goal to make it MMI 57, Freeland 56 with 1:27 remaining. Freeland regained the advantage by hitting on three of four foul shots, but MMI again narrowed it to one with a field goal. Rather than hold the ball, Freeland took a shot and missed, which MMI snared and sent to Jerry Hludzik, who was fouled with twelve seconds to play. Hludzik hit one of two to make it sixty all. Freeland missed a shot at the buzzer sending the teams into overtime.

The two teams continued their tight play in the overtime period. With thirty-eight seconds left the game was still tied at sixty-three. MMI had the ball but an errant pass was picked off by Freeland's John Machella, who got the ball to Jim Titus, who was fouled. His two foul conversions were the final points scored, and Freeland had stayed alive in the first-half race with the 65-63 win.

Saint Gabriel's now stood atop the Anthracite League mountain with a record of 4-0 while West Hazleton, Freeland, and MMI were a shade behind at 3-1. There was little doubt that all eyes would be on the Saints and Preppers when they met later in the week. Lambert Broad, MMI's president, announced all seats for the game with Saint Gabriel's would be reserved and that there would be no standing room tickets sold. Saint Gabriel's super fan Tommy Malloy already had his ticket and would find his usual seat in the balcony. If there was any trouble, he figured he could use the Tarzan ropes to make his way to the floor as he had done a decade earlier.

Needless to say, a capacity crowd was in their seats when the ball was tossed in the air by referee Jack Shema to start the game. The two teams battled through the first eight minutes to a twenty-two all deadlock. The second quarter was much the same and the team's left the floor at half tied at forty-four. The score was tied eleven times in the first half.

Late in the third quarter the Saints went on a spurt. Curry scored on an easy layup. Gallagher connected on two foul shots, and then Brown and Darraugh hit field goals while holding MMI scoreless. That ended the quarter with the G-Man on top 65-56. Up nine, Coach Anderson directed his team to hold the ball in the final quarter.

The strategy backfired. The Saints were guilty of shoddy ball handling as they kept losing the ball without attempting a shot. MMI took advantage of the miscues and just three minutes into the final period they narrowed the Saint Gabriel's lead to 66-64. A time-out by Anderson failed to slow the Preppers, and with a little over two minutes to play, Steve Makuta hit from just to the right of the foul line to put the Preppers up 75-70. One of the Saints' super sophomores, Jim Munley, then nailed a long jumper and followed that with another goal after stealing the ball.

Playing aggressive defense, the G-Men forced a jump ball that they controlled. They worked the ball to Curry, who took the ball to the basket and watched it just fall off the front of the rim as the whistle blew. Shema called a foul on Makuta with just forty-seven ticks on the clock. It was the fifth foul for the MMI ace, and he left the game after scoring twenty-nine points. Curry stepped to the line and missed his first shot but the second effort fell through cleanly. The two teams were tied at seventy-five.

MMI brought the ball in but, facing the Saints' full-court pressure, turned it over as a result of a walking violation. Jerry Gallagher missed a jumper but corralled the rebound and sent another shot toward the hoop, which was in and then out. In the fight for that rebound the ball went out of bounds. The crowd was suddenly silent as they waited to see who would be awarded possession. Referees Sam Esposito and Shema huddled together before making a call. When Shema called it in

MMI's favor the stands on one side of the small gym exploded in cheers. The Preppers wanted no part of an overtime game without Makuta. They advanced the ball up court, and Jerry Hludzik missed from the top of the key and the ball was deflected out of bounds by Saint Gabriel's. The Preppers inbounded the ball to Fritz Herring, who immediately fired a one-handed jump shot from the wing that dropped through as the buzzer sounded. MMI fans surged the floor and lifted Herring on their shoulders, carrying him off the court in their celebration. All of a sudden the G-Men, MMI, Freeland, and West Hazleton were all tied at 4-1 with two games remaining for each in the first-half race.

Attending Anthracite League games in this turbulent season was serious business as the owners of five vehicles discovered after the game. They arrived to find that the air had been left out of all four tires of their cars. To make matters worse the culprits had removed the tire stems. Since all five cars bore MMI license plates, the accusing finger was pointed at Saint Gabriel's fans. The identity of those responsible was never discovered.

West Hazleton faced the toughest road as they would face both Freeland and MMI in the final week. One thing the Wildcats had going for them is that both games would be played at Mother of Grace. Saint Gabriel's was viewed as having the easiest path to no worse than a tie for the first-half title with games against a struggling Jim Thorpe club and winless Weatherly. The local teams would return to the court on the day after the new president of the United States, Richard Nixon, took his oath of office.

What was being called decision week in the Anthracite League got underway on Tuesday, January 22, 1969. Saint Gabriel's was sluggish in their outing against Jim Thorpe, but even playing poorly they had too much for the Olympians. Curry, Darraugh, and Gallagher scored all but fourteen of the points the Saints racked up a 62-45 win. Before the game Darraugh had taken Farley aside and told the Saint Gabriel's junior that he wanted him to shoot more. "The shots are there—take them," he said. "It will open things up for the rest of us." Farley did just that, throwing up more shots than he had in a single game all season, but of the sixteen efforts he hurled at the rim only two found their mark. The junior guard took a lot of ribbing watching the game film the next day.

In the evening's marquee matchup Freeland traveled to Hazleton and virtually eliminated West Hazleton from the race for the first-half crown by downing the Wildcats 65-61 before what Ray Saul termed "a near capacity crowd." It was a close game all the way, but Freeland made foul shots when they counted late in the contest to seal up the victory. Ed Podany played one of the best games of his career for Freeland, scoring eighteen points and securing several key rebounds. George Petrylak put twenty-four on the board for West Hazleton while pulling down twenty-one rebounds, but it wasn't enough to get the Cats to the finish line.

MMI kept pace with Saint Gabriel's and Freeland by totally dismantling Marian Catholic 90-51. MMI Coach Dave Shafer admitted he was worried about a letdown after his team's big come from behind win against Saint Gabriel's. Those concerns were soon crased as his team piled up a 51-16 margin at half on the way to the win. With Saint Gabriel's facing Weatherly and Freeland getting Marian at home, a three-way tie for the first-half championship seemed probable providing MMI could take down the Wildcats on their home floor.

Weatherly, though winless in the league, had lost at home by just one point to both Freeland and MMI. Coach Anderson made sure the Saints' players were aware of that fact before stepping onto the Weatherly court. Sophomore Larry Walko had started every game for the Saints in the up-and-down season. Against Weatherly, Walko was certainly up as he scored thirty-one points in leading the G-Men to an easy 92-69 victory. Curry had another big night scoring twenty-four, and another Saint Gabriel's sophomore, Jerry Fallabel, scored eleven. The win guaranteed Saint Gabriel's a spot in a first-half playoff.

Freeland also secured a playoff spot by easily defeating Marian Catholic 93-64. MMI decided that it takes three to tango when they finished the first half 6-1 by beating West Hazleton 60-57. The Preppers beat back a furious fourth quarter comeback by the Wildcats to finish tied with Freeland and Saint Gabriel's in the first-half race. Saint Gabriel's drew the bye in the three-way deadlock, so MMI would meet Freeland on Monday at Mother of Grace gym, and the winner would face the G-Men two days later at a site to be determined.

Both MMI and Freeland played solid defense in their tussle advance to the first-half championship game. At the half MMI had a slim 13-12 lead in a game where points were hard to come by. In the second half, the Freeland players appeared to tire and MMI took full advantage, stretching their lead to 29-22 after three quarters. Things didn't change in the final eight minutes, and when all was said and done, MMI emerged with a surprisingly easy 55-38 win. The Preppers, who were the only team to defeat Saint Gabriel's in the first half would play them again with a claim to the league championship on the line. Surprisingly, the game was scheduled to be played on the Saints' home court at Saint Joe's after MMI agreed to play meet at that site to accommodate what was expected to be a heavy demand for tickets.

The *Standard Speaker* called the game a toss-up. Both teams could play rugged defense, and both teams could run through a quick pace—which probably favored Saint Gabriel's since Coach Anderson had a far deeper bench to call on than Coach Shafer. In a scheduling quirk, the same two teams would open second half play on the same court two days after the playoff.

The Saints called on their senior leaders in the playoff and both came through. Curry scored twenty-three and Darraugh, twenty-one as the G-Men led from the opening whistle in winning the first-half title 64-60. Only Steve Makuta scored in doubles for MMI, but the thirty-one points the region's leading scorer registered weren't enough to pull out a victory. If anything, the second-half race looked easier for the Saints since they would get both Freeland and MMI at home. West Hazleton on the road looked like the biggest obstacle to capturing back-to-back league titles for the first time in the history of the small parochial school.

For rookie coach Jerry Anderson, the win was especially satisfying. Winning had silenced those critical of his coaching decisions. His team was now 11-5 on the season and had won seven of their last eight. The Saint Gabriel's spirit was present, and this team was proving the boys in the purple and white could win without Paul Hoffman. With half the season gone, things couldn't have looked better. In truth, there were lingering dissension problems that would reappear before the seasons end.

18

CHARGING

CLOSE BUT NO CIGAR

O n the night of the first-half playoff game, the *Standard Speaker* received almost six hundred phone calls asking for the results of the game. After the game, numerous MMI fans complained about the game being played at Saint Joe's. Saint Gabriel's didn't want to play at Mother of Grace but would have played at Marian Catholic. It was MMI's coach Dave Shafer who agreed to play it on the Saints' home court.

Those same MMI fans found themselves in familiar surroundings just two days later when the Saints and Preppers went at it again. Unlike the playoff game, MMI made sure that the G-Men didn't hold the lead all the way in this one by racing to a quick 12-2 lead at the start of the contest. After a time-out Saint Gabriel's cut that margin in half, and after one quarter the G-Men were on the short end of a 16-11 score. The second eight minutes mirrored the first as the Preppers started strong to go up by nine, but the Saints fought back to make the score 26-23 at half.

In the third quarter MMI appeared to take command, going up by twelve led by Steve Makuta. The Saints couldn't find a way to stop the Preppers' ace, and after three periods the G-Men were down 45-37. Makuta was one of the best players in the region, and when he was on his game there was no stopping him. The game was almost the polar opposite of the one played just two days ago when the Saints had led all the way. On this night MMI had been in command from the opening tip.

At the beginning of the last eight minutes of play the G-Men went on a run, and with 4:46 to go they tied the score at forty-seven on two Curry foul shots. Curry then scored a rebound deuce, and Darraugh followed that with a driving layup. All of a sudden, Saint Gabriel's led 51-47. The Saints stretched that advantage to 57-50 with 1:40 left. At this point the G-Men tried to hold the ball but committed two quick turnovers that MMI converted into scores to draw within three. When Makuta scored with thirty-two seconds left, the lead evaporated to a single point. The Saints continued to freeze the ball, and for some reason MMI didn't commit an intentional foul. An errant pass was intercepted by the Preppers' Jim Kennedy with only three seconds left. He tried to throw the ball to a teammate down court, but Jerry Gallagher stepped in front, stealing the pass and cementing the win for the Saints.

It was the G-Men seniors who carried the day in this victory. Curry scored twenty; Darraugh, fourteen; and Brown added ten. Makuta had played another brilliant game, scoring twenty-six, but once again it wasn't enough. Coach Anderson was elated after the win, declaring, "We can beat anybody now. We played our worst ball for three periods and they played their best and we still beat them." A dejected Coach Shafer, who looked drained, simply stated, "I'm going to start getting out of the other side of the bed."

In his column, Ray Saul wrote that Saint Joseph's of Williamsport, who expected to meet Saint Gabriel's in the state playoffs, had a bevy of scouts at the game. The sports editor also made it a point to alert local fans to the fact Tony Kinney was only twelve points away from setting a new career scoring record at Hazleton High.

In other Anthracite League action, West Hazleton, Freeland, and Marian had all started the second half with wins. Both West Hazleton and Saint Gabriel's would be heavily favored to beat Marian and Cardinal Brennan in their next trips on the court, but Freeland was going to face an MMI team with their backs to the wall. For the Preppers, another loss would virtually eliminate any chances at a league title. The victory over MMI had made the Saints the leader of the pack in the race for the overall league title.

Saint Gabriel's was sluggish in the first half versus Cardinal Brennan. The boys in purple and white made their way to the locker room at half with a 21-15 lead. The Saints' defense stayed steady throughout the game and more than made up for their poor offensive showing. Led by Darraugh, Walko, and Gallagher, the G-Men secured their ninth win in their last ten starts, 57-52. Brown and Farley also provided some offensive support in the victory. Pat Curry, who had been playing his best ball of late, was held to a single field goal. For Cardinal Brennan, Joe Rizzardi scored half of his team's points in the loss.

West Hazleton remained undefeated in the second half by traveling to Marian and trouncing the Colts 81-52. The Wildcats were getting better and better with each outing as their talented junior class gained experience.

The big game of the night took place before a capacity crowd of about six hundred in MMI's gym. Facing their crosstown rivals for the second time, Freeland and MMI played the type of close and physical game the teams were known for. Neither squad led by more than five points through the entire contest, including with just four minutes to play when Freeland was clinging to a 54-49 advantage. From that point, on the Preppers took control, scoring nine points to the Whippets two to emerge bloodied but unbowed with a 58-56 victory. Makuta, who led the Preppers with twenty-four, scored five of those last nine points including a three-point play that gave the home team the lead. With the win, MMI remained in contention for second-half honors. The loss put Freeland in the same position—still alive but needing to complete league play without another loss to have a chance to wear the league crown.

On Thursday night, February 6, 1969, Hazleton High squared off against the East Penn League's first-half champs Allentown Dieruff before two thousand fans at Saint Joe's. Those present saw a great one as Hazleton took down the visitors 71-67 in overtime behind Kinney's twenty-nine points. Kinney's ninth point of the night made him the leading career scorer in Hazleton High's history. The ever gracious six-foot-one senior received the game ball from his happy coach Gene Evans after the game. Saint Gabriel's fans could only fantasize over how good their teams might have been over the last three years had Coach Phelps been successful in luring Kinney to Saint Gabriel's.

The next night the Anthracite League was back in action with a full slate of games. Saint Gabriel's, West Hazleton, Freeland, and MMI were all heavy favorites to emerge with victories. It didn't turn out that way. MMI traveled to Jim Thorpe where the

Preppers, who led through three quarters, fell flat in the fourth and came up on the short end of a 60-57 score in a contest decided in overtime. Makuta scored twenty-one for MMI, which put him over the 1,000 mark for his career, but that was of little solace in a game that effectively erased any title hopes for his team.

Saint Gabriel's avoided what could have been a second upset by getting it together in the final quarter to pull away from the Marian Colts and register an 82-63 win. The final score was deceiving in that the Saints led by only four points with two minutes to play in the third period. Darraugh once again led Saint Gabriel's in scoring with twenty-two. Brown added fifteen, and Curry, hobbled with an ankle injury, put twelve on the board. Yet another of the Saints' talented sophomores also hit doubles. This time it was the six-foot-three Joe Curry who scored ten. Curry was an emerging talent who was seeing more and more varsity playing time.

West Hazleton remained tied for first with Saint Gabriel's in the second half by pounding Weatherly 85-49 behind George Petrylak's twenty-nine points. The Wildcats would face a reeling MMI team in their next game on the Preppers' court and then have to face a Freeland team who would need a win to stay in the league's title chase.

Saint Gabriel's was 4-0 in the second half after easily dispatching Weatherly 83-49 at Saint Joe's. Walko, who scored thirty-one against Weatherly in the first meeting between the two teams, set the pace again hitting for twenty-five. Jerry Gallagher was right there with twenty. The Saints had three games left: at Jim Thorpe, a visit to West Hazleton, and Freeland at home. Win those three, and the Anthracite League trophy would return to Saint Gabriel's for the second consecutive year.

MMI appeared to make things a bit easier for the G-Men when they held on to beat West Hazleton 67-65. The Preppers carried a fourteen-point lead into the last quarter but had to hold off a tenacious comeback by the Wildcats that fell just short. Late in the game, West Hazleton came up with a steal and missed an uncontested layup that would have sent the game into overtime. Freeland beat Marian Catholic by sixteen and would face the Wildcats in just three days. As things stood, the G-Men were the lone undefeated team in the second-half race.

The Saints headed to Jim Thorpe as heavy favorites to handle the Olympians. It was just a week ago that Thorpe had upset

MMI, but few believed a second upset was in the offing. The local paper rated Thorpe's chances as "considerably less than slim." In the night's key contest, Freeland playing at home was given the edge over West Hazleton. After all, the Whippets had already beaten the Wildcats at Mother of Grace and needed a win to stay in the second-half race. Most believed West Hazleton would have to be at the top of their game to get a win.

Saint Gabriel's had played poorly in spots despite being undefeated in the second half, and the contest at Jim Thorpe certainly started as one of those nights. Throughout the first half, numerous turnovers and poor shooting plagued the G-Men. In addition, the referees were calling them close, and Jim Thorpe players were making regular trips to the charity stripe. At half, to the delight of the home crowd, the Olympians led 31-21.

In the second half, led by Hal Hydro, who scored thirty in the game, Thorpe actually widened their lead. With just over four minutes to play the G-Men trailed 60-46. At this point, Saint Gabriel's finally got to work cutting the margin to six with just under a minute to play at 70-64. The Saints were forced to foul and Thorpe's Fran O'Donnell missed the front end of a one-and-one. The Saints worked the ball inside to Curry, whose shot rolled off the front of the rim, just missing the chance for a three-point play when a foul was called. Curry sank one of two and with twenty seconds to play, Walko scored to make it 70-67. Once again, Thorpe's O'Donnell failed to convert on two foul tries, and Jerry Gallagher's goal made it 70-69. The Saints never got another chance as the Olympians ran out the clock. Jim Thorpe had made the most of their considerably slim chance, and now Saint Gabriel's was 4-1 and still had to face West Hazleton and Freeland.

West Hazleton, of course, was playing Freeland while Jim Thorpe was upsetting Saint Gabriel's. In describing the game, which happened to take place on Valentine's Day, Don Barnes wrote, "The Valentine's Day Massacre had nothing on the goings on at the Freeland YMCA last night." West Hazleton, with guns blazing, demolished the Whippets 73-49. Four talented juniors led the Wildcats with Tom Smith scoring twenty, George Petrylak nineteen, Billy Pavlick fourteen, and Laverne Mummey ten. The only Freeland player to hit doubles was Jim Titus with twenty-one. Though not a tremendous upset, the margin of victory caught the notice of the entire league—these Wildcats had caught fire. Tommy Smith was playing brilliantly, Petrylak was a strong presence underneath the basket, and both Pavlick and Mummey were providing steady guard play. In the hunt for this year's title, West Hazleton was certainly going to be a force to be reckoned with.

In the last upset of this crazy night, Marian knocked MMI clear out of contention by beating the Preppers 59-57. Coach Wink Gallagher's Colts were down ten after one quarter, but sparked by the play of Tom Andregic, they came back to beat the Preppers in the final minute of play.

All eyes were now on Saint Gabriel's and West Hazleton, who stood atop the second-half race with identical 4-1 records. Now the fans of Freeland and Jim Thorpe, who both had two losses, were thinking their teams still had a chance if they could win out. Thorpe and Freeland would meet the same night that the G-Men and the Cats squared off, and then the second half would end with the Olympians visiting West Hazleton and Freeland paying a call on Saint Gabriel's. Everything was, all of a sudden, up in the air.

A capacity crowd was expected as usual for the Saint Gabriel's-West Hazleton game. The two teams were rated equal talent-wise, and both could play aggressive defense. The home court advantage belonged to the Wildcats, as did the momentum that comes with playing your best basketball of the season. The *Standard Speaker* picked the Cats by about five. What the paper didn't know was that Darraugh, the Saints' leading scorer and team leader, had suffered a leg injury. His availability, much less his effectiveness, was a question mark.

When the two teams took the court on the night of February 19, 1969, they both knew a lot was riding on the outcome of this game. A Saint Gabriel's victory would likely wrap up the league crown for the G-Men while a Wildcat win would, in all probability, necessitate a playoff game between the same two teams. The fact the two teams had become archrivals in the past decade was something they carried onto the court with them as well. Saint Gabriel's had won four of the last five meetings, and these Wildcats were anxious to turn that around. In the words of Bill Pavlick, the West Hazleton point guard, "By the time I was a junior and a senior, Saint Gabe's was our main rival. We respected them, they had won those two state titles, they were as good as we were, and we all knew if we wanted a league championship we'd have to beat them. No doubt about it. As far as basketball was concerned, they were our biggest rival."

Pavlick was also West Hazleton's defensive ace, and as such would draw the assignment of stopping Darraugh, which was never an easy task. Not only could Darraugh shoot off the dribble, but he had such a quick release that if you gave him any room he made you pay. However, on this night Darraugh saw less than two minutes of action; he just couldn't perform on that injured leg.

From the opening tip, West Hazleton continued the fine style of play that had been their calling card as the season wore on and their young talent came of age. Midway through the first quarter, the score was tied at eight, but then the Cats went on a spurt and after eight minutes they led 18-11. Curry was having a good night inside for the Saints, but the same could be said of the Cats' Petrylak. The two played each other to a draw, both scoring twenty-three points.

With Darraugh out of the game, West Hazleton gradually pulled further ahead and after three quarters appeared to have the game under control with a sixteen-point lead 60-44. Then the Saints, led by some of their underclassmen, made a run, and with 3:30 to go, the Wildcat lead had been cut to 67-62. Coach Gatski called a time-out. With the ball and a five-point lead, West Hazleton went into a freeze. The Saints took risks going for steals and then were forced to commit intentional fouls to gain possession of the ball. To their credit, West Hazleton made good on the opportunities presented to them and when the final buzzer sounded, they were alone atop the league's second-half standings with an 81-66 victory.

Adding to Petrylak's twenty-three, Tom Smith scored seventeen for West Hazleton and Pavlick scored eleven in addition to playing an excellent floor game. For Saint Gabriel's, after Curry, the majority of the scoring came from two sophomores—Joe Curry, who hit for fifteen, and Jim Munley, who scored nine. Farley chipped in with eight points and drew praise from Barnes for his overall play. Barnes also wrote that the play of the G-Men underclassmen "insure St. Gabriel's being a tough outfit again next year." Freeland kept their second-half hopes alive by getting past Jim Thorpe 60-52. The Whippets now had to beat Saint Gabriel's in the final game of the regular season and hope West Hazleton would stumble against Jim Thorpe.

The day after the game, Ray Saul summed things up in his Speaking of Sports column, writing, "Keeping up with which team is in the driver's seat in the Anthracite School Basketball League is like listening to the old Abbott and Costello routine 'Who's On First?' West Hazleton is in command at the moment, but St. Gabriel's still has an ace in the hole with the first-half championship safely tucked away. The big question now is: Can Jim Thorpe play the spoiler again Friday night and defeat West Hazleton, setting up a playoff for the second half title?"

Both Saint Gabriel's and Freeland were hoping lightening in the form of the Jim Thorpe Olympians would strike a third time as they warmed up for their own contest. This was the last regular season game for six Saint Gabriel's seniors, and they were honored before the game. Pat Curry, Jimmy Brown, Jerry Gallagher, John Goryl, John Ammon, and the player the team voted as their MVP John Darraugh, were all introduced to tremendous ovations from the student body. Saint Gabriel's students appreciated the efforts these players had made on their behalf, and they took this last opportunity in Saint Joe's gym to show it.

John Darraugh was back at full strength, and just having him on the court helped spark the Saints. The G-Men jumped out to an early lead and maintained an eight- to ten-point margin throughout against the talented Whippets. When the final buzzer sounded, Saint Gabriel's was on top by a score of 70-61. Curry and Darraugh had gone out in style, scoring nineteen and fourteen points respectively. Two of the Saints' super sophomores also scored in double figures with Joe Curry hitting for twelve and Walko netting eleven. The G-Men had finished the first post-Hoffman season with a record of 16-7. They had captured the Anthracite League's first-half crown, and regardless of what happened in West Hazleton, would be playing for the league title. In addition, they had qualified to play in the Catholic state playoffs. Despite the criticism, Coach Anderson had also provided valuable playing time to a number of underclassmen that would form the foundation for the 1970 team who, unknown to most, would be the last in the school's history.

Jim Thorpe gave West Hazleton all they could handle before fading late in the game. West Hazleton emerged with a 65-52 win and the second-half title. After the game, a relieved Coach Ron Gatski remarked, "All I can say is I'm glad we won. Now I know what happened to MMI and Saint Gabriel's here. We murdered these guys at West Hazleton, but I had a hunch we might be in for a tough one, so we practiced hard against a press." The Olympians were within five with two minutes to go but were forced to foul when the Wildcats went into a stall. Coach Pip Radar was disappointed with his team's performance from the charity stripe. The Olympians hit eighteen out of thirty-four, and Radar felt that as much as anything contributed to the final result. When Gatski was asked where he'd like to meet Saint Gabriel's in the playoff for the league title he said, "Anywhere but Saint Joe's."

On Monday, February 24th, the announcement was made that the Saints and Wildcats would meet the following evening at Marian Catholic to decide the league title. The *Standard Speaker* rated the game dead even. West Hazleton was viewed as having improved over the course of the season and was said to be playing the most consistent ball. The G-Men were described as healthy again and anxious to defend their league title. The entire region was excited about this game between the two rivals. Needless to say a large crowd was expected.

By game time, more than 1,400 spectators filled the Marian stands and the temporary seats placed on the gym's stage. The G-Men seized the early advantage, working the ball for good shots and playing tight defense. Led by seniors Darraugh and Curry, who scored ten and eight points respectively in the opening half, the Saints led at intermission by a score of 32-25. The G-Men had controlled the boards in the opening sixteen minutes and, with the exception of Dave Scripko, the Wildcats weren't shooting with anything approaching consistency.

With about six minutes to play in the third quarter, the momentum shifted. The Saints committed multiple unforced turnovers and couldn't buy a basket. While West Hazleton wasn't tearing things up, they clawed their way back, and with two minutes to go in the third period they knotted the score at thirty-five. At the end of that period, having outscored the Saints 16-7, the Cats led 41-39.

The fourth quarter was much the same, and with two minutes left, West Hazleton led 53-45. The final score was 59-49. Over the final sixteen minutes West Hazleton dominated the game to the tune of 34-17. The Cats' defensive ace Billy Pavlick held Darraugh to a single point in the second half and Pat Curry only managed one field goal. Darraugh's eleven points still led the Saints in scoring, and Curry was a shade behind with ten. Farley just missed doubles with nine, and Walko, who fouled out with six minutes to play, had eight. In the third quarter the G-Men gave the ball up nine times without taking a shot, and for the game they were an abysmal fifteen for fifty from the field.

West Hazleton had caught the Saints on a bad night, but there was no denying that West Hazleton's aggressive play contributed to the Saints' miscues. Coach Anderson said after the game, "We beat ourselves. We start the Catholic playoffs Friday, but this was the big one that we wanted." Looking back on the game, Joe Farley remembers it as the most disappointing loss he experienced as a player. "My dad had played on the Saint Gabriel's team that won the school's first Anthracite League title, and I had a goal to play on one as well. I'll always remember that game as one we gave away. There were a lot of good teams in the Anthracite League that year, but to this day I think we had the best squad." Larry Walko has similar memories, saying, "We really should have won the league title my sophomore year. I really felt that we were the best team."

The loss took all the energy out of the Saint Gabriel's team. At practice the next two days, the Saints were sluggish and appeared beaten. With the state playoffs approaching they needed to break out of their funk and fast or they'd be heading to the exit door early.

The Saints traveled to Williamsport to take on that city's Saint Joseph's team in the state playoff opener. It was anybody's guess which Saint Gabriel's team would take the court. Would it be the one that had played so well for most of the Anthracite League season, or the one that had dropped three of their last four games? A large number of Saints' fans made the trip to find out.

The 1,200 spectators on hand for the contest held at the Williamsport High School field house didn't have to wait long for answer. As related by Don Barnes, "For the ten or twelve minutes they required to assert their authority over St. Joe's, the G-Men became the Saint Gabriel's of yore. Deadly shooting, crisp passing, hustle, defense, general know-how—they had it all." St. Joe's led briefly at 3-2 but that was quickly erased as the Saints jumped to a 21-11 lead after one quarter that they stretched to 46-24 at intermission. Saint Joe's Coach Ron

Cherba remarked at half that his team seemed awed by the Saints' performance. Darraugh nailed two quick twenty-five-foot jumpers to start the game but found himself sitting next to Coach Anderson after committing two quick fouls in the first three minutes. The G-Men ace played the entire third quarter but was ejected early in the fourth when he and a Saint Joe's player got into a slugging match. Both players were ejected, but not before Darraugh scored sixteen points in a little over eleven minutes of play.

The final score was 98-69, but that was closer than it would have been if Coach Anderson had not used his bench liberally. Twelve players saw action for the Saints and eleven of them scored. Senior John Goryl entered the game in the final quarter and scored eleven points. If the Saints could continue to play at the level they exhibited in Williamsport, they would indeed make some noise in the state playoffs. Next up would be another old foe—Plymouth St. Vincent's—and Saint Gabriel's would travel to the Wilkes-Barre area to take them on in the Kingston Catholic gym.

West Hazleton was also having success in the playoffs. On the night after the Saint Gabriel's victory, they beat Northampton 70-63 to advance to the District 11 final in the Class A state playoffs. Despite their many great teams, the Cats had never won a district title. As a matter of fact, six Anthracite League teams had qualified for the state playoffs and all six had won their first game. Digger Phelps would have been proud.

Another good crowd followed the Saints to Kingston, where the G-Men were slight favorites to handle St. Vincent's. This one wouldn't be easy as evidenced by the fact the Vinnies had given MMI all they could handle before losing by four earlier in the season.

The Saints fell to Saint Vincent's 84-78 in a game filled with controversy. The score was tied at sixty after three quarters only because of the number of times Saint Vincent's players were sent to the foul line. A number of G-Men were in foul trouble early, and three would eventually foul out of the game. Saint Gabriel's outscored the Vinnies from the field, hitting thirty-three of their shots while Saint Vincent's was making good on twenty-six. John Darraugh went out with a bang, scoring thirty points. The referees were calling them extremely close, but that seemed to be confined to the side of the court where the G-Men were playing defense. The Saints went to the foul line eighteen times, making twelve of those attempts, while Saint Vincent's players toed the line an incredible fifty-one times. The thirty-two foul tries they made proved the difference.

The next day in the paper Don Barnes confessed that he was "trying in the worst way to preserve a degree of neutrality in the burning controversy over whether the G-Men were jobbed by the officials in the loss to Plymouth St. Vincent's." The best he could do was admit there had been bad calls in the game but point out there were always some bad calls.

Clearly that wasn't what Coach Anderson was thinking when he heard the final buzzer. The first year coach rushed across the court to confront the referees as they were leaving the court. Anderson and one of the referees, Lou Febbo, had to be separated when it looked like they were about to exchange blows. As the coach was being pulled away, he yelled at the two men in stripes, "We'll be back."

Barnes called that confrontation unfortunate, but pointed out that if one forgot the officiating, "the thing that is really gnawing at the vitals of the G-Men's fans is the almost certain knowledge their team can take the Vinnies on a given night. There's no way of proving it, but I feel it's true, too."

It had been a season of ups and downs. Finishing 17-9 wasn't bad, but it certainly wasn't what the G-Men faithful were used to. It marked the first time in four seasons that the school couldn't say they had won a championship.

As Joe Farley entered the bus for what would seem like a very long ride home after the loss, he found a seat next to Jimmy Munley. "Jimmy," he said, "next year we can do something that no Saint Gabriel's team has done—not even Hoffman and Olexa. We can win the Anthracite League and the state championship in the same season. Next year starts tomorrow and it starts at Pine Street."

19

THE LAST QUARTER

PINE STREET

A couple of significant events occurred as the 1969 school year was drawing to an end. On April 14, 1969, Monsignor Maher announced at a school assembly that the parish would be closing Saint Gabriel's High School for financial reasons. A central Catholic school would be opened in the fall of 1970. Thus the class graduating in June of 1970 would be the last high school class to graduate from the parish school. That class already had a few stories to tell. The seniors-to-be had adopted the tune *Born to be Wild* as their unofficial class song, and apparently they became a little too wild for some of the good sisters. At the close of the 1969 school year, a decision was made that three of the juniors would not be permitted to finish their schooling at Saint Gabriel's. Among those three was Joe Farley. Farley, for his part, was not too concerned about the decision. After all, there was a whole summer to straighten it out.

Shortly after the school's closing was announced, Saint Gabriel's held its annual sports banquet. Jim Crowley of the famed Four Horsemen of Notre Dame was the main speaker and had the audience in stitches with his humorous remarks. Darraugh accepted his well-earned MVP award.

Though it was mid-April, there was still plenty of basketball news in the area. Gene Evans resigned his position as head coach at Hazleton High and the school board announced they were accepting applications. Former coach Fran Libonati announced he was not going to apply for the position, causing some to wonder if he was waiting on the new central Catholic job. Basketball was still being played by the seventh and eighth graders at Freeland Saint Mary's. Coach Ron Gerlach's club won their fifth straight Passaic Diocese championship when they beat Saint George's of Linden, New Jersey, 67-51. Saint Mary's finished the season with a remarkable record of 47-2. It wasn't unusual for Coach Gerlach to schedule more than fifty games in a season. Marian's legendary Coach Wink Gallagher resigned and the school hired Saint Gabriel's alum Bob Fulton to lead the Colts in their quest for an Anthracite League title.

Though Fulton was a Hazleton native, Marian had gone outside the local area to find its new coach. For the previous eight years he had been coaching in New Jersey, the last two years at Westfield High School. The previous year he had led Westfield to a Class A state title. With the hiring of Fulton, Marian declared they were quite serious about advancing their basketball program in the coming years. The results would come quicker than anyone expected.

As the warmer weather crept into the area, the *Standard Speaker* reported the news of what turned out to be an event-filled summer. On the entertainment side, in late May the Beatles had yet another number one hit when the tune "Get Back" jumped to the top of the charts. The controversial film *Midnight Cowboy* was released, and TV viewers caught the final episode of *Star Trek*. In July, Americans were captivated by the first moon landing. August brought with it the news that the actress Sharon Tate and seven others had been brutally murdered during a two-night killing spree later discovered to have been carried out on orders from Charles Manson by members of what he called his "family." That same month 400,000 young people showed up at a farm in Bethel, New York, for a music festival that came to be known as Woodstock. While all this was going on, a group of young high school boys were spending every day in a half-block area in downtown Hazleton known as Pine Street playground.

Pine Street had attracted Saint Gabriel's players in the past. Most notably, Paul Hoffman, Dennis Olexa, and John Darraugh had all polished their skills on the small tree-shaded court with the metal nets. But the summer of 1969 was the first time that what everyone expected would be the team's starting five and the sixth man made the playground a summer home.

The city of Hazleton had a superb playground system at the time. There were ten playgrounds scattered around the city that ran summer programs. Each of the playgrounds had two to three counselors who were assigned to guide the kids who spent their days at the various sites. The counselors were generally college-aged guys and gals home for the summer. The males usually ran the sports programs, and the females directed arts and crafts.

In 1969 the male counselor at Pine Street was Bruce Ellis. Ellis was a Hazleton High graduate who was attending Bloomsburg State College. He had fallen in love with the game of basketball and had a growing desire to coach. He had been a fixture at the playground for years and was well known by the regulars, who were more than happy to see him in charge. This was despite the fact that since he now had a job at the playground, he wouldn't be able to drive boys around looking for a game when too few boys showed up to play one at Pine Street. This particular summer, that was hardly ever a problem.

Almost every day the routine was the same—those who arrived first would shoot around or play one-on-one games, sometimes on the small biddy basketball court with the eight-foot baskets, as they waited for more players to appear. Once there were ten players present, sides would be drawn up and a full-court game to fifty by ones would commence. Those games were fast and furious as both teams looked to run on offense as much as possible. After the initial contest, it was a short walk to the local candy store where everyone grabbed their favorite beverage and drink it sitting on the store's porch. Then it was back to the playground for another, often more ragged game.

It was during these games that players got to experiment with things that local coaches had frowned upon for years. Behind-the-back dribbles and passes that would have drawn a stoppage of play by coaches during a practice were common place. Hook shots, reverses, underhand layups, and moves that were still in the experimental stage could be seen on a daily basis.

Then there were the little side bets, like the time Dennis Olexa said he'd buy anybody a soda who could steal the ball from him, only to have Hoffman say, "Let me give it a shot." On one day in particular, Hoffman stole the ball before Olexa completed his first dribble but, not missing a trick, Olexa said, "Hey, I didn't know we were starting."

Shooting exhibitions were popular too. Darraugh and Munley would knock down consecutive shots from ever increasing distances until observers would wonder, *Do these guys ever miss?* There was Paul Felicione, an older guy who hung out at the playground and was simply the best shooter anyone had ever seen. He could have put on a clinic for making consecutive free throws. Bruce Ellis still talks about watching Larry Nance win the first NBA slam dunk contest in 1984 by dunking two balls at the same time. When he saw it he thought to himself, *Heck, I saw Hoffman do that at Pine Street in 1968.*

By the time the official playground season opened, Bruce Ellis knew who his squad was going to be, and he thought he just might be able to steal a city championship with them. He decided to go with Jimmy Munley and Joe Farley as his guards. Ellis recalls Jimmy Munley was an outdoor gym rat, calling him a "playground rat." Ellis said back in those days, coaches didn't spend time correcting a shooter's technique, and Munley would have benefited from that. "He was really a good shooter—I can still see that high rainbow jumper—but he didn't have great technique, and I thought he took his shooting ability as far as he could on his own." With Farley he had what he called a "pure point guard"—a good shot and a great ball handler who could "see the floor and find the open man." He says Farley was dedicated to the game and the other guys looked up to him. "Farley was a year older, and that may have been the reason, but it was clear to me that he was viewed as a leader on the court."

Inside, Ellis decided to go with three players who, like Munley, had just completed their sophomore year of high school: Larry Walko, Jerry Fallabel, and Joe Curry. He called Larry Walko "tough, fearless and very strong," adding that if Walko "had been six six [instead of five eleven] he'd have been a Division 1 player." Ellis remembers Walko as a kid "who had full confidence in himself." He was always battling bigger kids, but he used his strength and positioning to gain an advantage. Walko also had a good mid-range jumper and, according to Ellis, "he'd take it outside and stick it."

Then there was Jerry Fallabel. "Fallabel was tall [six foot three], had great hands, and could run the floor." In Fallabel, Ellis felt he had a player totally dedicated to the game. "He worked so hard that summer developing a jumper and did it successfully. Back then, kids who played inside usually didn't have that jump shot, but he did."

Rounding out the inside men was the six-foot-three Joe Curry. The first thing that came to mind as far as Ellis was concerned when it came to Curry was "ladies man." According to Ellis, Curry had a lot of interests besides basketball, but as far as the game went Ellis described Curry as "very talented." Curry had a "Chet Walker ball fake" and was a "hell of a one-on-one player." Ellis remembers Curry hustling kids on the playgrounds for sodas playing one-on-one. "He [Curry] used to beat Dennis [Olexa] one on one and it drove Dennis crazy," said Ellis, who also remembers Curry as the only player to best Hoffman in a one-on-one contest. Curry was a young man who was trying to find himself. Ellis summed up Curry by saying, "With the right attitude, he could have been devastating."

The sixth man would be a G-Man entering his junior year, Tommy Boyle. Boyle could play inside or outside and possessed a quick and accurate jump shot. He was also a battler who had no qualms about going against bigger men underneath the basket. Ellis believes all six of those players would have picked themselves as the best on the team if asked. When pressed to pick a top player himself, Ellis went with Fallabel. But Ellis wasn't concerned with individual play. He knew there was talent there, much of it still young, but what attracted him to this group was the way they came together as a team. Ellis said he never substituted much that summer because those five "had a chemistry that was obvious when they were on the court together."

Scarcely a day went by when the six Saint Gabriel's players couldn't be found at Pine Street. On Saturdays Joe Entiero, who had played on the 1964-65 Saint Gabriel's team, would usually show up with a few older guys to take on next year's G-Men. Another frequent visitor was Tony Farnell. Farnell was a former Hazleton High and Kutztown State athlete who had gone into coaching and just been named the assistant basketball coach at Gannon College in Erie. One day, Farley and Farnell were playing one on one when Farley rebounded his own missed shot, put his shoulder forward, and rammed into Farnell as he put the ball back up. Farley's shoulder struck Farnell in the lip, splitting it open and sending the coach sprawling backwards. As Farley began to apologize, Farnell shook his head and said,

"Good move—that was an offensive foul, but 99 percent of the refs would have called it on me."

After the game as the two were resting on one of the courtside park benches, Farnell said, "I think you guys will beat Hazleton this year. You've got five guys that can shoot and that doesn't happen often at Saint Gabe's. Your coach won't have to worry about facing gimmick defenses. You guys handle the ball and see the floor good enough to handle a press, and none of you have to carry the team. If someone has a bad night, it's likely that one of the other guys will pick up the slack. You have the makings of an easy team to coach."

One thing was certain as the summer went on: the Saint Gabriel's players at Pine Street were becoming a truly cohesive unit. After securing a rebound Walko, Curry, and Fallabel knew exactly where Farley or Munley would be to receive an outlet pass to start a fast break. They grew to recognize their teammate's favorite spots on the court, and if any of them were open in those spots, the ball was delivered into their hands instantly. Their ability to communicate on the court grew on a daily basis. They learned to blend their talents, and in time they shared a common goal. Winning became a team goal and individual accomplishments seemed to matter less as the long days grew shorter.

If the Saint Gabriel's boys weren't playing enough basketball during the day, in late June they got another idea. They decided to stage a forty-two-hour marathon basketball game. With no adult help or supervision, they pulled it off. The game started promptly at noon when the local radio personality Vince Laporte tossed up the ball to start the game. It came to a halt forty-two hours later. The *Standard Speaker* covered the game with a small write up that caught the eye of some of the West Hazleton players. A few of them showed up one day at Pine Street with the proposal that a forty-eight-hour game be played in West Hazleton. John Stoll of West Hazleton was the driving force behind the idea, which included publicizing the game as between Saint Gabriel's and West Hazleton and passing a hat during the contest at various times to collect money for charity.

That game was set to begin at 8 p.m. on Wednesday, July 16th, and would end Friday at that same time. The playground at the elementary school in West Hazleton was packed when play began. Makeshift lighting surrounded the court, but it wasn't all that illuminating. After the first half hour of play, the score was close. Tommy Boyle went up for a shot from the foul line but saw an opportunity to hit Joe Farley for an easy basket underneath. Instead of shooting, he fired a pass that caught Farley square on the left hand ring finger. As the ball bounced out of bounds, Farley clutched his hand in pain. Looking down he could see the finger was already swelling and couldn't move it. He was replaced by a substitute. Farley's dad (John "Swish" Farley) came down to have a look. He told his son to sit tight; he'd be right back. He arrived with tape and a couple of popsicle sticks. Taking his sons hand, he put the sticks on either side of the finger, squeezed and then wrapped the tape around them. When finished, he surveyed his work and said, "Okay, get back in."

The game was played in shifts, and the local paper carried pictures of players resting on the sides of the court during play. The local radio station did play-by-play for a time, and a local television station showed film of the game during their sports report. Local interest in the two Anthracite League teams was high.

With the marathons behind them, the Pine Street team set their sights on winning the city playground championship. Looking over the rosters of the other teams, it was clear that James Street and D. A. Harman would provide the chief competition. James Street would be led by Tony Kinney and other Hazleton players including Eddie Parsons, Joe Duda, and Filmore Williams. Harman with Hazleton's Tony Manfredi, Sam Mumaw, Bruce Leib, and Wally Kisthardt joining a couple of G-Men—Pat Curry and Brian McBride—had all the makings of a very tough outfit. Arthur Street couldn't be overlooked with Steve Falatovich and Robby Marusak providing a strong outside game. Joe Maddon, who would later manage the Chicago Cubs to an historic World Series victory, was also slated to play for Arthur Street.

Around this time Joe Farley met with Coach Jerry Anderson, who complained that the latest marathon had been advertised as a game between West Hazleton and Saint Gabriel's, which meant he couldn't attend. Farley explained the West Hazleton boys had handled all the publicity and then asked the coach for help in making sure he could start school at Saint Gabriel's in the fall. Anderson said he had little influence in the matter and suggested Farley visit Monsignor Maher directly to press his case.

Midway through the summer, Harman led the northern division of the playground league with a record of 5-0. They had beaten James Street and, in a battle that went back and forth, outlasted Pine Street 71-70 in a game played at Harman. That site provided quite a home court advantage as players had to get used to playing on a court that was anything but level. Shooting from one corner, the basket stood at a height of nine and a half feet, while on the other it was over ten feet.

The big surprise in the early summer was Pine Street's win over James Street. Few observers believed that the youngsters at Pine Street could hang with a team that had Tony Kinney and Joe Duda, much less beat them. Word spread that Bruce Ellis conducted daily practice sessions at Pine Street and had developed an offense designed to take advantage of the offensive strengths possessed by each of his players. The latter rumor was true. What was also true was the fact Coach Ellis had developed a real trust in this team and the way they had come together during the summer. This was evidenced by the fact that he declined an offer by John Darraugh, who was working the summer at a basketball camp, to return to Hazleton to play for the city championship.

By the close of the regular season, Pine Street had won the southern division and Harman had won the north. The two teams would meet in a best of three series for the summer league title. The first game was scheduled for Friday, August 15th, at Pine Street.

By game time the little court just off Pine and bordered by Oak and Hemlock Streets was surrounded by onlookers standing three deep. Alumni of the three local high schools were all represented, with Joe Entiero, Yosh Grobelny and Fran Libonati among the observers. If anyone needed more evidence as to how important the game was locally, all one needed to do was check out the referees. The striped shirts were being worn by Ray Saul and the region's most acclaimed official, Joe Barletta.

The Pine Street players huddled around Bruce Ellis while Mike Tracy delivered his final instructions to the visitors. From the opening tip, the home team grabbed the momentum. For the first eight minutes they could do little wrong. Not only were the Pine Street players clicking offensively, but they were making the opposition work for any shooting opportunity when they had the ball. After the first eight minutes, Pine Street had a comfortable 31-12 lead.

Things turned around in the second quarter when Farley picked up his third personal foul early in the period and took a seat on the bench. With Mike Decosmo hurt, the home team lacked depth at guard, and Munley was forced to move from his preferred spot as the shooting guard to the point. Led by Sam Mumaw and Bruce Leib, Harman stormed back and brought the deficit at halftime to under ten at 45-36.

In the third period the teams traded baskets. Pine Street maintained their lead for the majority of the quarter. With about a minute to play in the third, the home team still led by eight, but Harman scored the last four points of the quarter to make it 68-64. The final quarter was played almost dead even, and Pine Street held a six-point lead with two minutes to play when Farley picked up his fifth personal. With his point guard on the bench and mindful of Harman's second-quarter success, Ellis directed his team to hold the ball. The strategy worked, and Pine Street emerged with an 85-82 win to go up 1-0 in the series.

After the game the two teams congratulated each other, though both were already thinking about game two, scheduled for the following night at James Street. Pine Street placed all five starters in doubles in the win. Farley led the way with twenty-one. Curry scored sixteen, while both Fallabel and Munley added fifteen. Walko was a shade behind with fourteen. Harman was led by Sam Mumaw's twenty-one and Bruce Leib's seventeen while Pat Curry tallied sixteen for the visitors. Bruce Ellis brought his team together, reminding them they hadn't won anything yet. Then he took Farley off to the side, saying, "Joe Barletta told me that you're the most improved player in the area." Farley smiled, obviously pleased with the praise, and responded, "I think he meant Joe Curry."

Though they were one up, Bruce Ellis still considered his Pine Street squad underdogs. In his view, this team was still a year away, and winning at Pine Street was expected. There was no doubt that those friendly surroundings carried with them a distinct home-court advantage. There were spots on that court where Ellis knew that his squad could shoot 50 percent blindfolded.

Wally Kisthardt, who had been out of town during game one, was back for the second contest. Coach Ellis decided to match up Farley on the Harman guard. Game two was much more a defensive battle than the first game had been. Through three quarters, neither team had a lead of more than six points. Pine Street trailed by four heading into the final quarter, but couldn't find the range, scoring just eight points in the final eight minutes. Sammy Mumaw, who Larry Walko described as a real banger underneath, took Harman on his shoulders and carried them to a 61-52 win to knot the series at 1-1. Mumaw scored thirty-one in the contest. Two of his teammates, McBride and Kisthardt, also hit doubles with eleven and ten points respectively. Once again, Farley paced Pine Street with fifteen, but Walko was the only other member of the south side team to hit doubles with twelve.

The deciding game was also played at James Street the very next night, making it the third game in as many days. A large crowd gathered to take in the contest. They saw a good one. Jimmy Munley had a hot hand for Pine Street, and his teammates got him the ball often, passing it back to him outside after the Harman defense collapsed on Curry, Walko, and Fallabel. After three quarters, Harman clung to a slim 62-61 lead. Bruce Ellis decided to go to a zone defense in the final eight minutes, hoping to protect Curry, Walko, and Farley, all of whom had collected four personal fouls. It didn't work as both Curry and Walko fouled out early in the final quarter. In the last two minutes, Pine Street was forced to foul to get the ball and Harman made them count. When it was all over, Mike Tracy's team had captured the city championship 86-78. As the teams left the court a local fan who always made an appearance to cheer against anything associated with Saint Gabriel's yelled, "Hey Farley, it'll be just like that in December," making a reference to the Hazleton-Saint Gabriel's game scheduled for that month.

Pat Curry carried the load for the winners in this one, scoring twenty-five, but he was helped by Mumaw with twenty-two and Jimmy Famalette who scored twenty, including twelve of fourteen from the foul line. Leib was also in doubles with fourteen. Munley was outstanding for Pine Street, scoring twenty-six. Farley and Walko hit for thirteen and ten, while Curry and Fallabel just missed doubles with nine each. Harman won it on the foul line where they made twenty-six of forty-two attempts compared to the sixteen for twenty-five that the Pine Street players put on the board.

After the game the Pine Street players returned to their home playground and sat in the concession stand drinking sodas. Coach Ellis told them he was proud of their performance, that they had gone the distance, indeed further than anyone would have predicted, and never quit. Farley reminded everyone they'd have a chance to beat those same players over the Christmas holidays. Walko said, "I'll be there." Farley responded, "I hope I am." The remark got laughs all around.

20

A TALE OF TWO SEASONS SEASON ONE

Reverse Layup

In late August the 1969 yearbooks were available to be picked up in the Saint Gabriel's gym. Students would get their book and then hang around the auditorium getting their friends to sign their book while they returned the favor. A subdued Farley picked up his yearbook and was headed to the exit when he ran into Jerry Fallabel. He asked Fallabel to sign his book. Fallabel wrote, "To the best guard in the city. I tried to get you back. Good luck at Marian. See you at Pine St. next year."

When school started after Labor Day in September of 1969, Joe Farley found himself at Marian Catholic. He had taken Coach Anderson's advice and had a face to face with Monsignor Maher. That didn't go well. The monsignor appeared bothered by the intrusion and seemed to want to end the get-together as soon as it began. Visits from Farley's father and grandfather Norbert Corrigan also proved fruitless, so a decision had to be made on where the young man should attend his senior year.

Marian's new coach Bob Fulton was a former G-Man. Farley's cousin Francis "Snapper" O'Donnell, who remained the only Saint Gabriel's player ever to win the MVP award in the dream game, knew Fulton. It seemed that in the late fifties, Bob had scrimmaged with the Saints when his younger brother Cy was in high school. O'Donnell had come to know the new Marian coach at these practices and offered to go see Fulton to explore the possibility of Farley attending Marian. After a few discussions, the matter was settled, and Farley decided to become a

Marian Colt with the idea that he would still be eligible for the majority of the season after sitting out the ninety days required by the transfer rule in effect at the time.

So it came to be that on the first day of school Joe Farley was sitting in the office of Marian's vice principal Jack Malarky. Mr. Malarky worked out a schedule for the new student and then took Farley on a quick tour of the school. Walking calmly down the hall through a group of students, the vice principal suddenly grabbed a large male student and lifted him roughly against the school's wall. The look on the student's face was one of complete surprise, and Farley was stunned as well. To this day, he doesn't remember what the boy had done to warrant such attention. Thinking about the incident, he decided Malarky probably did it to make an impression. It worked.

Farley maintained a low profile at the new school though he quickly made a number of friends whom he had played against in previous years. The Colts with a new coach were a big question mark in the Anthracite League that year. For Farley, he couldn't wait for November 1st and the start of practice. All he wanted was a chance to get on the court against Saint Gabriel's where he could show Monsignor Maher that he had made a big mistake.

If Malarky made an impression that first day of school, Bob Fulton sure made one that first day of practice. There was not a moment's rest. Drills were timed to the second, and then it was immediately on to the next station. Fulton himself didn't need a whistle. Whenever he wanted attention, he'd raise two fingers to his mouth and out would come the loudest sound you'd ever heard. Farley thought he was in shape, but he'd never gone through a two-hour practice like the ones held in the Marian gym. If Phelps had his twenty minutes of death, Fulton had taken that and turned it into 120 minutes of death. When the session ended with a series of suicides (sprints to the first foul line touched by hand then half-court then three quarters and finally full court), the exhausted Colts headed to their locker. By the time Farley arrived home, he couldn't lift his legs to get out of the car. He lifted them to the curb using his hands. Walking up the steps to enter his home was a slow and painful journey. He was thankful to make it to his bed.

Meanwhile, formal practices had begun at Saint Gabriel's, and it appeared that in the last year of the high school, the

G-Men would start five juniors. Robby Marusak or Tommy Boyle would step into Farley's position. Behind the scenes, Fallabel, Curry, Walko, and Munley were, unknown to Farley, trying to convince the two assistant pastors, Father Doherty and Father Langdon, to get their point guard back to Saint Gabriel's. Years later, Jerry Fallabel would remember, "We never stopped trying to get him [Farley] back."

Farley didn't know what his former teammates were up to, and they were likewise unaware of what was happening at Marian. Farley was learning the game of basketball like he never had before, and Bob Fulton was a master at both teaching the fundamentals of the game and inspiring kids to work their butts off for him. The man was like a holy trinity—he seemed teacher, coach, and psychologist all in one.

The first thing you learned under Fulton was that every moment of practice was timed and not a second was wasted. He also alternated his practices. If today was two hours of offensive drills, tomorrow would be two hours of defensive drills. Fulton didn't believe in anything but man-to-man defense, and he went about teaching it like it had never been taught in the area. He taught his players to take offensive fouls, and the players learned to do it, though Fulton would spend the next two years educating officials on the rule before it began being called consistently in his favor. Fulton also encouraged creativity with the basketball. He had his players practicing behind-the-back and through-the-legs dribbling. With all the playground ball Farley had played, that was right down his alley. After the first few days, Farley realized that Marian had a chance to surprise some people. He began thinking, *I can be part of a league champion right here.*

At the end of practice, Fulton always had the entire team run a series of suicides. On one of the final days of the first week after the sprints had been run and the players were in the process of catching their breath, Fulton said, "Who is the best foul shooter here?" Farley didn't waste a second and answered, "I'm right here." Never one to waste a teachable moment, Fulton immediately told the team that he would have expected they'd all have the confidence to claim the honor. Then he threw Farley the ball and said, "Now we'll do a little exercise called social pressure." Then he set up the situation. "We're down 49-48" (Fulton could never imagine a team scoring fifty points against his defense) "and there's no time left on the clock. Joe's shoot-ing a one-and-one. He makes them both we win and head for the showers. He makes the first and misses the second, we run a single suicide. If he misses the first shot, we run a double."

As Farley walked to the line, he remembered thinking, *Great, you're new here and you put yourself in this situation. You bet-ter make these.* He stepped to the line, took a deep breath, and sent the ball toward the basket. The shot hit the front of the rim, bounced to the back, then returned to the front of the rim, where it hung for what seemed like an eternity before it fell to the floor without entering the cylinder. Farley dropped his head for just a second as Fulton whistled the team to line up for the double. After that run was completed, the coach said, "Joe, you owe me another one. We don't drop our heads after missing a shot. Give it to me tomorrow after practice. If I forget, remind me." Then the psychologist appeared: "Joe's a great foul shoot-er—someone must have moved the basket during that shot." He then called the team together and said the Serenity Prayer, which was how Marian ended every practice. The following day at practice when Fulton asked for the best foul shooter, every player in the gym quickly claimed the title, and Farley reminded the coach that he owed him a set of suicides.

About a week later, Farley was in the hall changing classes when Fulton called him over. "Joe," he said, "I've got some bad news. The PIAA ruled last night that you are ineligible for the year because you crossed district lines. Their ruling is correct based on the letter of the law, but in your case I felt they should have made an exception. You weren't recruited to come here; you wouldn't be here if you'd had a choice. We tried to get them to reconsider based on the spirit of the law, but they wouldn't budge. If you have questions I'll talk to you about it after prac-tice." Farley couldn't believe it. His high school career was over. Fulton encouraged Farley to stay with the team and keep prac-ticing, and Farley agreed to do so. As the season approached, it was difficult for the young man to believe he was not to play a second during a game that year. He phoned members of the PIAA who had made the decision, but there was no changing their minds.

On Tuesday, November 18th, the big sports news reported by the *Standard Speaker* was Notre Dame breaking a forty-five-year tradition of spurning bowl bids by accepting a bid to play either

Texas or Arkansas in the Cotton Bowl. On the same page, Ray Saul's first preseason basketball preview featuring the sports editor's view on the G-Men's chances this season. Considering the fact that the Saints would return but one starter and would be short on experience, Saul still said the team had talent and height and would be one of the region's top teams.

Walko, the sole returning starter, was seen as the key on a team that would need to mature early. Munley was viewed as "one of the best ball-handlers and dribblers in the region." Boyle fit nicely into the Saints' running game and helping off the boards. Of the three seniors on the team, Emil Polchin at six four would be the tallest player on the club and was expected to contribute. Coach Anderson was optimistic, though he called West Hazleton the team to beat. He felt this year's squad had improved defensively and was more balanced on offense than last year's squad. The G-Men would open their exhibition season on November 28th by taking on Scranton Prep at Saint Joe's.

When Saul interviewed Coach Bob Fulton on the chances of his Marian Colts in the upcoming season, Fulton came right to the point. "We will press full court, man-to-man on defense, all of the time. If we win it will be because of good defense. We plan to diminish the element of chance as much as possible by using the man-to-man defense. Each man has exact responsibilities in the man-to-man. In a zone, the responsibilities are not as clear cut." Saul saw Ed Stulginsky, a senior, and two juniors, Frank Yusella and John Teprovich, as key to the Colts chances. There was one talented sophomore on the squad named Bobby Schlosser. Saul noted that Joe Farley, a transfer from Saint Gabriel's, was ineligible at the moment and might be ineligible for the entire season. In the writer's view, adjusting to a new system and a new coach would make it tough to compete for a league title against the likes of West Hazleton and Saint Gabriel's.

If there was any doubt about which high school basketball team Saul saw as at the top of the class in the area, it was erased on November 25th by a bold headline that took up the length of the front page of the sports section and read, "West Hazleton Poised on Brink of Great Basketball Year." The Wildcats were said to have it all—height, depth, experience, and ability. With players like Tommy Smith, George Petrylak, Brian Minnig,

Laverne Mummey, Bill Pavlick, and Dave Scripko, Saul wrote that this group might just be the best squad in the school's history. Coach Ron Gatski saw the young Saint Gabriel's squad as the biggest obstacle to his team's defense of their league title but added, "Everyone will be pointing for us."

Hazleton High, as usual, would start their season later than most local teams to give their football players more of a chance to get accustomed to the basketball court. Hazleton was another team that would be breaking in a new coach, but Dave Shafer knew the region well, having coached at MMI. The Mountaineers were expected to have a solid club despite the loss of Tony Kinney. With Ed Parsons, Tony Manfredi, and Sam Mumaw inside and Wally Kisthardt running the offense, beating the Mounts wouldn't be easy. On the down side for Hazleton, the East Penn League was expected to be stronger than it had been in years.

On the evening of November 28th a good-sized crowd found their way to Saint Joe's to watch the G-Men open their season. Offensively they were very impressive as five players hit double figures. Defensively their press was ineffective and Scranton Prep often broke it for layups. Midway through the third period, Saint Gabriel's looked like they were going to run away with it when they piled up a seventeen-point lead. But the team from Scranton fought back to take a one-point lead at 66-65 with three minutes to play.

The two teams traded a couple of scores before the only senior to play for the Saints, Emil Polchin, dropped in a field goal to put Saint Gabriel's ahead to stay. When the buzzer sounded, the G-Men were on top of an 80-72 score. Watching his former teammates celebrate the victory Joe Farley had to admit they looked good considering their lack of varsity experience. Coach Anderson thought so as well, saying, "Everyone thinks we're a year away from a big year, but I feel we can make this one a big season too. There's a lot of work to be done, but I think these kids can do it." Three players from the Pine Street squad—Curry, Fallabel, and Boyle—led the Saints in scoring with fourteen apiece.

At Berwick that same night West Hazleton sounded a warning to all the other teams in the region by destroying Berwick High 85-38. Coach Gatski used ten players and they all scored. The Cats two big men led the way with Smith netting twenty and Petrylak adding nineteen. West Hazleton also played great defense as not a single Berwick player managed to hit double figures. It appeared from their openers that Saint Gabriel's and West Hazleton were indeed the teams to beat in the Anthracite League.

The following week things started in earnest. Seven of the eight Anthracite League teams were in action. Saint Gabriel's was the overwhelming favorite to handle Crestwood at Crestwood. The game drawing the most interest involved Marian at Mahanoy Area. Bob Fulton would be making his debut on the road in a game rated almost even. Hazleton would open its season later in the week against Bethlehem Freedom at Saint Joe's.

As impressive as the Saints were in their opener, few expected Crestwood to be much more than a warmup where Coach Anderson would get a chance to clear his bench. After eight minutes, with Crestwood leading 17-16, it appeared that somebody forgot to let the Comets in on that secret. The G-Men were up three at half, but eight minutes later trailed 53-48. The closest the Saints got the rest of the way was 62-60. From there on in it was all Crestwood. Stunned Saint Gabriel's fans sat silent in the bleachers staring at a scoreboard that read Home 74, Visitors 62. This particular squad of G-Men had a lot of questions to answer. Looking back on the loss, Coach Anderson remembers his team couldn't hit anything that night and never really got it together. "We were the better team by far—that loss was a fluke."

Marian, playing Mahoney Area in their first game, drew the attention of the fans in the gym from the moment they left their locker room. First, every player on the team dribbled a ball onto the court. Then they didn't warm-up by doing layups; instead, they formed a circle and, led by a player in the middle, began doing stationary ball-handling drills. When they finally formed two lines, the fans, who expected to see layups, got another surprise. Marian's Bobby Schlosser stood on the foul line, accepting a pass from one of the two lines. As the two players went by him on the way to the basket, he delivered behind-the-back, through-the-legs, and no-look passes to his teammates. At the conclusion of the warmup, he spun the basketball on his finger, walked toward the basket, and shot the still spinning ball. It goes without saying that no one in the area had ever seen anything like it.

Bob Fulton burst onto the scene in a big way. Mahanoy Area seldom lost, especially on their home court, but on this night they went down convincingly 63-45. Frank Yusella, a talented junior guard from Tamaqua, led the Colts in scoring with nineteen, and John Teprovich, always a dangerous offensive weapon, was right there with fifteen. The *Standard Speaker* called the victory one of the biggest basketball wins in Marian's history.

Back in Hazleton at the Mother of Grace gym, West Hazleton completely dominated North Schuylkill 100-69. Dave Scripko came off the bench for the Wildcats and scored twenty-three to lead a parade that saw four other Cats hit doubles. West Hazleton was living up to its lofty preseason billing.

Dave Shafer didn't have Fulton's luck in his first game as Hazleton fell to Bethlehem Freedom 61-56. It was a tough loss for the Mounts, who led most of the way and were up by ten in the third period. Hazleton could have been wearing Harman's playground jerseys on this particular night based on where their points came from. Sam Mumaw had seventeen and Jim Famalette and Wally Kisthardt were just a shade behind, adding sixteen and fifteen. Another Harman player, Bruce Leib, scored seven.

The night after the Hazleton loss there were a number of interesting games on tap. MMI was traveling to Wilkes-Barre to take on Saint Mary's. This game drew attention because Saint Mary's new head coach was Jack Cryan, who was back in the high school ranks after a year at King's College. Mahanoy Area came to Hazleton to take on the G-Men at Saint Joe's. Based on how easily Marian handled the Golden Bears on their home court, the Saints were viewed as the solid pick. Meanwhile, Marian Catholic took on Panther Valley, a school that Marian had never beaten in any varsity sport.

Jack Cryan ran his record to 2-1 as his Marymen defeated MMI 46-39. A freshman by the name of Joe Feno, who would later play on a state championship MMI squad, scored four for the Preppers. Things were not so merry at Saint Joe's, where Mahanoy Area beat Saint Gabriel's 66-62. Walko scored twenty-seven and Munley added sixteen, but those two got little support from the other Saints. The G-Men had now lost two straight and would face a strong Scranton South Catholic team on the road in one week. The fans of the G-Men were growing concerned over the poor start, especially in light of the fact that West Hazleton routed their third straight opponent by beating Shikellamy 103-80, and Marian Catholic downed Panther Valley 61-42.

The Marian win was their home opener, and it was played before a packed house. Marian's 300-member Pep Club stood throughout the contest, and as Don Barnes pointed out, they and everyone connected to the school were convinced that Bob Fulton was Moses sent to lead the Colts out of the basketball wilderness. Don Barnes witnessed the Fulton effect, writing, "There's an electrifying crackle in the air when he lifts a finger. It's said his players worship him."

Fulton was pleased with his team's effort. He praised the Colts' hustle, but never one to miss a teachable moment, added, "We went into our 'Victory Plan' with about six minutes to play, and I wasn't too happy with what happened in the next four minutes. When we go into our Victory Plan, we feel we have a big enough lead to force the other team to come out after us. When they do, we have to get somebody loose for an easy one, but our kids got too excited and didn't get things done the way they should have."

Barnes was calling them the "New Marian Catholic," noting they were even flashy at times with an occasional behind-the-back pass. That was Bob Fulton as well. Where other coaches in the area tended to discourage what they called "showboating," Fulton taught it and appreciated it when executed properly. Folks were beginning to wonder whether a Saint Gabriel's alum had taken a team and supplanted his alma mater as the chief threat to beat West Hazleton.

The following Saturday morning, Marian finished their practice at noon, and by early afternoon Joe Farley was back in Hazleton. It was December 6th, and he hadn't stopped into the old school since the picking up his yearbook. It was a short two-block walk from his home on Cedar Street to the high school. It was a sunny, mild day with temperatures in the upper thirties. He entered the front door, immediately turned right, and headed down the steps toward the gym.

He could hear the sound of the basketball as he descended the stairs. It was Joe Curry, Larry Walko, and Jerry Fallabel who greeted him as soon as they saw him. They wanted to know about Marian and Bob Fulton. Farley told them he had never seen anyone like the Marian coach. He told them that Marian was for real and so was Fulton. "They play, man," he said, "but the player two passes away plays in what Fulton calls a help or open position, and it's like you're facing a zone as well."

Joe Curry asked him about his eligibility, and Farley said it didn't look good. Curry asked, "Would you come back here?" Without hesitation, Farley said he would, but there was no chance of that.

Curry told him not to be so sure. "We've been working at it and we're making headway. Do you want us to keep it up?"

"Absolutely," said Farley, "I'd give anything to put on a uniform this year."

As he was leaving, Farley looked back over his shoulder and yelled, "What the hell happened to you guys against Crestwood?"

The trio kind of groaned and Walko responded, "We just played terrible, and we haven't bccn playing well. We should be undefeated."

Farley said, "Let me know if you guys hear anything or if there's something I can do to help." Farley left the school, glad he had made the trip. Maybe there was hope.

The following Tuesday, Saint Gabriel's had a much needed night off, but there was plenty of other local action. Coach Dave Shafer registered his first win at Hazleton High when the Mounts traveled to Allentown and upset Allentown Allen in the "Little Palestra" 76-69. Five Mountaineers—Famalette, Kisthardt, Parsons, Mumaw, and Leib—scored more than ten in the balanced attack. West Hazleton continued to turn in impressive performances by beating Shamokin 81-50. Marian Catholic's "Colt Power" defense was on full display in a 78-32 win over Pleasant Valley. Marian point guard Frank Yusella, who scored fifteen, was blossoming under the tutelage of Coach Fulton.

The Saints traveled to Scranton to take on South Catholic a week after the loss to Mahanoy Area. After a slow start, it looked like the G-Men had righted the ship when they overcame an early nine-point deficit to take a two-point advantage to the locker room at half. Early in the final quarter the Saints appeared to be breezing to a victory when they stretched their lead to fifteen.

What followed was a total collapse. South Scranton hit two foul shots with five seconds left, sending the G-Men to their third straight defeat 70-69. The Saint's solid inside trio of Fallabel, Curry, and Walko combined for a total of just nineteen points in the thirty-two minutes. The G-Men would be back in Scranton to face Scranton Prep in just a few days. Saint Gabriel's had looked so impressive in beating Prep in their opener less than a month earlier, though now it felt like years ago.

The Saturday after the game, Joe Farley was sitting at home having lunch when he heard a knock. It was Fallabel, Curry, and Walko. The three delivered a message. "You can come back to Saint Gabriel's if you want." Farley had a hard time believing it but did as directed by his three Pine Street teammates and headed to the parish rectory to see Father Doherty, who confirmed the news. The only requirement was that Marian's principal would have to supply Saint Gabriel's with a letter confirming Farley hadn't caused any trouble at Marian during his time there.

That Monday Farley met with Coach Fulton and brought him up to date on the developments. Fulton advised Farley to give the matter some thought and to make sure the move back was something he wanted and was in his best interest. In Farley's mind, there was no question. The travel to Marian—first to school and then later to practice—was taking a toll. At Saint Gabriel's, maybe the PIAA would reconsider and restore his eligibility. He told Fulton he wanted to make the switch. The coach said he'd work with the officials at Marian to make it happen.

It took a week before everything was worked out. The letter from the Marian principal was delivered to Saint Gabriel's. Coach Fulton told Farley the letter stated that Farley arrived at Marian a perfect gentleman and was leaving the same way. The pressure of the final week did get to the young man, and for the last three days at Marian, he was forced to leave class in the afternoon due to violent headaches that forced him to lie down in the dark. The headaches stopped the day after he returned to Saint Gabriel's.

While Farley was in limbo between the two schools, the Saints took on Scranton Prep for the second time. The game was nip and tuck most of the way. As a matter of fact, the teams were tied multiple times in the final quarter. With just eight seconds to play, the G-Men were up 70-68. Scranton Prep's Paul Gallagher was at the foul line shooting a one-and-one. His first shot dropped neatly through, but his second bounded off the right side of the rim into the hands of Joe Curry, and Saint Gabriel's secured a one-point win. Curry played his finest game to date scoring twenty, and three other Saints—Fallabel, Polchin, and Marusak—also hit doubles. The main thing was breaking the team's early losing streak.

Marian Catholic faced the undefeated Palmerston Blue Bombers and the Colts were ice cold. Only two of their first twenty-four shots found the net. Midway through the second quarter, the Colts were down by fourteen. The rest of the contest was played fairly evenly, but Marian couldn't overcome the sluggish start and lost for the first time, 58-43. After congratulating the winners, Coach Fulton assessed the game, accepting the blame himself for his team losing its poise on both offense and defense. Fulton did say, "I never expected to see us give away that many layups to anyone—uncontested layups."

West Hazleton continued to dominate area teams. The Wildcats, led by Petrylak and Mummey, traveled to Wilkes-Barre where they had no trouble disposing of Coughlin 90-66. Area fans were anxious to see how the Cats would fare in their game against Nanticoke in just three days. Nanticoke was unbeaten and the defending Class A District 2 champions. Hazleton improved to 3-1 on the year by beating Easton 59-50, and it began to look like the Hazleton-West Hazleton holiday matchup would get top billing as far as the competition between the city teams went this season.

On the night West Hazleton faced its toughest test to date, Saint Gabriel's obtained a measure of revenge by beating Crestwood 93-45 at Saint Joe's. In avenging their previous defeat six G-Men scored double figures, and ten of the eleven who played registered points. Evening their record at 3-3, the Saints were showing signs of life.

Nanticoke arrived at the Mother of Grace gym riding a regular season thirty-one game winning streak. They left without it. West Hazleton broke an early 2-2 tie, and then never trailed in the contest that ended 74-57. Smith, who was now being touted as an all-state candidate, scored twenty-four and was a big reason the Wildcats controlled the boards, corralling forty-nine rebounds to just twenty-eight for the visitors. West Hazleton was now 7-0 and only had Hazleton left before starting Anthracite League play. Ray Saul was writing he didn't see a team in the Anthracite League that could challenge the Cats. The *Reading Eagle* rated West Hazleton the number one team in the region.

The only other Anthracite League team to make the *Reading Eagle* list was Marian, who clocked in at nine.

It was Christmas week when Joe Farley stepped onto the court at Saint Joe's to practice with the G-Men for the first time this season. Farley had spent the afternoon battling the last of his headaches and visiting his local doctor. Given a clean bill of health, he was at practice early and more than a little surprised to see some of the Saints take the court wearing their Pine Street shirts. It seemed some of the Saint Gabriel's players weren't thrilled to have Farley back because of the potential loss of playing time, and Farley's former playground teammates had decided to wear the shirts to show their support for him. Coach Anderson, seeing the situation, sent the team minus Farley back to the locker where he had a talk with them.

Farley then asked if he could talk to the team. He started out by saying everyone might just be jumping the gun because the school was still waiting on a ruling relative to his eligibility. He noted he had played with most of the guys present for years and wanted them to know all he cared about was winning. He said, "I'll be cheering for whoever is playing at any time during the full thirty-two minutes." He added that he hoped the rest of the team felt the same way. He left the locker and when the team was summoned to the floor, the Pine Street shirts were gone. If a crisis was diverted it turned out to be a needless one. The PIAA maintained that Farley remained ineligible for the year. It appeared his main role would be imitating the next opponent's point guard at practices.

A very white Christmas season resulted in the postponement of multiple games, including Saint Gabriel's versus Lehighton the day after Christmas. The snow wreaked havoc with the Hazleton Mountaineers. Due to a cancellation they were going to be playing three games—at Pottsville and at Saint Joe's against West Hazleton and Saint Gabriel's—in five days. The week got off to a rocky start for the Mountaineers when they fell apart in the second half during an 81-59 loss to Pottsville.

More than two thousand fans made their way to Saint Joe's for the Hazleton-West Hazleton contest. Most of them parked downtown and walked to the game as there were absolutely no spaces available close to the gym due to the snow. Hazleton stayed with the Wildcats for eight minutes before Smith caught

fire and led unbeaten West Hazleton to a 66-55 win. If West
Hazleton had any weaknesses, they were hard to find. They
were rugged underneath, played good defense, had depth coming off the bench, and they could shoot. Ray Saul began writing
about a possible undefeated season for the Cats. The Mounts'
Coach Dave Shafer complimented West Hazleton, but said his
team still had a lot of basketball in them starting with Saint
Gabriel's in two days.

The Saints had experienced a long layoff. Their game with
Lehighton was finally cancelled due to the weather, so Coach
Anderson was using the time to prepare for Hazleton. He told
Joe Farley, "You're going to play the part of Wally Kisthardt
[Hazleton's point guard]." Farley jokingly replied, "Fine, but I'm
gonna have to lose my jump shot."

Hazleton and Saint Gabriel's met for the last time on
January 2, 1970. Farley was there at tip-off, though not the way
he imagined he'd be when he expressed his wish the previous
August sitting in the Pine Street playground concession stand.
He was sitting on the G-Men bench wearing the Saint Gabriel's
blazer varsity players had donned on game days since the reign
of Digger Phelps.

The G-Men played the Mounts toe to toe throughout the first
half. Munley had a hot first quarter, scoring six of his twelve
points in those eight minutes. Walko and Curry were battling
inside against Parsons and Mumaw, and at halftime it was anyone's game with Hazleton holding a slim 26-23 lead.

At the start of the second half, Hazleton went on a run
outscoring the G-Men 10-1 in just two minutes before Coach
Anderson called a time-out to get things under control. His
team fought back in the next six minutes to narrow the margin
to 44-37 with eight minutes to play. The last quarter began
the same way the third had as Hazleton scored fourteen unanswered points in a little over two minutes. The final score was
Hazleton 74, Saint Gabriel 54. The margin was deceiving. Aside
from about four minutes of play where Hazleton outscored the
Saints 24-1, the game was virtually even.

Substitute Pat Curry for Ed Parsons, and the Hazleton team
was basically the Harman team that Pine Street had come very
close to beating just a few months earlier. Still, what mattered
was Saint Gabriel's was hobbling into Anthracite League play
with a record of 3-4. Coach Anderson felt inexperience had hurt

his squad in some of the games to date, but he expected the Saints would make some noise in league play. Ray Saul revised his preseason projections and picked the G-Men to finish behind both West Hazleton and Marian in the league race.

At practice the day before Saint Gabriel's was to begin league play against Cardinal Brennan, the team's starters were on offense going against the reserves. Gradually, Coach Anderson switched personal around until Farley, Fallabel, Curry, Walko, and Munley were all on defense. The five, seeing what had happened, began playing with energy usually reserved for big games. The chemistry between the five was obvious as they played with one thing in mind: keep the opposition from scoring. For twenty minutes they dominated on the defensive side of the court. They yelled encouragement to each other, praising good defensive plays, looking to help if any of one of them was caught out of position or beat by an offensive player. They crashed the boards, fiercely determined that the offense was only getting one shot. Though it was clear they itched to go on offense each time they stole the basketball or secured a rebound, each change of possession halted the action and the ball was put in hands of the offense. Finally, Anderson sent Farley to the sidelines. It was the only time that season the five players who had worked so hard all summer together took the floor as a unit.

Cardinal Brennan provided little opposition as the Saints handled them easily 87-59. Fallabel came to life and scored nineteen, and all eleven players scored for the G-Men. It was a positive start to a season that was about to get tougher with Marian coming to Saint Joe's in just three days. While the Saints mauled Brennan, Marian and West Hazleton went at it in the Colts' gym. Marian proved they were for real. With thirty-four seconds to go, West Hazleton was trailing by one but had possession of the ball. The Wildcats worked the ball to Petrylak, who drove to the basket and was fouled with just seventeen seconds to play. Petrylak was three for six from the line to this point, but he stepped to the stripe and nailed both shots, putting West Hazleton ahead 55-54.

An ill-timed Marian pass on their last possession resulted in a turnover, and the Cats escaped the packed Hometown gym with a win. After the game while Coach Gatski praised the Marian defense he admitted he didn't expect the game to be close. According to Don Barnes, Coach Fulton was almost apologetic after the game. Fulton appeared to be taking the blame for the defeat, saying it was the first time a team he coached had lost a game after being at least even with two minutes to play. Pointing a finger squarely at himself, he said he should have spent more time in practice on his two-minute drill. He finished his interview saying, "They're a fine team, but I'm proud of the way our boys played them."

As Saint Gabriel's prepared for Marian, they leaned heavily on Farley. Farley had been a member of the Marian team for more than a month. He had run their offense and he understood their defense. He explained Marian even had jump ball plays. They'd call for an offensive tap play if they thought they could control the tap and defensive if they didn't. Their players would circle the ball differently depending on the call. He said they would play a man-to-man defense full court the entire game. Farley stressed that they would look to create offensive foul situations, particularly if you beat your man and were heading to the basket. Beating one Marian player wasn't going to get you a clear lane to the hoop. Another Marian player was going to pick you up. If you did beat your man, it was going to be just as important to look for a pass as a shot. At the close of practice the night before the game Coach Anderson put Farley on the spot in front of the entire squad, asking for a prediction. Farley, playing the Irish politician, responded, "There's more talent on this court than there is on the one in Hometown."

Saint Gabriel's offense gave Marian trouble, and Coach Fulton said it possessed wrinkles his team hadn't run up against in previous games. The G-Men started quickly, handled the Marian press, and were strong off the boards in the first eight minutes to go up by five 15-10. Marian settled down in the second stanza and grabbed a slim two-point lead at intermission despite going a dismal three of ten from the foul line. Both teams were supported by a large and very vocal fan base, and Saint Joe's literally rocked in the second half as Marian edged ahead by six 43-37.

The Saints struggled to get closer. With just over a minute to play Larry Walko scored to narrow the Colt lead to four at 61-57, but Marian responded by hitting for five straight points and it was over. The final was 68-61. After the game Coach Fulton had nothing but praise for Saints' Larry Walko, whose twenty-six points and yeoman work on the boards still wasn't enough to carry his team to victory. Curry scored eighteen, but Munley and Fallabel managed just three between them. West Hazleton was now the clear favorite to win the first-half title. Marian fans would be cheering for the G-Men in two weeks when the Saints were scheduled to take on the Cats at Mother of Grace.

The Marian loss was just the latest blow to what was the final basketball team that would wear Saint Gabriel's purple and white. By mid-January, the *Standard Speaker* was reporting that the G-Men would face Weatherly "amid rumors that dissension was rocking the basketball boat" at the small parish school. The G-Men traveled to Weatherly and won 81-64, but as the paper noted, the Saints played without Curry and Fallabel, who were said to have "elected to disassociate themselves from the team." In his sports column, Ray Saul reported that the two had quit the squad, making the Saints even bigger underdogs in the upcoming contest with the Wildcats. The truth was Fallabel had made such a choice, but Coach Anderson had made the choice for Curry, dismissing the talented junior for violating team rules.

Even without Fallabel and Curry, the G-Men had too much for Jim Thorpe as the Olympians fell to the Saints 75-65. After a close first half Saint Gabriel's turned a four-point lead into a twelve-point margin after three quarters and coasted from there. West Hazleton prepped for their meeting with the G-Men by traveling to Freeland and easily handling the Whippets 88-54.

Playing at Mother of Grace against a team like West Hazleton would be tough for a school the size of Saint Gabriel's under the best of circumstances. To try to compete with the Cats minus the services of Fallabel, Curry, and Farley was an impossible task. It was over at half with the Wildcats holding a comfortable 47-23 lead. Walko and Munley led the Saints in scoring. Marusak hit doubles as well, and to their credit the G-Men fought to the end as did their fan base who began chanting "We'll meet again" as the final seconds ticked away. The more levelheaded among them may have cautioned "Be careful what you wish for" based on the results on this night. With the impressive 90-65 win, it was clear sailing to the first-half crown for the Wildcats.

The day after the game Farley and Coach Anderson talked briefly about the current situation involving Fallabel and Curry. Farley, unaware Curry had been dismissed for violating team rules, said the team needed them both. Anderson said he wanted

Fallabel back, but Curry would not be permitted to rejoin the team. Looking back on the situation over forty-five years later, Anderson said that "dismissing Joe Curry was the toughest thing I ever did in my coaching career." Anderson said he had given Curry multiple chances but felt that the talented young player had basically tied his hands. Curry did some things Anderson just couldn't allow, and the whole situation haunts the coach to this day. Hearing Anderson reflect on the situation, one can't help think that he wished he could have found other options to deal with the tall, but at this point troubled, junior.

Anderson did visit Fallabel and his parents to make his case that Fallabel come back and play. Whether it was the personal visit or some other factor, Fallabel returned to the team. Fallabel says he wanted to play and had left the team because he was upset over the playing time he was getting. After the summer at Pine Street, he said, "We knew how good we were, and I didn't think the best players were getting the time on the court that they deserved." After the loss to West Hazleton, the Saints' record was a disappointing 6-6. They won the last two games in the first half to finish with a league record of 5-2. West Hazleton was undefeated and captured the first-half championship. The Saints would meet the Wildcats at Saint Joe's in the last game of the regular season. Few doubted the game would have a significant bearing on the outcome of the league's second-half race.

With no playoff needed, the Anthracite League teams had a week off before starting second-half play. Father Doherty surprised Farley by showing up at Saint Joe's after practice during this time frame. Doherty, unlike Father Deviney, seldom showed up at practices. He called Farley over and said, "Joe, how would you like to play this year?" The question confused Farley, who thought that matter was decided, but he admitted he would love to. Doherty said he had talked to a friend about Farley's situation and followed up on the suggestion to check the Pennsylvania Catholic Interscholastic Athletic Association rules. Pulling the rule book from his pocket, he said that according to PCIAA rules, Farley was eligible to play thirty days after a transfer. Farley stood there, mouth open, and asked what it meant. "Well," Doherty replied, "I asked Coach Anderson if he wanted you and he said, 'Are you kidding? He's my best guard and I can't use him.' I showed him the rule, and we checked it out. You'll be eligible for the state playoffs." Doherty then said it was possible Farley could play in the Anthracite League games against other non-PIAA schools (Marian, Cardinal Brennan, and MMI) if the league members agreed. Doherty said a league meeting had been called to decide the matter.

The meeting took place later that week. Each school had a representative. Coach Gatski was there for West Hazleton and Bob Fulton was there for Marian. Gatski and the other PIAA schools took the position that they didn't care since Farley wouldn't play against them in any case. Gatski threw the ball squarely into Fulton's court, saying the decision probably affected Marian the most and that he was willing to leave the decision up to Fulton. When Father Doherty informed Farley of the results of the meeting, he said that it basically came down to a decision by Bob Fulton, and Bob Fulton had recommended Farley be permitted to play. As luck or fate would have it, the first game the Saint Gabriel's guard would be eligible to participate in would be against Marian Catholic.

21

SEASON TWO
THE
UNLIKELY CHAMPIONSHIP

BUZZER BEATER

arry Walko says he remembers a different feeling on the team that came along with Farley's eligibility. He says Farley brought an "energy" and "drive" to the team. "Playing became fun again. That's what that run we went on was—fun."

"If I brought anything with me," says Farley, "it was my own excitement. I had worked hard all summer only to be ineligible. Then I practiced for three months without the hope of playing. So when Father Doherty found that PCIAA rule, I was pretty excited. For me, a game in February was going to be my first as an active participant. The other guys on the team had been through a lot of ups and downs. They may have needed some new energy, and I certainly had that."

Armed with his new status, Farley decided to make another run at Curry. He was thinking there might be a chance of getting the boys from Pine Street back on the court. He urged Curry to go talk to the coach. Curry said he'd been down that road with no results. He said Anderson wasn't going to budge, and he wasn't going to beg. As it turned out, even if Curry had returned, it would not have gotten the starting five from Pine Street back on the court. Munley was hurt. Munley had been one of the bright spots in the up-and-down year. He had scored consistently, handled the ball well, and played good defense. But he developed a back problem that rendered him almost immobile as far as basketball went. In his own words, "walking was a chore" and the doctors couldn't pinpoint a cause.

While most of the Anthracite League teams were enjoying the week off, Hazleton High, who finished third in the East Penn League first-half race, beat Allentown Allen by ten to improve to 3-0 in the second half and a tie for first with Allentown Central Catholic in that league's second-half race. Five Mountaineers hit doubles led by Kisthardt with sixteen. Parsons scored fourteen and hauled down twelve rebounds.

The G-Men opened the second half on February 3, 1970, at Freeland. Though Freeland was notoriously tough at home, the Saints entered the game as solid favorites. As it turned out, the Whippets gave Saint Gabriel's all they could handle. Freeland was actually ahead by nine midway through the second quarter before the G-Men closed with a rush to take a 41-39 halftime lead. After three periods Saint Gabriel's was clinging to a two-point advantage before surging ahead in the final eight minutes to win by a 78-67 margin. The good news was Fallabel played his best game of the year scoring twenty, and Marusak hit for eighteen to fill the void created by Munley's absence.

West Hazleton opened their second half by easily defeating Jim Thorpe for their sixteenth straight win. Marian was impressive, beating Cardinal Brennan 89-43. Saint Gabriel's would meet Marian in just two days at Marian.

The game was originally scheduled for Friday but had been moved to Thursday at Marian's request due to a scheduling conflict. The *Standard Speaker* installed the Colts as the favorite since they had beaten Saint Gabriel's at Saint Joe's and were a difficult on their own court as evidenced by their whisker one-point loss to West Hazleton. The loser of the game wouldn't be out of the second-half race, but their chances would be much diminished.

Joe Farley found a seat in the bleachers while the Saint Gabriel's JV team headed to the locker room to prepare for their game. Though it was about forty minutes before the start of the first game, some fans were already in place. A Marian student who had been in one of Farley's classes when he attended school there sat down beside him and asked how he was doing. After the initial pleasantries, she said, "You know everyone here is mad at you." Farley, surprised, asked for an explanation. She said the Marian fans considered Farley a traitor who had come to their school as a spy and was now sharing all the team's secrets with the Saint Gabriel's squad. Farley laughed and said, "Well, that didn't help a month ago. We'll have to see what happens tonight."

Once the JV game began Farley sat with Fallabel in the row behind the Saint Gabriel's bench. He could barely sit still and told Fallabel he wanted to go to the locker room. Doing so would violate a team tradition where the varsity sat behind the JV team until the end of the third quarter as a show of support. Fallabel told him to calm down and sit tight. Farley did neither as the first-half of the JV dragged on for what to Farley seemed like an eternity. At half the two got up and walked around, where they ran into Marian's assistant coach Tinker Knies, who wished the two of them luck in tonight's game. When the JV team returned to the court, Farley convinced Fallabel to head to the locker room. At the end of that quarter, Coach Anderson arrived in the locker room with the rest of the varsity team.

"Where were you guys?"

Farley answered, "Right here, getting ready."

The coach responded "From now on, until the end of the third quarter, get ready with the rest of us behind the JV team."

The stands were packed by the time the two varsity teams took the court. After completing their warm-ups, the Saint Gabriel's team gathered around their bench for the introductions of the starters. Fallabel and Walko were introduced first for the G-Men, and they took the court to the sound of polite applause from the many Saint Gabriel's fans on the visitors' side of the court. Then the public address announcer said, "For Saint Gabriel's at the guard position—Joe Farley." The Marian faithful, led by their Pep club, erupted in chorus of boos. As Farley shook hands with Walko and Fallabel, he said, "Just a few of the many friends I made while I was there." The formalities were over; it was time to play ball.

The first paragraph in the story authored by Don Barnes pretty much summed up the game. Barnes wrote, "St. Gabriel's— the NEW St. Gabriel's that is—made a shambles of Marian's vaunted defense last night as the G-Men rode roughshod over the Colts at Hometown, 76-55, to take a temporary half-game lead over the field in the Anthracite League second half race." Barnes noted that the game marked the availability for the first time of Joe Farley, a senior who had transferred to Marian and then returned to Saint Gabriel's. Barnes said Farley would be a big asset in the Catholic playoffs, but rightly asserted, "It was more than Farley that did in the Colts in last night."

According to Barnes, one observer said this Saint Gabriel's team clicked like a unit in a way that they hadn't all season. All five starters scored in double figures, but as Barnes noted, the Saints' players owned the boards, ran the fast break to perfection, and seemed to find the open man at every available opportunity. Polchin scored twenty for the G-Men and did everything Joe Curry could have. Walko hit for nineteen, Fallabel twelve, and the two G-Men guards scored ten each.

Farley remembers it as the best high school game he ever played. "I didn't have a turnover, I had twelve assists, I went five for five from the field. I think the only mistake I made was missing a foul shot." Coach Anderson recalls the game as the turning point in the season. "I could see it and the kids could feel it. We were playing with the attitude that nobody could beat us. I had a feeling after that game that we might not lose another game all year."

After he showered, Farley returned to the deserted gym floor. Tinker Knies was there, and Farley said he'd like to talk to Coach Fulton. Coach Knies said he'd check but Coach Fulton generally liked to be left alone after a loss. After a few minutes, Fulton came out of the Marian locker. Farley told him that he knew it was Fulton who had made the decision allowing him to play, and he wanted to thank him. Fulton said Farley deserved the chance to play. "There are times you have to think about more than winning or losing if you want to see the whole picture before making a decision." The two wished each other luck the rest of the way.

The next night Hazleton High beat Easton to take sole possession of first place in the East Penn's second-half race. Smith and Mummey led West Hazleton to a 76-58 win at Weatherly. Ray Saul wrote Saint Gabriel's had breathed new life into the Anthracite League race, and they had done it without Munley. Don Barnes was crediting the "Anthracite League Fathers with something approaching clairvoyance" for scheduling the G-Men to face the Cats in the last game of the regular season at Saint Joe's "where the Saints are best and the seats are most plentiful."

The next test for the Saints was Cardinal Brennen at Saint Joe's. It would be the only home game that Farley would be eligible to take part in as a senior. The game proved to be no contest and Coach Anderson substituted freely, using fourteen players. Twelve of them scored. Fallabel led the way with twenty, Boyle scored thirteen coming off the bench, and Farley scored twelve. That same evening West Hazleton took no chances with Marian beating the Colts 80-56. The Colts hung tough for a half before fading against the talented Wildcats. Both West Hazleton and the G-Men appeared to be on a collision course for the end of the year meeting. Hazleton High's reign alone at the top was short-lived when they were upset 67-65 by Allentown Dieruff.

On Friday the 13th while the Church Hill Cinema was showing five horror films, Saint Gabriel's traveled to Freeland to take on MMI. MMI was a private, non-PIAA school, so Farley was eligible to play. It would be the final Anthracite League game he would be permitted to participate in, and he wanted to make the most of it. Pine Street's Bruce Ellis was attending school at Bloomsburg College and he had been urging the coaching staff to take a look at Farley. Ellis had told Farley that Bloomsburg's head coach Earl Voss intended to make that night's game.

Farley made his presence felt in the early going, getting two steals that he converted into layup goals as the Saints jumped to a 6-0 lead. The small MMI gym offered plenty of offensive opportunities, and the G-Men took full advantage of them in rolling up a 102-78 victory. Fallabel scored twenty-five and Farley hit for twenty-four in the Saints' win. It was the first time Saint Gabriel's had reached the century mark this season and it came, according to Don Barnes, as "Cardinal Newman scouts [the Saints' first opponent in the state playoffs] cowered in the balcony." Barnes also wrote that as of late, "the Saints are playing a different brand of ball." West Hazleton kept pace, winning for the nineteenth straight time. It now appeared certain that Saint Gabriel's was the only thing standing in the way of an undefeated season for the Wildcats.

Jim Thorpe was up next for the Saints and though Farley couldn't play, he made a point of reminding his teammates that a year earlier Thorpe had cost the G-Men a tie for the second-half title. It appeared that history wasn't going to repeat itself when the Saints jumped to an early 13-4 lead. The Olympians played deliberate ball throughout, and though Saint Gabriel's maintained a comfortable advantage, they never quite put the visitors away until late in the third quarter when a mild run extended the advantage to 39-20. Even then the Thorpe players didn't quit as they outscored Saint Gabriel's in the final quarter. Still, when the buzzer sounded the G-Men were on top 54-41.

West Hazleton was 20-0 after dispatching a game Freeland squad 75-54. If the G-Men and the Wildcats won their next game, as they were expected to do, they would meet at Saint Joe's for the league's second-half title.

The headline in the *Standard Speaker* said it all: "West Hazleton, St. Gabriel's Stay Unbeaten in Second-Half Race." The Wildcats survived a slowdown game by MMI that ended 46-30 after the Preppers trailed by just four at half 21-17. Meanwhile, the Saints had a little more trouble than expected against Weatherly, breaking a game that was 29-26 at half open in the third quarter on the way to an 81-65 win. Saint Gabriel's fans were mighty happy Fallabel had rejoined the team as he scored twenty-eight in the contest. Walko scored twenty-one and Boyle hit for seventeen. The stage was now set for the two rivals to slug it out for the final time at Saint Joe's. Don Barnes described the matchup as "one of the tastiest dishes the league has served up in a while" and predicted "there'll be plenty of epicures on hand to savor it."

West Hazleton remained on top of the *Reading Eagle* rankings of high school teams in the Anthracite region. Hazleton High was ranked fourth and Saint Gabriel's made their first appearance in the rankings at number nine. Ray Saul noted the presence of the three city teams in the top ten. It also appeared the state playoffs would provide a measuring stick for Digger Phelps's prediction that in a few years some of the Anthracite League teams would be on par with those in the East Penn League as it was looking like West Hazleton was going to draw the top East Penn League team in their first playoff game.

On Tuesday, February 24th, the Hazleton weather was mild with temperatures in the low twenties. The night before, Hazleton defeated Bethlehem Catholic 66-55 to join in a four-way tie for the East Penn second-half title. Hazleton would play Pottsville at the Harrisburg Farm Show Arena in the first game of a doubleheader. The winner would advance to the second-half championship game against either Allentown Dieruff or Allentown Allen.

Saint Gabriel's students and fans cared little about that news; their thoughts were all on this evenings contest with

West Hazleton. West Hazleton was one of four unbeaten Class A team's left in the state, and they were the favorite to end a perfect regular season with a win against the Saints. The G-Men were 14-6 but seemed to have righted their ship after a shaky start. As stated in the *Standard Speaker*, both teams were capable of playing outstanding basketball. If both played at the top of their game, the contest had the potential to be a classic. If either experienced an off night, that team would be in real trouble.

All year long at Saint Gabriel's High School, every annual event held marked the last celebration of that event. That evening at Saint Joseph's it was no different. It was the last time a Saint Gabriel's High School team would play in what had become their home gym. It was the last Anthracite League game for the small parochial school that had competed in the circuit since its creation. It was the last game between these two high schools that had participated in so many classic games together in their long history. It was the last Saint Gabriel's senior day where, per tradition, the senior players and cheerleaders were honored by the school body.

The four senior players and the student manager were introduced and stood together at mid-court. Tom McNelis had served as student manager for three years. He had stopped playing competitive basketball after he was diagnosed with a heart murmur as a freshman. He certainly deserved as much recognition as any of the players. Two of the four seniors, John Breslin and John Ferry, had stayed with the team through three seasons knowing they would see limited playing time. The teams before their senior year had been dominated by upperclassmen, and this year's team was largely made up of talented juniors. But they richly deserved the thanks of the student body and fans gathered that night. They had made every practice minute count and through their work their team had improved.

Only one other senior was in uniform—Emil Polchin who had stepped up when Joe Curry was dismissed from the squad. Polchin's play underneath had been a key in the Saints turning this season around. The other senior was in street clothes, ineligible to play on this night. For Joe Farley, sitting out this game made for the most frustrating night of his season. After the seniors were introduced, the public address announcer asked the fans to stand for the Saint Gabriel's alma mater and the national anthem. The students stood, and for the last time at a basketball game sang the school song. Their voices rose and the cadence quickened as they belted out the last verse of the song's lyrics:

> Hail to Saint Gabriel's High
> Whose hallowed name
> Echoes a trumpet call
> To Victory and fame.

As always, the students and the many Saint Gabriel's fans among the more than two thousand who filled the gym erupted into cheers at the song's finish.

Fallabel was back after missing the first game against the Wildcats, but Munley, though in uniform, wasn't expected to play. Thus, of the five players that had been expected to carry the load for the Saints this season, only two were on the court when Referee Joe Barletta tossed the ball into the air to start the game. The Cats got off to a fast start and jumped to a 21-12 lead after one quarter. The two teams played the second eight minutes almost dead even and headed to lockers at intermission with West Hazleton holding a 31-21 lead. At the start of the third quarter the momentum swung to the home team. Led by Fallabel and Walko, the Saints knotted the score at forty-two in just three minutes and Coach Gatski called a time-out. When the teams returned to the court Smith scored two quick buckets to put the Cats back on top for good.

The G-Men fought hard to the very end, but when it was over, West Hazleton was on top 80-68 and had not only defended their league championship but finished 22-0. The veteran Wildcats prevailed, but as Don Barnes noted, the Saint Gabriel's team "needed no apologies for their performance." The Cats' backcourt, with Munley ailing and Farley out of uniform, dominated their opposition, outscoring the Saints' guards 31-8. Inside Fallabel, Walko, and Polchin had battled Smith, Petrylak, and Minnig all night and had more than held their own. Only two other teams had scored more than sixty-eight points against the Wildcats all year, and in both those games West Hazleton had topped the century mark themselves.

After the game Coach Gatski admitted that this was the first time he was really worried before a contest. Jerry Anderson was proud of the way his team battled, though he admitted that his club hadn't exactly helped itself by committing twenty-two turnovers. Anderson added that he expected to do very well in the Catholic state playoffs. Ray Saul wrote that the Saints would benefit by the availability of "outside shooter" Farley in those playoffs. As soon as the game was over, that's what Farley wanted the Saints thinking about. He talked to both Fallabel and Walko in the locker room after the game while the West Hazleton players were celebrating their win by singing a raucous version of the *Battle Hymn of the Republic* in the adjoining locker room. Pulling the two G-Men aside, Farley said, "Now I'm as eligible as anyone. Let's go win a state title."

The G-Men had only one practice session to prepare to face Williamsport Bishop Neumann in a game scheduled to take place in Wilkes-Barre at King's College two nights later. Bishop Neumann was a new central Catholic school that had replaced Williamsport Saint Joseph's, a familiar playoff foe. Bishop Neumann had come of age as the season progressed and was on a five-game winning streak. The *Standard Speaker*'s pre-game preview said the G-Men would be favored if they started the same club that had faced West Hazleton, but the team would be strengthened by the availability of Farley, who the paper described as "a premiere playmaker at the guard slot." The preview noted that if Munley were available, the Saints' backcourt tandem "would be really devastating."

If Saint Gabriel's had to rely on the outside shooting of Farley against Bishop Neumann, they would have made a first round exit. As a matter of fact, none of Saint Gabriel's players save Fallabel shot very well, but the G-Men still had enough to handle the Knights from Williamsport 64-50. Even though the Saints were never seriously threatened, observers agreed they'd had a bad night. Only two of the G-Men hit doubles: Fallabel, who scored thirty-one, and Larry Walko, who hit for twelve. The third leading scorer for the Saints was Farley with six. In the second game of the doubleheader, West Scranton Central Catholic beat Pocono Catholic 68-65. The two winners would meet on March 1st and whoever emerged victorious in that one would meet Wilkes-Barre St. Nicholas in the Diocese final. The word was St. Nick's was the team to beat, and that the Wilkes-Barre team had the size and skills to go all the way.

Saint Gabriel's wasn't the only local team to have a bad shooting night. In their East Penn League playoff, Hazleton shot just 31 percent from the floor in their ten-point loss to Pottsville. The defeat was an especially tough one for Hazleton because it cost them a spot in the state playoffs.

The G-Men traveled to Scranton to take on the West Scranton Chargers on a Sunday afternoon. After a close first quarter the Saints opened up an eleven point 40-29 halftime lead and looked like they might blow the game wide open. But in the third quarter West Scranton came to life, and Saint Gabriel's was guilty of multiple turnovers. With eight minutes to play the G-Men's lead had been whittled to 47-46. Four minutes into the final quarter, that lead widened to 59-50, and with less than a minute and a half to play, Saint Gabriel's looked safely home with a 68-62 lead. But the Chargers scored two quick goals to get within a field goal. Forced to foul, they sent Farley to the line and he hit three of four from the charity stripe to make the final score 71-66 and move the G-Men into the Diocesan championship to be played Wednesday back at King's College.

The Saints showed more balance in this game with Farley scoring twenty and Polchin hitting for sixteen while Walko and Fallabel netted fifteen and thirteen respectively. Turnovers had become a major concern for the Saints, and they surely didn't want to repeat their performance from the foul line where they had converted only nine of twenty-two attempts. Don Barnes summed the situation up by writing that the G-Men would need a better performance to even stay in the game with Saint Nicholas. The Wilkes-Barre team was 20-2 on the season and was unbeaten in the Catholic League. As Barnes wrote, "Knowledgeable neutral observers who saw St. Gabriel's against Bishop Neumann last week flatly stated St. Nick's would run all over the G-Men if they didn't get their game in shape for the finals."

On the same Monday that the Hazleton paper carried the story of the Saint Gabriel's victory, Ray Saul reported Jack Cryan was a patient at the Mercy Hospital in Wilkes-Barre. Cryan was expected to be confined for several weeks with a back problem. The back injury he had suffered in college playing soccer caused frequent back pain during his time in Hazleton. Few at the time knew just how serious Cryan's condition actually was.

Saint Nick's was no doubt a formidable opponent. They scored an average of 81.2 a game and were giving up just 46 in each contest. They were led by a smooth left-handed guard named Joe Dougherty who was scoring twenty-six points a game and was deadly from virtually anywhere on the floor. At the other guard position, Rich Miscavage at six three was going to give the Saints' matchup problems. Miscavage was splitting the nets for eighteen points in each contest. Inside they were led by the six five Bob Descisk, who would be the tallest player on the court. He was hauling down twelve rebounds a game and was scoring eighteen. The team was coached by Tony Konieski, who was on record as saying he had a team that could go all the way.

The Saints, displaying balanced scoring, had four players averaging in double figures. In his five appearances, Farley led the parade at 14.8 and Walko was contributing 14 even. Fallabel's average of 13 a game was deceiving in that he had come to life late in the year and turned into the Saints' most reliable offensive performer. Polchin the tallest G-Man at six four was contributing 10 each contest. The fifth starter and the team's defensive ace, Marusak, was hitting 7.4 per game. Coming off the bench for the Saints was Boyle, who could play both inside or outside and score from anywhere.

Some of the G-Men, including Farley and Walko, had seen Saint Nick's in action. They had accompanied Coach Anderson on a scouting trip to watch the Cardinals take on Jack Cryan's Saint Mary's squad. Saint Nick's easily won that encounter. At the conclusion of the Saints' final practice prior to meeting the Cardinals, Coach Anderson called Farley aside and asked, "So how would you rate Saint Nicholas?" Farley responded, "They're better than Marian and they'd give West Hazleton all they could handle. This is going to be quite a ballgame." How right he was.

More than 2,500 people had found their way to the spacious King's College gym in Wilkes-Barre to watch the G-Men and the Cardinals battle for the Diocesan Crown. In the Saint Gabriel's locker, Coach Anderson paced back and forth in front of his team. "This is the last year Saint Gabriel's will exist as a high school," he began. "You boys are the last team that will ever wear those purple-and-white uniforms. Some of you had parents that attended this school. Some of you had aunts and uncles and even grandparents graduate from Saint Gabriel's. Some of you had relatives who played on teams in the past. All those people are depending on you now. It's up to you, tonight! Go out there and see that Saint Gabriel's goes out a winner. Let's play the ball we're capable of playing."

The game itself had two different beginnings. The G-Men shot out of the gate to a 5-1 lead but then came apart at the seams as Saint Nick's outscored the Saints 16-1. Coach Anderson called for a time-out to settle his team. It seemed to do the trick, but after eight hard-fought minutes the Saints trailed 19-10. In addition, Joe Farley had picked up two quick fouls trying to deal with Saint Nick's six-three guard Rich Miscavage.

Midway through the second period, Farley picked up his third personal and was replaced by Brian McBride. Munley was in uniform but operating at less than 50 percent. Fallabel and Marusak were playing steady games and keeping the Saints in it. At halftime Saint Gabriel's was on the short end of a 35-28 score. Snapper O'Donnell, who had played for the Saints a decade earlier, was making a halftime visit to the men's room where he overheard two Saint Nick's fans talking about the next game to be played in the Harrisburg area. The one fan said that the parish had already chartered seven buses to transport the Cardinal fans to that contest against the defending state champions, Saint Francis Prep. The two went on talking about making plans to attend that game. It was clear to O'Donnell that in their minds, this one was already over.

The two teams played an even third quarter, Saint Nick's maintaining a seven-point lead at 45-38 with eight minutes left to play. Farley now had four fouls and hadn't scored a field goal. His contributions offensively had been limited to several assists and three foul shots. Up in the stands, Farley's mother Mary was sitting with Swish Farley and her cousin Tommy Malloy (the same Tommy Malloy who had made the leap from the balcony when the riot broke out at the Saint Gabriel's-White Haven game a decade before). Malloy tapped his cousin on the shoulder and said, "Mary, he should have stayed at Marian."

Early in the last quarter the G-Men made a move, scoring five points in the first minute to make it 45-43. When Fallabel hit a short jumper with just over four minutes to play, the score was tied at 47. Having seized the momentum, some in the crowd might have thought the Saints were going to win this one going away, but they turned the ball over on their next two possessions and Saint Nick's took advantage to take a 54-49 lead with two minutes left. Fallabel scored again to make it 54-51, and with fifty seconds to go the G-Men got the ball back and called a time-out. In the huddle Coach Anderson gave surprising instructions: Forget the offense, get the ball to Farley, and let him play one on one. Anderson was going to put the ball into the hands of a player who hadn't scored a field goal in the first thirty-one minutes. Just as they were going to break the huddle, student manager Tom McNelis could stay quiet no longer. "Let's go, guys," he shouted. "Our parents and grandparents went to this school."

As instructed, the G-Men got the ball to Farley who faked left and went right and took a quick jumper that hit nothing but net. Saint Nick's inbounded the ball to Miscavage, who began to advance it up the right side of the court. Farley, with four fouls, remembers thinking *It's now or never* as he timed his lunge and stole the ball mid-dribble and without hesitation went unimpeded to the basket for an easy layup. The Saints led for the first time since early in the first quarter 55-54.

The Cardinals didn't panic as they took the ball down court and got it to the six-five Bob Desciak right around the foul line. He turned and coolly dropped in a shot to regain the advantage for Saint Nick's. Farley hurried and inbounded the ball to Brian McBride, who immediately said "Oh no" and passed it back to Farley as soon as he stepped inbounds. Farley looked at the clock as he began dribbling the ball toward the basket on the far end of the court—twelve seconds to play. Farley remembers he never gave a thought to passing the ball. What surprised him was the fact that none of the Saint Nick's players challenged him. He took the ball to the right, again stopped just inside the foul line, and let go a shot that hit the backboard and dropped neatly through the basket. Half of the gym erupted in a thunderous cheer as Saint Nick's called a quick time-out.

In the huddle, Jerry Anderson made what he called "the biggest boneheaded decision of my coaching career. If things had turned out differently they would have run me out of town, and I would have deserved it. I was concerned about them hitting a shot from half court, so I ordered the team to play a tight man-to-man defense." Miscavage took the ball out under his own basket. Farley waved his arms in front of him. The referee handed him the ball, and Miscavage reared back like a quarterback and let it fly. Joe Dougherty had broken free handled the long pass and appeared to be on his way to scoring the winning goal. Larry Walko came flying out of nowhere as Dougherty went up for the layup. Under Waldo's defensive pressure, the effort fell off the front of the rim as the buzzer sounded. The Saints were alive and well in the PCIAA playoffs following what Don Barnes called "the most extraordinary comeback ever made by the G-Men in their colorful and illustrious basketball career."

The Saint Nicholas fans were either sitting stunned or screaming at the refs that Walko had fouled Dougherty on the final play. The Saints fought their way through their fans who had stormed the court to get to their locker. Once they were gathered inside, Jerry Anderson threw the game ball to Farley, saying, "You earned this" before making a beeline toward the bathroom. Left on their own, the jubilant G-Men decided to visit the Cardinal locker to congratulate the losers on playing a fine game. When Coach Anderson, returned the locker was empty. *Oh my God*, he thought to himself. *They called a foul on Walko.* Anderson hurried back to the court, which was still empty. In the stands he saw the Saint Nicholas fans sitting in silence in their seats.

As reported by Don Barnes, when Anderson was "finally able to talk" he said his team's balance was the key factor in the game. He had special praise for Fallabel, calling him the region's next great player, and Marusak, who he described as a fighter who "doesn't know how to quit." Barnes described the Saint Gabriel's fans after the game as delirious. He said fans were calling the outcome "unbelievable" and "a miracle." Barnes himself shared in their reaction, writing that considering it was against a team as talented as Saint Nicholas, "In its way, it was almost miraculous."

The G-Men couldn't take a long time celebrating, but they did have a little fun with Farley the day after the game, making a big deal out of the headline in the Wilkes-Barre paper that declared in bold letters "Walko's Defensive Play Saves Saint Gabriel's." Underneath in much smaller lettering was the message "Farley's Third Goal Decisive." The day after at school, some of the nuns had serious doubts the team could go much further. Sister Margaret Joseph said to Farley, "You fellas have done all you can. Don't worry about what happens Friday." The good sister was referencing the game for the eastern title against Saint Francis Prep just a day away. Farley remembers thinking, *I'm not worried—we aren't going to lose.*

On the same night that Saint Gabriel's pulled the rabbit out of a hat against Saint Nick's West Hazleton was matched up against East Penn League champion Allentown Allen in the Class A District 11 semifinal game. The Wildcats led by as many as seventeen points in the final period before holding off a furious Allen rally to hold onto a 68-64 win. West Hazleton would play another East Penn League team, Pottsville, in the district final. Once again, the West Hazleton guards played very well as Mummey and Pavlick scored fourteen each in the win. Two other Wildcats, Smith and Scripko—a weapon off the bench—also made it into double figures in the win. Digger Phelps's five-year-old prediction was somewhat vindicated by the game's outcome.

The Saint Gabriel's faithful may have had some trepidation heading into the game for the eastern PCIAA Championship. After all, they were facing Saint Francis Prep, a team that had won not only back-to-back state titles but had beaten an undefeated Saint Gabriel's team with Paul Hoffman, Dennis Olexa, and Mike Heffernan on the roster. If the fans were nervous, their team was not. Looking back, Walko remembers his feelings at the time. "All I was thinking is basketball is fun again. I never thought about losing." Farley was telling everybody that this team was going to win a state title. Fallabel recalls that he never thought about the possibility of losing.

That said, beating Saint Francis would be no easy task. Saint Francis was led by six-four Billy Taylor, a junior who led his league in scoring—no small feat in a league that include Harrisburg Bishop McDevitt, York Catholic, and Shamokin Lourdes, all Class A schools. Taylor was averaging 22.9 points a game. Pete Christ, a junior like his Hilltopper teammate, was contributing 15.8 a contest. If Saint Francis had any weakness, it was a lack of depth.

The Saints left early to make the rather lengthy trip to McSherrytown where the game would be played in Delone Catholic's new gym. The G-Men made a stop on the way at Trinity High School, where they went through some light drills before that evening's game. Trinity students who caught the Saint Gabriel's players in action were overheard speculating on just how bad Saint Francis would beat these guys.

Coach Anderson was worried about how the Saints would contain Taylor, and he stressed to Polchin how important boxing out the Hilltopper ace was going to be. Three buses carrying Saint Gabriel's fans arrived just four minutes before tip-off. They made it in time to see a good one.

Taylor controlled the opening tip for Saint Francis and Rick Norton took a fifteen-foot jumper. As the ball bounced off of the rim, Polchin did as instructed, placing his own six-four body between Taylor and the basket. Taylor wasn't fazed. He went up and reached over Polchin to control the rebound, and in the next moment launched his own shot that touched nothing but net. Watching from the bench, Coach Anderson muttered to no one in particular, "We're in trouble."

Fortunately, the G-Men were running their offense to perfection, getting good shots and, more importantly, making them. The Saints hit on ten of sixteen first quarter attempts to take a 21-20 lead after eight minutes. Taylor scored eleven of his team's first quarter points while Farley and Fallabel had six each for Saint Gabriel's.

In the second period the G-Men lost their hot hand, making only four of the twenty-two shots they attempted. They did continue to out rebound the Hilltoppers and make all four foul shots they were awarded. At halftime, Saint Francis was clinging to a 35-33 advantage.

Early in the third period, Fallabel picked up his third personal foul. That seemed to light a fire under the talented junior. Fallabel scored ten points in the period, Marusak seven, and Farley six as the G-Men took a 58-54 lead. However, with just ten ticks remaining on the clock, Fallabel picked up personal foul number four. Farley recalls that was the only time in the whole game that he felt nervous.

Boyle started the fourth quarter while Fallabel took a seat on the bench. When Taylor drove down the middle for a goal with a little over six minutes to play, Saint Francis took a 59-58 lead. It disappeared in the time it took Boyle to connect on two quick jumpers from the left wing. At the five-minute mark, Fallabel returned to the game and Farley hit two buckets from beyond the Hilltoppers' zone defense. All of a sudden it was 68-61 G-Men. The closest Saint Francis got the rest of the way was 71-67. When the Saints went into a stall, the defending state champs were forced to foul and the G-Men hit three out of four. It ended with a score of 74-67. The G-Men had earned a spot in the state championship game.

Billy Taylor, hailed as the "best schoolboy basketball player in these parts" by the *Hanover Evening Sun*, led all scorers with thirty-four points while collecting seventeen rebounds. Fallabel and Farley were the key offensive players for the G-Men scoring twenty-two and nineteen. Despite the stats, in thinking back on the game, Farley maintains that the two quick field goals by Boyle were the keys to victory. He recalls, "When he [Boyle] nailed that second one, you could see the energy drain out of them." After their slow start, the G-Men had won twelve of the previous thirteen games. But they all knew the big one was the one coming up.

While the Saints were getting ready for the state championship game, G-Man alum Paul Hoffman with St. Bonaventure was playing in the NCAA tournament. Led by senior Bob Lanier, the Bonnies were one of the top teams in the country. Hoffman, a sophomore, was averaging double figures, but he made big news when he held Niagara's Calvin Murphy to the lowest point total of his career. Murphy scored twenty-three, but seventeen of those came in the second half when the game was already decided. For the first twenty minutes, Hoffman held the Niagara ace to just six points. After the game Hoffman remarked, "He got a little hot in the second half or I got a little tired."

On the night after Saint Gabriel's claimed a spot in the state championship game, West Hazleton demolished East Penn League representative Pottsville 76-54 at a game played in the Harrisburg Farm Show Arena. A crowd of more than 6,500 watched the Cats win their first district title in the history of the school. In making history, the Wildcats improved their record to 24-0. Later that week, Harrisburg William Penn ended West Hazleton's season and knocked them out of the Class A state playoffs by beating the Cats before ten thousand fans in Harrisburg.

Saint Gabriel's would face Uniontown Saint John's for the Class C title at Trinity High School outside of Harrisburg. By mid-week Father Doherty announced he had chartered five buses to make the trip with the possibility of adding more. The game would be played on Saturday, March 14th, and it would mark the end of an era. Saint Gabriel's would be sending a high school basketball team onto a court for the final time.

Saint John's would serve as yet another tough test for the Saints. The Johnnies sported a record of 20-3. Of the three loses one was to Frazier, last year's Western Class B champion, by a score of 63-60, and the other two loses were to Mapletown, the team that beat Frazier out this season in the WPIAL. The two losses to Mapletown were by a total of six points. Saint John's was led by a slick guard named Pat Bradley who was averaging 28.2 a game and had scored thirty-three in the western final. The *Standard Speaker* expected the battle-hardened G-Men to hold their own against the westerners.

On the day of the game, the Saint Gabriel's team left shortly after lunch and checked into a hotel just across the Susquehanna River from the state capital. That afternoon the Saints lounged in their hotel rooms watching Paul Hoffman and his St. Bonaventure teammates beat Villanova for a spot in the final four. Unfortunately for the Bonnies, they lost Bob Lanier to an injury late in the game; he'd be unavailable the rest of the way.

It was a short trip from the hotel to Trinity High School where the Saints did some light shooting before heading to the locker to prepare for the game. The buses loaded with Saint Gabriel's fans made it in plenty of time for this game. Though placards were not permitted in the gym, two Saint Gabriel's graduates who lived in the Harrisburg area snuck one in to announce their support for the Saints. The two, Elizabeth and John Butler, were Farley's aunt and uncle. They had to give up their sign when threatened with ejection from the gym.

From the opening whistle, the G-Men knew they were in for a battle. On Saint John's first trip down court, Pat Bradley let fly from about thirty feet and the ball didn't touch anything but net as he put his team on top. Through the first eight minutes, the teams flew up and down the court, and when the buzzer sounded they were tied at twenty. The G-Men controlled the boards and were a more balanced team but had no answer for the Saint John's ace.

Just a minute into the second period, Farley drove for the basket and collided with Bradley. The two fell to the ground and the whistle blew. The referee cupped his hand on the back of the head as he called Farley for the charge. The offensive foul was his third personal of the game and Coach Anderson quickly sent Brian McBride into the game. Farley found a spot on the bench for the remainder of the half. Sparked by Bradley's nineteen first-half points, Saint John's led 39-35 at intermission.

The two teams picked up where they left off in a game that kept going back and forth. By the time the final buzzer sounded there had been seventeen lead changes and nine ties. One of those ties came at the close of the third quarter with the scoreboard showing fifty-four for both teams. Walko was playing what he would later call "one of the best high school games of my career," and with Fallabel and Polchin, the G-Men maintained control of the boards. The three big men were also doing the bulk of the scoring for the Saints.

As the team took the court for the final eight minutes, Farley said, "Let's go—we have eight minutes to make it happen." The fourth quarter started with Polchin hitting a foul shot followed by five straight lead changes as the team's traded field goals. The last change came on a jump shot by Marusak that gave the G-Men a 61-60 lead. Boyle then hit a foul shot followed by field goals by Walko and Farley, and it was 66-60 with four minutes to play. At this point the G-Men began to hold the ball, taking nothing but extremely good shots. With fifty-six seconds left the Saints were up 75-70. Before it was over, the boys in the purple and white hit two foul shots and a field goal by Robby Marusak with six seconds left to make the final score 79-70. The Saints had done it. They were state champions.

Pat Bradley had done all he could, scoring twelve of his game high thirty-five points in the last eight minutes, but it wasn't enough to counter the balance of the G-Men. As Don Barnes reported, "In the final analysis it was St. Gabriel's overall balance that made the difference. Where St. John's had only two players in double figures, the G-Men had four, led by Larry Walko with 21. Illustrating the difference in balance was the fact that Joe Farley, who scored only two points in the first three periods, came up with six points in the last quarter when the issue still hung in the balance."

When the final buzzer sounded, the Saint Gabriel's fans stormed the court to congratulate their team. There was joy everywhere one looked—except on the Saint John's bench and among their fans in the stands. Farley felt a hand on his shoulder and turned around to see Joe Curry, who said, "Congratulations. I was cheering against you guys." As Farley shook Curry's hand, he said, "You can come back. I did. Get down to Pine Street this summer."

The floor was cleared and awards were presented to both teams. As the newspaper was gathering the Saints together for a photo, somebody told Farley that the local radio station wanted to talk to the Saint Gabriel's starters. Farley arrived to talk to WAZL's Vince Laporte as Walko finished up. Laporte asked, "Well Joe, how does it feel to be a state champion?" Farley answered, "It feels great. I never thought Marian was going to make it." Then he thanked Bruce Ellis for the work he had done with the Saint Gabriel's squad over the summer. By the time he returned to his teammates, the photo had been taken. The team then carried Coach Anderson off the floor and deposited him in the shower. When the state champs arrived back in Hazleton, the coach got another surprise. Some of the fans celebrated the win by picking up the coach's Volkswagen and placing it on the steps of the convent.

Forty-six years later Coach Anderson and Joe Farley sat together at a table in Berwick at the O'Donnell Winery. Anderson had brought with him the game ball from the final game. He asked Farley to get it to Larry Walko. As the two sat there and discussed that unbelievable season, they agreed totally on one thing: There was no way a Saint Gabriel's basketball team could have stepped on a court and left as losers in the school's last game. After all, as Tom McNelis reminded us, "Our parents and grandparents went to that school."

AFTERWORD

POST Game

"We didn't realize how lucky we were." That's how Bob Farley, the Voice of the G-Men, summed up his time at Saint Gabriel's during part of what could aptly be labeled as the golden age of G-Men basketball. Writing this book, reading about and sharing in the memories of those who were touched by the magic of those days, has left me feeling much the same way. On May 28, 1970, the forty members of the last class to graduate from Saint Gabriel's High School received their diplomas from Monsignor Maher. As the good monsignor handed over mine, he said, "I never thought you'd make it." The following September the new Hazleton central Catholic school, Bishop Hafey High School, graduated its first senior class.

In the summer of 1970, Jerry Fallabel, Jimmy Munley, and I returned to Pine Street to play for the city playground title. Dennis Olexa returned, as well as the Pine Street coach. Since I was already attending class at Bloomsburg College, there were times that Olexa would pick me up at the college on game days and then drive me back afterwards. On other occasions I used my skilled thumb to obtain a ride. It was on one of the days I hitched a ride that a family who had dropped their daughter off at school picked me up as they were heading home. The girl's dad was driving, and in the course of making conversation, he asked me where I went to high school. When I told him Saint Gabriel's, he said, "I should stop and let you out." It turns out his daughter was a Wilkes-Barre Saint Nicholas grad, and he and his wife had been at the game where we had prevailed just a few months before. Since I had told him I was heading back to Hazleton to play in a basketball game, I admitted that I had been a player in that game. I didn't share the fact that I had scored the winning goal as I thought that information may indeed have resulted in my ejection from the vehicle.

Under Olexa's leadership, we beat James Street, coached by Tony Kinney, in two straight games for the city title. We won game one 68-62 as Jerry Fallabel scored twenty-eight, I hit for nineteen, and Jimmy Munley added sixteen. The second game ended with us on top 60-54 as Munley scored eighteen, Fallabel sixteen, and I chipped in with fourteen. Bruce Ellis was coaching Pine Street's intermediate or junior high team, and they won the city title as well, and they would for three straight years under Ellis. Joe Curry had decided not to play.

That summer it was Hazleton High doing the recruiting. Since Saint Gabriel's had closed, the PIAA had ruled that its athletes could attend any school they wished and be eligible to play immediately. Hazleton officials concentrated their efforts on Fallabel, Munley, and Walko. By the summer's end, Fallabel and Munley had decided to enroll at Hazleton High.

That January Hazleton High and Bishop Hafey met on the basketball court for the first time. Jerry Fallabel scored twenty-six and Jimmy Munley added ten as the Mountaineers took down the Vikings 83-59. Tommy Boyle and Larry Walko led Hafey in scoring with fourteen and thirteen respectively.

On January 21, 1971, Jack Cryan lost his battle with cancer. The former Saint Gabriel's coach passed away at the home of his parents in Trenton, New Jersey. He was twenty-seven years old. The following night Bishop Hafey defeated West Hazleton 64-54. Larry Walko scored twenty-five points in the contest. In the dressing room after the game, Walko, who Cryan had recruited to Saint Gabriel's, approached Ray Saul and said, "Mr. Saul, put it in the paper that this one was for Mr. Cryan."

Hazleton High, led by Jerry Fallabel, Wally Kisthardt, Jimmy Munley, and Charlie Liott, won the District 11 title. The Mountaineers advanced to the eastern state semi-final where they lost to Norristown 54-49 before more than 9,000 fans in a game played at the Farm Show Arena. Fallabel led the Mounts in scoring with fifteen and in rebounds with fourteen. Hazleton, which had won the East Penn League championship, finished the year with a record of 23-4.

That same night on March 20, 1971, Coach Bob Fulton's Marian Colts took on Pittsburgh Saint Basil in the Class B PCIAA state championship game at Saint Vincent's College in Latrobe,

Pennsylvania. The Colts became state champs in Fulton's second year at the helm with a dominating 67-48 victory. I had helped the Marian freshman coach Ron Gerlach with his team at times during the year and had made the trip to Latrobe with the Marian team.

* * *

Writing this book involved taking quite a trip down memory lane. In so many ways, it was a joy. Sitting down and talking to the players on Coach Phelps's Saint Gabriel's team was a pleasure. I watched Pete O'Donnell play in my grade school years, and I was among the many younger players who idolized the star of our high school team. I still remember how thrilled I was when he was named the coach of my biddy basketball team. A lawyer now, we met in his office and he couldn't have been nicer as I probed his memory for his thoughts on events now a half century gone.

O'Donnell's teammate and co-captain Ray McBrearty welcomed me to his home and regaled me with his recollections on his former coach. We all know the heights Phelps reached in the years after he left Hazleton. McBrearty does a pretty good imitation of Coach Phelps, and the two have stayed in touch over the years.

Talking to Paul Hoffman, Dennis Olexa, and Mike Heffernan was invaluable. The big three, who to this day agonize over their loss to Saint Francis Prep, were more than open about their Saint Gabriel's experience. It's clear that the three still hold each other in high esteem. Both Olexa and Hoffman, who are already members of the Hazleton Sports Hall of Fame, believe that Heffernan should be part of that exclusive club.

Meeting up with the guys I played with was a wonderful experience. John Goryl, Jerry Fallabel, Larry Walko, Jimmy Munley, and Tommy Boyle shared some stories I had forgotten about. We had quite a few laughs and were happy to find we're all doing well.

Sitting and talking with Coach Anderson was more than worthwhile. I got the sense that here was a guy who still cared about those kids he coached almost fifty years ago. To hear and see him clearly struggle with his decision to dismiss Joe Curry from the team in 1970 made quite an impression. To hear him talk about Larry Walko's last high school game, and how bad he felt that Larry spent much of it on the bench because of what Anderson maintains to this day was poor officiating, opened up a side of the man I never knew when I played for him. Of course, his memory of me as "a real cocky kid" may explain why.

The family reunion that took place talking to my cousins Mike and Francis O'Donnell was illuminating. I found out that at one time or another we had all either voluntarily or not separated ourselves from the basketball team while in high school. It must run in the family. One thing I think we agreed on was our All-Time Saint Gabriel's team, which would have included the three of us, my dad "Swish" Farley, and Paul Hoffman.

The get togethers with some of the players who opposed Saint Gabriel's on the court proved more than helpful. West Hazleton's Billy Pavlick, Hazleton's Ed Parsons and Tony Kinney, and Marian's Tom Andregic and Bobby Schlosser provided the viewpoint of what it was like playing against the G-Men those days. Meeting with these men really brought home the wealth of basketball talent that roamed the Hazleton area in the late sixties.

Finally, Bruce Ellis was a rich resource when it came to Pine Street playground. Truth be told, he should have received a state championship award when we won it in 1970. His efforts with us that summer made us all better. To this day, Jimmy Munley credits Bruce with any athletic success he achieved.

When I talked with all these folks about this project, some of them had questions for me. A few wanted to know if I was going to rate the coaches and players. Others asked if I would be stating an opinion as to which team was the best. Some asked about my own situation, wondering if I regretted the eligibility problems I ran into my senior year.

Let's take the last question first. At the time the situation had me totally frustrated, but I was determined to make the best of it. There's only one thing I'd change: I would want to be eligible for that last game against West Hazleton. Frankly, I don't regret the time I spent at Marian at all. Though I only got to play for him for a little over a month, being coached by Bob Fulton was something I wouldn't trade for a full season of play. I don't believe it's an exaggeration to say that I learned more about the fundamentals of the game in my time at Marian than I had in all my previous basketball experience. Bruce Ellis said of Fulton, "He was special. His kids loved him and he was ahead of his time. There are coaches teaching man-to-man defense today that don't do it effectively as he did fifty years ago." I agree wholeheartedly with Bruce, and like I wrote earlier, Fulton was more than a coach—he was a teacher and psychologist as well. He never gave you any reason to doubt him. When you played for Bob Fulton, you learned a heck of a lot more than just basketball. As a great man once told me, "Sometimes you have to think about more than winning and losing if you want to see the whole picture." From today's vantage point, I wouldn't change anything inside the frame.

When you start talking about the best players at Saint Gabriel's, it all starts and ends with Paul Hoffman. Nobody I talked to ranked anyone near Hoffman, not only among players at Saint Gabriel's but throughout the region. Bruce Ellis, who has continued to follow high school basketball over the years, maintains that Hoffman is the best player the region has produced. Other players universally mentioned include Pete O'Donnell, Dennis Olexa, and Larry Walko. Some Saint Gabriel's fans forget about Jerry Fallabel because he spent his senior year at Hazleton. Other players mentioned include Joe McFadden, Joe Sernak, Tom Sharkey, Joe Entiero, Jimmy Barrett, Ed O'Donnell, Mike Heffernan, John Darraugh, and a few folks even mentioned yours truly. To this day I believe Joe Curry would have been on that list had he decided to continue his high school career.

When I picked an all-time team at the start of this project, I went with Hoffman, Olexa, Pete O'Donnell, Fallabel, and Jerry Moye. I included the star of the 1947 team because he went on to have a very successful college career playing Division 1 Basketball at Fordham. Now, at the end of the project, I'd have Jerry coming off the bench. My starting five would be Hoffman, O'Donnell, Olexa, Fallabel, and Walko.

When it came to the best players among the teams the Saints faced, one name topped all the others: Tony Kinney. The youngster that Phelps tried unsuccessfully to recruit to Saint Gabriel's was mentioned by almost everybody, and I'd have to agree with them. Other prominent Hazleton players that would make the list would include Sam Mumaw, Ed Parsons, and Wally Kisthardt. From West Hazleton, Tommy Smith, George Petrylak, Billy Pavlick, Dennis Mummey, Rich Sypek and Yosh Grobelny deserve mention. Pat Searfoss and Henry Panckeri from Weatherly were great ball players. Jim Thorpe's Bobby Brown and Dennis Balliet come to mind, as does Steve Makuta and Jack Hollis from MMI. Frank Yusella and John Teprovich from Marian were both excellent players as well.

As far as coaches go, there is no denying that the most successful Saint Gabriel's coach in the 1960s was Jack Cryan. He won both a league and a state title and truth be told, he probably should have won two of each. He had an outstanding record of 47-7, which could easily have been 50-4 were it not for an injury to Paul Hoffman and an ill-timed time-out call.

Digger Phelps was only in the area for a year, but he brought new ideas and a knowledge of the game that was indeed unique to the area. Nobody pressed from the opening whistle until Phelps came to town. He finished a game short in both the first and second half of Anthracite League play but led the Saints to their first state title. He did have some pretty good talent when one remembers that he had the two leading scorers in the history of the school playing on the same team.

Jerry Anderson was probably under appreciated. Bruce Ellis summed up Anderson's situation well, saying, "His biggest problem may have been that he wasn't Jack Cryan." Cryan was a tough act to follow. As Ellis pointed out, Cryan's players loved him. "Olexa would have taken a bullet for Jack Cryan." Judged on his record, Anderson came close to matching Cryan in winning both a state and an Anthracite League title. He won the state title in 1970 and lost the league title in a playoff game the year before. In his two years at Saint Gabriel's, he went 36-16, and he did it without Paul Hoffman.

The main issue people wanted my opinion on was which Saint Gabriel's squad was the best. Most would pick the 1968 team, and with good reason. Paul Hoffman in his senior year was by far the best player around the region and certainly one of the best in the state. Dennis Olexa as a senior was one of the top five guards the area has ever produced. Bruce Ellis says there wasn't a high school in the state that wouldn't have had Olexa in their starting lineup. Add Heffernan, Darraugh, and Pat Curry to the mix, and that was quite a team. They won a league title and went undefeated through the regular season. All they lacked was depth, and they do carry the black mark of that loss to Saint Francis Prep when Hoffman was hurt.

The 1967 squad can make a case for itself. They were one bad half and two points from an undefeated season that would have netted them a league title to go with the state honors they won. They had size and speed. There were times Hoffman played guard on this team when Cryan wanted to go big. Their blemish was the failure to win the league title.

Coach Phelps's 1966 team probably had less overall talent than the Saint Gabriel's squad that played for Chip Kender the year before. When I talked to Pete O'Donnell, he wondered how well that 1965 team might have fared had Phelps arrived a year earlier. This team won the state title easily after narrowly escaping their first playoff test against Williamsport Saint Joseph's. The Anthracite League was very balanced in 1966, and this team finished in the runner up position in both halves. Certainly a good team that improved as the year went on, but not the equal of the two teams that followed.

The 1969 team should have won the Anthracite League title. In John Darraugh's senior year, he provided a spark that led the Saints to a first-half title after a poor exhibition season. Losing to West Hazleton in a playoff for the league championship after having the game well in hand for sixteen minutes was a major disappointment. Darraugh, who would go on to coach at Hazleton and Allentown Central Catholic and passed away too young, deserved better that year. Without a championship, this team, like the 1965 team in Hoffman's freshman year, isn't in the conversation.

It is hard to really gauge the 1970 state title team. It is a team of what ifs. What if I had been available the whole year? What if Joe Curry and Jerry Fallabel had never left the team? What if Joe Curry had come back? What if Jimmy Munley had stayed healthy the entire season? The questions actually provide some clues as to the strengths of this team. We won thirteen of our last fourteen, which indicates the youthful talent on the team matured as the season went on. The team clearly had depth. There was not a single second in the entire season that the 1970 team put the five best players in the school on the floor at the same time. The team still finished second in the Anthracite League to what was probably the best West Hazleton team in the school's history, and they won a state title. They beat some pretty good teams in those state playoffs as well. It's really impossible to say how good this team might have been. A fair observation is that they were a good team that improved as the year went on and overcame obstacles that would have stopped others on the way to the state title.

One last thought on the 1970 team. When I sat down with Larry Walko, he insisted that my return was the reason we won the title. While I appreciate his thoughts, I have to disagree. We won because a number of things came together. The juniors on the team kept getting better as the year went on. Whenever we needed a lift, somebody stepped up. Emil Polchin came on and filled in superbly for Joe Curry when he left the team. Jerry Fallabel became a dominant offensive force as the year went on. Robby Marusak may have played the most consistent game relative to any of the starters during the playoff run. Tommy Boyle was terrific coming off the bench, and he pulled us through against Saint Francis Prep. Larry himself proved an impossible matchup for many teams because of his speed and strength. He played a fantastic game in the state final against a Saint John's team that gave an outstanding effort. If ever it took a total team effort to win a title, it was in 1970.

Given the above, none of the teams were perfect, but the 1968 team had the best starting five. For a small Catholic school, they were a cut above. When I sat down to talk with Tommy Boyle in his office in Hazleton, he said something that stuck with me. That January of 1971 when Bishop Hafey played Hazleton High School before an overflow crowd of 3,000 people at Saint Joseph's, seven of the ten players on the floor to start the game had worn purple and white uniforms the year before. Joe Curry may have been in the stands. Had Saint Gabriel's stayed open just one more year, the players under the roof at Saint Joe's that night might well have supplied the final answer to the best team question.

INDEX

ABOUT THE AUTHOR

JOE FARLEY was born and raised in Hazleton, Pennsylvania. He was a member of the last class to graduate from Hazleton Saint Gabriel's High School where he demonstrated his academic prowess by graduating thirty-seventh in his class of forty. While attending Saint Gabriel's, Mr. Farley was the starting point guard on the school's 1970 state championship basketball team. He then attended Bloomsburg State University where, after four dimly remembered years, he graduated with a degree in education.

In 1975 Mr. Farley began a 35-year career working for the Commonwealth of Pennsylvania. After his retirement in 2010, he began work on the Keystone Tombstone series with his co-author Joe Farrell. To date there are thirteen volumes in that series. Farley and Farrell also authored Gotham Graves volumes one and two. Mr. Farley also penned *Song Poems in Search of Music*, which was released in 2014.

He and his wife Sharon reside in New Cumberland, Pennsylvania. They have three children.

Made in the USA
Columbia, SC
22 November 2017